T0383320

MEDICAL
INTELLIGENCE
UNIT 16

Heat Shock Proteins in Myocardial Protection

Rakesh C. Kukreja, Ph.D.
Division of Cardiology
Department of Medicine
Medical College of Virginia
Virginia Commonwealth University

Michael L. Hess, M.D.
Division of Cardiology
Department of Medicine
Medical College of Virginia
Virginia Commonwealth University

LANDES BIOSCIENCE
GEORGETOWN, TEXAS
U.S.A.

EUREKAH.COM
AUSTIN, TEXAS
U.S.A.

Heat Shock Proteins in Myocardial Protection

Medical Intelligence Unit

Eurekah.com
Landes Bioscience
Designed by Michelle L. McGillivary

Printed in the U.S.A.

Please address all inquiries to the Publishers:
Eurekah.com/Landes Bioscience, 810 South Church Street, Georgetown, Texas, U.S.A. 78626
Phone: 512/ 863 7762; FAX: 512/ 863 0081

ISBN: 1-58706-021-3

While the authors, editors and publisher believe that drug selection and dosage and the specifications and usage of equipment and devices, as set forth in this book, are in accord with current recommendations and practice at the time of publication, they make no warranty, expressed or implied, with respect to material described in this book. In view of the ongoing research, equipment development, changes in governmental regulations and the rapid accumulation of information relating to the biomedical sciences, the reader is urged to carefully review and evaluate the information provided herein.

Library of Congress Cataloging-in-Publication Data

Kukreja, Rakesh C.
Heat shock proteins in myocardial protection/Rakesh C. Kukreja, Michael L. Hess.
p. ; cm. -- (Medical intelligence unit)
Includes bibliographical references and index.
ISBN 1-58706-021-3 (alk. paper)
1. Heat shock proteins. 2. Neovascularization. 3. Myocardial. 4. Growth factors. I. Hess, Michael L. II. Title. III. Series.
[DNLM: 1. Myocardial--drug effects. 2. Angiogenesis Factor--therapeutic use. 3. Heat-Shock Proteins--metabolism. WG280K96h 1999]
QP552.H43 K85 1999
612.1'3--dc21 99-088376

CONTENTS

EDITORS

Rakesh C. Kukreja, Ph.D.
Division of Cardiology
Department of Medicine
Medical College of Virginia
Virginia Commonwealth University
Richmond, Virginia, U.S.A.
Chapter 4

Michael L. Hess, M.D.
Division of Cardiology
Department of Medicine
Medical College of Virginia
Virginia Commonwealth University
Richmond, Virginia, U.S.A.

CONTRIBUTORS

Mohammed Amrani
Department of Cardiothoracic Surgery
National Heart and Lung Institute
Imperial College Harefield Hospital
Harefield, Middlesex, United Kingdom
Chapter 2

Richard Carroll
The Hatter Institute
and Center for Cardiology
Department of Cardiology
University College
London Medical School
Grafton Way, London, United Kingdom
Chapter 1

Richard N.M. Cornclussen
Department of Physiology
Cardiovascular Research Institute
Maastricht University
Maastricht, The Netherlands
Chapter 5

Dipak K. Das
University of Connecticut
School of Medicine
Department of Surgery
Surgical Research Center
Farmington, Connecticut, U.S.A.
Chapter 10

Wolfgang Dillmann
Department of Medicine
University of California, San Diego
San Diego, California, U.S.A.
Chapter 3

Caroline C. Gray
Department of Cardiothoracic Surgery
National Heart and Lung Institute
Imperial College, Harefield Hospital
Harefield, Middlesex, United Kingdom
Chapter 2

Jeffery B. Hoag
Division of Cardiology
Deparment of Medicine
Medical College of Virginia
Virginia Commonwealth University
Richmond, Virginia, U.S.A
Chapter 4

Shiro Hoshida
Cardiovascular Division
Osaka Rosai Hospital
Sakai, Osaka
Chapter 9

A. A. Knowlton
VA Medical Center
Houston, Texas, U.S.A.
Chapter 8

Nilanjana Maulik
University of Connecticut
School of Medicine
Department of Surgery
Surgical Research Center
Farmington, Connecticut, U.S.A.
Chapter 10

Xianzhong Meng
Department of Surgery
University of Colorado Health Science
Center
Denver, Colorado, U.S.A.
Chapter 6

Ruben Mestril
Department of Physiology
Loyola University
Cardiovascular Institute
Maywood, Illinois, U.S.A.
Chapter 3

Kazuhiro Nagata
Department of Cell Biology
Chest Disease Research Institute
Kyoto University
Kyoto, Japan
Chapter 11

Junichiro Nishizawa
Department of Cardiovascular Surgery
Tenri Hospital
Nara, Japan
Chapter 11

Jan A. Post
Utrecht University
Biology Faculty
Department of Molecular Cell Biology
and Institute of Biomembranes
Utrecht, The Netherlands
Chapter 7

Yong-Zhen Qian
Guilford Pharmaceuticals
Baltimore, Maryland, U.S.A.
Chapter 4

Robert S. Reneman
Department of Physiology
Cardiovascular Research Institute
Maastricht University
Maastricht, The Netherlands
Chapter 5

Chris T.W.M. Schneijdenberg
Utrecht University
Biology Faculty
Department of Molecular Cell Biology
and Institute of Biomembranes
Utrecht, The Netherlands
Chapter 7

Luc Snoeckx
Department of Physiology
Cardiovascular Research Institute
Maastricht University
Maastricht, The Netherlands
Chapter 5

Ger J. van der Vusse
Department of Physiology
Cardiovascular Research Institute
Maastricht University
Maastricht, The Netherlands
Chapter 5

Arie J. Verkleij
Utrecht University
Biology Faculty
Department of Molecular Cell Biology
and Institute of Biomembranes
Utrecht, The Netherlands
Chapter 7

Magdi H. Yacoub
Department of Cardiothoracic Surgery
National Heart and Lung Institute
Imperial College, Harefield Hospital
Harefield, Middlesex, United Kingdom
Chapter 2

Derek M. Yellon
The Hatter Institute
and Center for Cardiology
Department of Cardiology
University College
London Medical School
Grafton Way, London, United Kingdom
Chapter 1

PREFACE

Myocardial ischemic syndromes pose a major medical problem and a significant economic health care concern. Reperfusion, although used in the clinical arena as essential to the survival of acutely ischemic heart muscle carries with it the risk of "reperfusion injury". Therefore the salvage of additional myocardium is highly desirable. It was almost a decade ago that Currie and co-workers demonstrated that whole body heat shock activated a powerful endogenous protective mechanism that significantly improved myocardial salvage following prolonged ischemia and reperfusion injury in the heart. A characteristic feature of this heat shock response was the expression of a family of proteins known as heat shock proteins. These proteins have a role in cytoprotection as well as repair of cells and tissues against the deleterious effects of stress and trauma. Altered expression of these proteins has been extensively documented in association with a diverse array of diseases such as ischemia/reperfusion injury, cardiac hypertrophy, fever, inflammation, metabolic diseases, infection, cell and tissue trauma, aging, and cancer. Interstingly, some studies have now shown a direct correlation of the heat shock proteins produced and the degree of myocardial protection. In addition, mice engineered to overexpress heat shock protein particularly the 70 kilodalton molecules have been shown to be resistant to myocardial ischemia/reperfusion injury. A closer examination of this group of proteins and their involvement in cardioprotection during myocardial protection is extremely important to understanding the myocyte's ability to protect itself against ischemic injury. In addition, it is also important to explore other mechanisms such as protein kinase C and/or opening of ATP-sensitive potassium channels, that may be activated in association with heat shock proteins following whole body hyperthermia. The purpose of this book is to present a thorough description of the current state of knowledge, the controversies in this growing field and the potential of treating ischemic heart disease with heat shock proteins in patients.

We like to express our deep gratitude to the leading investigators in the field who have contributed their valuable time in preparing their chapters. In addition, we are thankful to Dr. Ronald G. Landes for his continuing interest and encouragement in publishing the book in this interesting field. We hope that this book will serve as an important compendium to our understanding of the role of heat shock proteins in myocardial protection.

Rakesh C. Kukreja, Ph.D
Michael L. Hess, M.D.

Chapter 1

Stress Proteins in Myocardial Protection

Richard Carroll and Derek M. Yellon

In all organisms examined heat stress results in the synthesis of a specific group of proteins known as the heat shock or stress proteins (Hsps). Cells that accumulate these proteins adapt and become resistant to further heat stress, a protection that seems directly dependent on stress protein induction. Numerous reports also suggest that stress protein accumulation is associated with protection against differing stresses in various mammalian tissues. This chapter reviews the evidence that stress proteins are directly responsible for the adaptation that increases the resistance of cells to various forms of injury. We will examine the role of stress proteins in protecting the adapted heart against both ischemic as well as non-ischemic injury. In addition we shall discuss the involvement of stress proteins in the phenomenon of ischemic preconditioning relating specifically to the delayed adaptive process that follows short coronary artery occlusions which give rise to the so called "second window of protection".

Acute myocardial infarction is the most common cause of death in the Western world. The treatment of this condition is no longer simply supportive, awaiting the complications of ischemic injury, but has entered a new era where the mortality of acute myocardial infarction can be approximately halved by thrombolytic agents and aspirin,[1] with the greatest benefit seen in those treated soon after the onset of symptoms. The lack of a reduction in mortality when thrombolytic treatment is administered late is most likely due to the fact that the prolonged coronary occlusion has resulted in such severe necrosis of the myocardium that little benefit can be derived by restoring blood flow.[2] Therefore any intervention that could delay the onset of tissue necrosis could buy valuable time by extending the effective temporal window for thrombolysis. Attempts to limit myocardial infarct size over the last decade with exogenous pharmacological agents have been largely unsuccessful,[3] prompting us to explore the heart's endogenous protective mechanisms to ascertain if this route may provide us with the knowledge required to protect the myocardium from severe ischemic injury.

Heat Stress and the Stress Response

All organisms respond at the cellular level to stresses such as heat by the preferential synthesis of a group of proteins known as the heat shock or stress induced proteins. This stress response relates to the process whereby general protein synthesis is inhibited whilst the synthesis of stress proteins is enhanced. A range of studies have now demonstrated the importance of these proteins in both the stressed and the unstressed cell, where they perform functions that seem essential to the maintenance of cellular integrity. Over the last decade interest in this group of proteins has grown with the recognition that manipulation of stress protein content in cells appears to be associated with enhanced cell survival following subsequent injury. Indeed studies suggest that stress proteins may be capable of delaying ischemic injury to the myocardium (see editorials[4-6])

Heat Shock Proteins in Myocardial Protection, edited by Rakesh C. Kukreja and Michael L. Hess.

and as such could be exploited to our advantage by offering a future approach to increase the effective time window for thrombolysis.

Are Stress Proteins Protective?

It is known that stress proteins have the ability to interact with other proteins by altering their conformation e.g., heat shock protein 70 (hsp70) and mitochondrial protein import; protecting them from inappropriate and premature interactions e.g., hsp90 and the steroid receptor; encouraging the correct refolding of denatured proteins e.g., hsp90 and Fab or citrate synthase; aid in the degradation of denatured proteins e.g., with the use of ubiquitin; detect subtle changes in the conformation of other proteins e.g., hsp70 and clathrin triskelions; and stabilize the cytoskeleton e.g., alpha β-crystallin interacting with actin and desmin. All these interactions suggest that stress proteins maybe capable of increasing cell viability and integrity both during and following denaturing stresses. Therefore, if upregulated, these proteins may allow the cell to behave in a more efficient manner when it is subjected to subsequent potentially lethal ischemic stress. Similarly, a change in post translational state and increase in function, such as the phosphorylation of hsp27, or translocation to a different subcellular compartment such as the perinuclear localization of hsp72 will enhance the protective capacity of these proteins.

Evidence for the Ability of Stress Proteins to Protect the Cell

Thermotolerance

When prokaryotic, or eukaryotic cells are acutely exposed to temperatures several degrees above their normal ambient temperature, the cells or animals will die within a predictable period of time. However if the cells are initially exposed to the elevated temperature for a shorter time period and allowed to recover at normal temperatures, it has been shown that they can survive a subsequent period of otherwise lethal heat stress. This universal phenomenon is known as acquired thermotolerance.[7] Stress proteins induced by the first period of sublethal thermal stress are attractive candidates to explain the acquisition of thermotolerance.

The evidence that stress proteins are involved in thermotolerance is strong. For example with regard to hsp70 in eukaryotic cell lines, thermal tolerance and stress protein induction are temporally related;[8] the degree of stress protein expression following stable transfection in cells correlates with the degree of thermotolerance;[9] cell lines expressing abnormal hsp70 with a missing ATPase domain retain thermotolerance;[10] cells microinjected with a monoclonal antibody recognizing a shared epitope on constitutive and inducible forms of hsp70 are thermosensitive;[11] mutants selected for multiple copies of the hsp70 promoter region are thermosensitive[12] (in this study copies of the hsp70 regulatory region presumably competed with the endogenous hsp70 encoding genes for factors that activate hsp70 expression, since hsp70 induction was reduced by 90%); and stress proteins incorporating amino-acid analogues (i.e., nonfunctional stress proteins) result in thermal sensitization.[13] Other stress proteins may also be important since rodent cell lines stably transfected with hsp27 (homologous to alpha β crystallin) are "naturally" thermotolerant,[14] whilst cells with an hsp104 protein deletion are unable to acquire thermotolerance.[15] In addition transfection with antisense RNA for hsp90 (to specifically hybridize with and prevent the translation of native hsp90 mRNA) also prevents the acquisition of thermotolerance.[16]

However, it is not certain whether thermotolerance represents better recovery following heat stress or actual attenuation of injury during the thermal stress. Laszlo[17] has demonstrated that protein synthesis and RNA synthesis are similarly depressed following heat stress of thermotolerant and naive fibroblasts. However recovery of both processes was enhanced in cells overexpressing hsp70 (either by transfection or by prior treatment with sublethal thermal stress or sodium arsenite). In contrast other investigators[18] have found evidence for protection during thermal stress since conformational changes within proteins, detected by both -SH group targeted electron spin resonance and mobility by thermal gel analysis, occur at a higher temperature in thermotolerant eukaryotic cell lines. Clearly, protection may occur both during and following the thermal denaturing stress and these mechanisms are not mutually exclusive.

The arguments are further complicated by the fact that thermotolerance in some situations can occur in the absence of stress protein induction, leading to the speculation that two types of thermotolerance exist, stress proteins being responsible for the acquisition of long but not short-lasting thermotolerance.

Crosstolerance

If sublethal heat stress induces stress proteins that protect against subsequent lethal heat shock, can other non-thermal stresses that also induce stress proteins give rise to similar thermal tolerance? Interestingly, this does seem to be the case. In addition, and of more relevance to experimental cardiology, thermally induced stress proteins seem capable of protecting against stresses which themselves induce stress protein synthesis. Such cross-protection is known as crosstolerance.

There are numerous studies that support the concept of crosstolerance first suggested by Li and Hahn.[19] These workers demonstrated that a hamster cell line could be rendered resistant to both adriamycin and heat toxicity by pretreatment with ethanol. Later studies have demonstrated similar findings but with very different stresses. For example, whole body heat stress in rats protects retinal pigment cells from light injury, protection being temporally dependant on hsp72;[20] pretreatment with hydrogen peroxide protects against subsequent oxidative stress;[21] heat stress protects against subsequent oxidative stress in a number of models (for review, see ref. 22); heat stressed human breast cancer cells are rendered resistant to doxorubicin, an effect that seems related to hsp70 and hsp27 cell content;[23] and heat stressed neuronal cells are resistant to the excitotoxic effects of glutamate, an effect dependent on protein synthesis and related to hsp70.[24,25]

Control of Stress Proteins in the Heart

The primary transcription factor involved in the regulation of expression of heat shock proteins is heat shock factor-1 (HSF-1), which appears to be the factor mediating transcription regardless of the mode of stress. In the quiescent state, HSF-1 exists in the cytoplasm as a monomer. With stress, phosphorylation causes trimerization and migration of this complex to the nucleus. Here it binds to the heat shock element, (HSE) which is present in the promotor region. Serine phosphorylation is imperative before transcription can occur, and after a few hours dephosphorylation causes inactivation.[26,27] However, activation and binding of HSF alone is not adequate to initiate transcription, and it appears that concomitant factors are required such as ATP depletion[28] or an increase in denatured proteins in the cell.[29] In heat stressed HeLa cells, there is a parallel increase in the half life of hsp70 mRNA.[30] Using a model that placed modified hsp70 coding sequences under the control of a metallothionein promoter, Petersen and Lindquist measured the half life of mRNA from copper driven transcription at 15 minutes. In the heat shocked cell, the half life was measured at 4 hours.[31] Several heat shock proteins, notably hsp70 contain no introns and therefore splicing is not needed before translation, but others require splicing, capping, and have the half life of mRNA closely regulated. Finally, protein methylation and, particularly in the case of hsp27, phosphorylation appear to be important in the functional status of the finished protein monomer whilst oligomerization or co-localization with other stress or structural proteins is necessary for final functionality as in the case of the interaction between hsp60 and hsp10.

Stress Proteins and the Heart

Stress proteins have been detected in the myocardium of a variety of mammalian species. Their synthesis has been shown to be increased by whole body temperature elevation[32-34] and other stressful stimuli including ischemia,[35] brief ischemia and reperfusion,[36] anoxia,[37] hypoxia,[38] pressure or volume overload,[39] mechanical stretch,[40] cytokines[41] and drugs such as vasopressin,[42] isoproterenol,[43] hydrogen peroxide,[44] L-type (slow) calcium channel blockers[45] and other cardiotoxic drugs and heavy metals.[46] Our group have recently shown the ability of the ansamycin antibiotic, Herbimycin-A, to protect cultured cardiomyocytes, with induction of hsp72.[47] The implication of these findings is that stress proteins may play an important role in the cardiac stress response. Although many of these stimuli induce members of the 70 kD family of stress proteins, there appear to be differences in the pattern of stress protein induction when other families of stress proteins are considered. For example, cardiotoxic drugs preferentially induce a 30 kD stress protein.[46] It is possible that each stress induces its own subtly differing profile of stress proteins best suited to meet the cellular consequences of that particular stress.

Heat Stress and Myocardial Protection

Following the suggestion that, (a) tissues with thermally pre-elevated stress proteins are resistant to stresses that normally induce stress proteins (crosstolerance), and (b) myocardial ischemia causes stress protein induction,[35,36] investigators have been interested in examining whether myocardial tissue entering ischemia with a pre-elevation of stress proteins is resistant to infarction.[48-51]

Currie et al[48] were the first investigators to show that temperature elevation to 42°C in rats resulted in concomitant cardiac stress protein and catalase induction, and an attenuation of ischemia/reperfusion injury. Using an isolated heart model, these investigators demonstrated that following ischemia/reperfusion, contractile function is enhanced whilst creatine kinase release is dramatically reduced in heat stress compared with control hearts. These findings have been confirmed by our group in both the rat[52] and the rabbit.[50] Moreover, we have observed improvements in additional parameters of protection in the heat stressed rabbit heart,[50] including preservation of high energy phosphates, reduction in oxidative stress during reperfusion (as measured by lower levels of oxidized glutathione) and significant mitochondrial preservation following ischemia. There does however, appear to be some species variation in the metabolic changes associated with protection following heat stress. In the rabbit for example, higher levels of high energy phosphates mirror the enhanced contractile activity of heat stressed hearts during reperfusion.[50] In the rat however, the enhanced contractile activity following ischemia in the heat stressed groups is not associated with changes in high energy phosphate content.[48,52,53]

The protective effects of whole body heat stress have also been shown in the hypertrophied heart which ordinarily has an increased susceptibility to ischemic injury. In the hypertrophied rat heart 24 hours after whole body heat stress, preliminary evidence suggests that ischemic changes are diminished whilst contractile function is enhanced.[54]

The studies summarized to this point have demonstrated protection expressed in terms of myocardial contractility and metabolic state. The ability of whole body heat stress to reduce the extent of myocardial infarction as examined by triphenyl tetrazolium staining has also been examined. In a preliminary study in the rat model, infarct size is reduced following 30 minutes of regional ischemia, with protection being temporally related to elevated stress protein levels at 24-72 hours following whole body heat stress.[55] In addition, our group[56,57] has demonstrated a similar reduction in infarct size following 45 minutes of regional ischemia and 2 hours reperfusion in the buffer perfused rabbit heart removed 24 hours after whole body heat stress.

Interestingly, in contrast to isolated heart studies, controversy surrounds the ability of whole body heat stress to reduce infarct size in vivo. In the rabbit, heat stress 24 hours prior to ischemia was unable to reduce infarct size following a 45 minute coronary occlusion[58] although protection was found following a 30 minute occlusion by Currie et al.[51] A similar dependence on the length of coronary occlusion is seen in the rat. Donnelly and co-workers[59] have demonstrated a reduction in infarct size in the rat following a 35 minute, but not a 45 minute, coronary occlusion initiated 24 hours after whole body heat stress. Moreover, in this model the reduction in infarct size, following a graded heat stress procedure, is related to the degree of stress protein induction.[60] The apparent dependency of protection on the length of ischemic insult is difficult to explain. One possibility is that the protection conferred by heat stress is only moderate, and that as the severity of the ischemic insult increases the protection becomes less evident. A similar phenomenon occurs with ischemic preconditioning in dogs where a marked reduction in infarct size occurs with 60 minutes of coronary occlusion, but not with 90 minutes.[61] Another apparent anomaly is the fact that although infarct size is reduced after a 30 minute coronary occlusion 24 hours following whole body heat stress in the rabbit, no protection is seen at 48 hours after heat stress at a time when cardiac stress protein content is still increased.[51]

Other investigators have been able to demonstrate in vivo protection following hot blood cardioplegia of the pig heart.[62] In another rather novel approach,[63] a microwave diathermy probe was applied to the canine heart. Although such regional hyperthermia was shown to increase stress protein mRNA expression, there was no concomitant protection against infarction. However, the time course of this study was such that appreciable stress protein accumulation was unlikely to have occurred in the one hour between thermal stress and coronary ligation. In addition, the spatial relationship between heat-treated myocardium and the subsequent area of hypoperfusion during coronary ligation was not documented.

The cause for the discrepancy between in vivo and in vitro studies is not clear. However, observations from our laboratory suggest that whole body heat stress may activate a blood-borne component that overrides the beneficial effect of cardiac stress protein induction. This inference was made after noticing that blood from a heat-stressed support rabbit, when used to perfuse an isolated rabbit heart, significantly increased infarct size.[64] It may be that whole body heat stress, despite conferring myocardial protection, causes confounding physiological changes which have negative effects on infarct size. This is consistent with the finding that cytotoxic T-cells directed against myocardial heat shock proteins are induced in rats by stresses that elevate myocardial heat stress protein content,[65] and that these cells are cytotoxic in vitro to heat stressed myocytes from the same species. In addition, the possibility remains that the duration of recovery after heat stress and length of the ischemic insult may also influence the ultimate infarct size and appearance of cardioprotection.

Heat Stress Proteins and Ischemic Preconditioning

Acquired thermotolerance, where sublethal hyperthermia protects against subsequent lethal hyperthermia, is similar in concept to ischemic preconditioning, with sublethal ischemia protecting against subsequent lethal ischemia. One could speculate that stress proteins synthesized in response to the first brief episode of preconditioning ischemia are involved in the protection against the subsequent injury. In agreement with this idea Knowlton et al[36] demonstrated that brief bursts of ischemia, such as those used in preconditioning protocols, can induce hsp70 mRNA and protein accumulation. The mechanism by which stress proteins are induced by short episodes of ischemia may be secondary to the free radical stress induced by reperfusion, since in the isolated rat heart stress protein induction following a 15 min infusion of xanthine plus xanthine oxidase is quantitatively similar to that induced by ischemia with reperfusion.[66] However, in a study by Knowlton et al,[36] elevated levels of the hsp70 protein were only manifest at 2-24 hours after the ischemic insult. In contrast the protective effect of preconditioning is lost approximately 1 hour after the initial brief ischemic episode.[67]

The involvement of stress protein in ischemic preconditioning has been further questioned by a study[68] which indicates that the protective effect of preconditioning can be observed under conditions where de novo protein synthesis has been almost entirely inhibited. Thus, it is unlikely that stress proteins are involved in the protection observed in early ischemic preconditioning. However, the changes in mRNA coding for stress proteins indicate an adaptive response to ischemia which may predict a delayed protection dependent on stress protein synthesis.

Indeed this is what we found when we either heat stressed or administered repetitive sublethal ischemia to rabbits hearts and were able to demonstrate a significant limitation of infarct size 24 hours later. Furthermore, there was a significantly increased expression of the 70 kD hsp in both the hearts that had the prior heat stress as well as the prior ischemic insults.[57] Reports using the dog model[69] have also demonstrated effects of a second phase of protection existing at 24 hours after preconditioning with four repeated, 5 minute episodes of ischemia. Interestingly, a similar phenomenon appears to occur within the brain, where ischemic pretreatment with two, repeated episodes of 2 minute bilateral carotid occlusions is capable of limiting the neuronal cell loss that follows a subsequent more prolonged bilateral carotid occlusion.[70-72] For this protective effect to be manifest, the short occlusions must precede the long occlusion by at least 24 hours, a time interval known to result in cerebral heat stress protein accumulation in an identical model.[73] It is interesting to speculate if myocardial adaptation to ischemia may explain the apparent benefit of a 7 day or more history of angina prior to myocardial infarction,[74] although likely collateral vessel formation and concomitant medication make any definite conclusions impossible. In contrast other attempts to induce myocardial protection by ischemic pretreatment have been unsuccessful. For example, Donnelly et al[59] compared the protective benefit of heat stress with 24 hours of recovery to 20 minutes of ischemia with 8 hours of reperfusion. Following a subsequent 35 minute occlusion in the rat, heat stress pretreatment reduced infarct size, whilst ischemic pretreatment did not. However, as heat stress resulted in a more marked stress protein accumulation, the authors concluded that ischemic pretreatment failed to protect because of insufficient stress protein accumulation.

Other methods of stress protein induction have included immobilization stress which has also been shown to protect against subsequent ischemia/reperfusion injury assessed by CPK leakage, contractile function and reperfusion arrhythmias.[75,76]

Heat Stress and Protection Against Non-Ischemic Injury

The observations that cardiac tissues synthesize stress proteins in response to a variety of stresses has encouraged investigators to explore the breadth of protection that follows heat stress. In this regard Meerson[77,78] has demonstrated that stress protein induction by either heat or immobilization protects the isolated rat and rabbit heart against a subsequent calcium paradox, a finding confirmed by ourselves in the isolated rabbit heart.[79] The fact that oxidant stress is capable of inducing cardiac stress proteins[44,66] has prompted Su et al[80] to examine the protective benefits of prior heat stress with exposure to H_2O_2 as the final stress. In a rat myocyte culture model, heat stress is capable of inducing acquired thermotolerance and limiting myocyte injury on subsequent H_2O_2 exposure.

Several lines of evidence suggest that the inducible isoform of hsp70, hsp70i is a cytoprotective protein conferring tissue tolerance to ischemia/reperfusion injury. For example, Hutter et al showed that the rise in myocardial hsp70i content correlated with both the degree of hyperthermia and the extent of subsequent ischemic tolerance.[60] Our group showed that the post-hypoxic functional recovery of papillary muscles from rabbits pretreated with hyperthermia correlated with the hsp70i content of an adjacent papillary muscle from the same animal.[81] More recently, studies with transgenic mice that overexpress hsp70i[82,83] and studies involving transfection of the gene encoding for hsp70 into isolated myogenic cells[84-86] and cardiac myocytes[87] show more convincingly that the protein directly confers protection against ischemic injury. While there is good evidence then that the presence of hsp70 is associated with an ischemia-tolerant phenotype, the extent to which this particular stress protein accounts for myocardial protection following heat stress is unclear.

Mechanisms of Cardiac Protection by Stress Proteins

All studies using heat to elevate stress protein synthesis result in a large number of physiological perturbations which may in themselves have cardioprotective properties. For example, Currie's group[48,88] have shown that heat stress also results in an increase in the endogenous levels of the anti-oxidant enzyme catalase. Moreover, they have demonstrated[88] that inactivating catalase with the irreversible inhibitor, 3-aminotriazole (3-AT), results in an abolition of the protective effect normally observed at 24 and 48 hours after heat stress. This protective role of catalase would be dependent upon its ability to minimize the damage caused by secondary free radical generation to sulphydryl containing enzymes, DNA and lipids[89] by catalyzing the conversion of H_2O_2 to water. Following a period of prolonged ischemia the importance of catalase is increased since there is a marked reduction in the activity of SOD as well as in the ratio of reduced to oxidised glutathione.[89] In agreement with such a mechanism, it has been observed that a reduction in the levels of oxidised glutathione in the coronary effluent following ischemia/reperfusion in heat stressed hearts occurs, suggesting that a second, alternative line of antioxidant defence exists in these hearts.[90] The picture however becomes more complicated since cardiac mRNA levels for catalase are not increased by heat stress.[91] The increase in catalase may therefore result from post-translational mechanisms. An alternative suggestion is that stress proteins may modulate the catalytic activity of catalase by direct interaction with the enzyme.[92]

In myocytes exposed to stresses that would otherwise cause protein denaturation and loss of function, it appears that particular stress proteins play roles in preventing protein unfolding. Located cytoplasmically, the hsp70 isoform hsc70 is expressed during normal growth and development and is one of the archetypal "molecular chaperones", catalyzing the folding and translocation of newly synthesized proteins.[93] Hsc70 is thought to bind to nascent polypeptide chains and prevent incorrect folding or aggregation. Subsequent ATP dependent release allows correct folding of the protein. Hsp70 also has a significant role in the translocation of proteins across organellar membranes and as such is found on both sides of organelles such as endoplasmic reticulum and mitochondria. Translocation takes place via protein complexes which form proteinaceous channels, and emerging polypeptides on the luminal side are chemically crosslinked to hsp70. ATP dependent release then allows correct protein folding. Similarly, grp78 is located on the lumenal side of the rough endoplasmic reticulum and associates with polypeptide chains emerging from the ribosome. More importantly, hsp70 appears able to act as chaperones in the refolding of previously denatured polypeptides[94,95] and to prevent the stress induced denaturation and aggregation of certain proteins.[96,97] This has lead to the theory that refolding and antiaggregating properties determine its role in cellular protection against stresses.[98] A specific mitochondrial matrix associated isoform of hsp70 (mhsp70) has been identified. In yeast, it has been shown that pretreatment with sublethal heat stress maintained the coupling between oxidative phosphorylation and electron transport following a later, more severe thermal stress.[99] In the same experiment, when the initial heat stress was given to cells pretreated with cycloheximide, at a concentration sufficient to abolish hsp72i synthesis, protection was lost. Similar protection of mitochondrial function has been shown against ischemia in the rabbit heart following heat stress pretreatment.[50]

During conditions of stress, hsp70 has been shown to translocate to the nucleus and to accelerate recovery of nucleolar morphology following heat shock, possibly by the formation of a complex between hsc70 and nuclear topoisomerase I. Ciavarra et al showed that hsc 70 was able to reactivate heat-denatured topo I in vitro, and this may be an extension of its role in protein folding under normal conditions.[100,101] Distinct from its chaperoning and anti-aggregative properties, it has recently been shown that hsp70 family proteins prevent the activation of a variety of stress activated protein kinases. As opposed to necrotic death, severe stresses such as heat shock, oxidative stress, UV and chemical stressors can commit the cell to programmed cell death, the triggering of which requires activation of the c-Jun N-terminal kinase, (JNK). Using human lymphoid tumour cell lines, stably transfected with plasmids encoding hsp72 under the control of a tetracycline regulated transactivator, Gabai et al showed that the high levels of hsp72 expressed on the withdrawal of tetracycline from the culture medium were protective against lethal heat stress and that this was mediated by an anti-apoptotic mechanism.[102]

Recent reports suggest that the injury occurring during the calcium paradox can be influenced by procedures that cause stress protein synthesis.[77-79] The precise mode by which the calcium paradox damages the heart is a matter of controversy, but free-radical production is probably not involved.[103] It is thought that during the period of low calcium exposure changes occur in the structural proteins of the myocyte so as to increase fragility, and, on calcium repletion the return of contractile activity causes myocyte mechanical disruption.[104] A similar process involving cytoskeletal disruption may also occur during ischemia.[105] Heat stress proteins are known to alter the physical properties of actin and desmin[106] and may themselves form an integral part of the cytoskeleton.[107] Hsp27 is constitutively expressed and present in large quantities in the mammalian heart, with concentrations of up to 1700 ng hsp27 per 1mg total protein in explanted human hearts.[108] Hsp27 is widely accepted to be located primarily in the cytoplasm and particularly in the perinuclear zone. Upon the induction of a significant stress, hsp27 has been shown to translate to the nucleus. During recovery from stress, the protein relocates to the cytoplasm,[109] and this would be in keeping with a role for protein renaturation and chaperoning in the nucleus. In the cardiomyocyte, small stress proteins seem to play a special role in the protection of the cytoskeleton and myofibrils and this is in keeping with their particularly high levels in cardiac tissue. Electron microscopic double antibody labelling studies have demonstrated colocalization of both hsp27 and αβ-crystallin in sarcomeres of myofibrils.[110,111] In the adult cardiomyocyte, hsp27 has been shown to colocalize with actin in the I-band and in some cases, the M-line, confirming this functional proximity. However, how hsp27 effects its regulatory or protective function has yet to be elucidated. The cytoskeletal microfilaments are one of the earliest targets in cellular oxidative damage; in keeping with its intracellular location and proximity to actin, recent evidence shows that phosphorylation of hsp27 regulates actin filament dynamics in cells in response to a variety of cell stresses and cytokine stimuli. Guay et al showed that chemical stress or stimulation of CCL39 cells with cytochalasin D increased phosphorylation of hsp27 and prevented actin destabilization. This protective effect was completely abolished by pretreatment with the p38 MAP kinase inhibitor SB203580.[112] Similarly, by expressing the non-phosphorylatable form of human hsp27 (pmhsp27) in Chinese hamster CCL39 cells and comparing the response with control cells or cells overexpressing the wild type human hsp27, Huot et al showed that the overexpression of wild type protein conferred significant protection against H_2O_2 or menadione induced reactive oxygen metabolites, but that the pmhsp27 variants were as sensitive as control cells to damage. Visible fragmentation of F-actin with the formation of aggregates in the perinuclear region was observed in the injured cells.[113] In combination with hsp27, αβ-crystallin has antiprotease activity which may be important for cardiac metabolism by protecting against the protease activity of ubiquitin. It too can be phosphorylated in three serine residues but the regulatory significance of this is unclear. It is present in the heart in high concentrations of up to 3 μg/mg protein and does not appear to be induced by heat stress.[114]

In mammalian mitochondria two stress proteins appear to be involved in protection. Both hsp60 and hsp10 are coded for by the nuclear genome and together form the chaperonin complex,[115] the primary site for folding of mitochondrial proteins and multimeric enzyme complexes. Hsp60 exists as a cylindrical structure made up of 14 hsp60 molecules and requires for the proper folding of mitochondrial proteins a cofactor made up of between 7 and 14 hsp10 molecules. It appears that nascent proteins enter the center of the cylinder where the chaperonins interact with the exposed hydrophobic regions. Multiple ATP-dependent cycles of release and binding then occur, leading to refolding and then ultimate release of the protein. During ischemia, this chaperonin complex is likely to maintain the integrity of mitochondrial proteins. Recently, Lau et al transfected both primary rat neonatal ventricular and H9c2 cells with hsp60 alone, hsp10 alone, or cotransfection with both. They found that protection against simulated ischemia was only conferred by the cotransfection.[116]

Yet another possible mechanism of protection is that during heat stress, protein synthesis (apart from the stress proteins) is inhibited. A similar response has been noted during other forms of stress in cardiac tissue[117] and it has been postulated that such a response allows the cell to redirect energy into more vital cell processes during and following times of stress.[5] A 17 kDa stress protein which inhibits protein translation has been isolated from cardiac tissue and is expressed in response to heat and pressure overload, providing yet another possible mechanism by which heat stress may confer myocardial protection.

Although the specific changes that result in myocyte death during ischemia are poorly understood, alterations in the structural conformational of proteins will inevitably occur secondary to, changes in pH, ionic concentration and free radical stress. The general protective properties of stress proteins may be able to attenuate or correct these changes.

Conclusions

Stress proteins are induced in the heart by various physiological and pathological conditions such as ischemia, these findings together with other information have led to the hypothesis that stress proteins may have play an important role in adaptation to stress. This hypothesis has been examined by elevating the stress protein content of the heart by heat and other means prior to ischemia. The protective effect of elevated temperature on the ability of the heart to survive a subsequent stress has now been demonstrated by a number of different laboratories using different animal species with various endpoints.

Stress proteins are induced by the brief periods of sublethal ischemia known to cause ischemic preconditioning. However, this induction of stress proteins has not as yet been shown to be directly responsible for the protection observed. However studies in which direct transfection of cells with hsp70 genes and/or transgenic mice in which hsp have been an overexpressed do clearly indicate a direct protection role for these proteins.

The weight of evidence presented suggests that stress proteins increase the resistance of the heart to ischemia and may offer an endogenous route to myocardial protection. Such a route represents an obvious pathway for therapeutic intervention. Future investigators, by using either pharmacological or genetic manipulations, will address the problem of cardiac stress protein induction independent of physical stress. It is hoped that by such methods eventually it may be possible to protect the heart by a specific but non-abusive stimulation of its own adaptive protective mechanisms.

Acknowledgments

Dr Richard Carroll is sponsored by the British Heart Foundation. We also thank the Hatter Foundation for continued support.

References

1. ISIS-2 collaborative group. Randomized trial of IV streptokinase, oral aspirin, both or neither among 17187 cases of suspected acute myocardial infarction. Lancet 1988; 342:349-60.
2. Reimer K, Jennings R. The "wave phenomenon" of myocardial of myocardial ischemic cell death. II. Transmural progression of necrosis within the framework of ischemic bed size (myocardium at risk) and collateral flow. Lab Invest 1979; 40:633-644.
3. Hearse H, Yellon, DM,. Why are we still in doubt about infarct size limitation? The experimental viewpoint. In: Hearse DJ & Yellon DM , ed. Therapeutic approaches to myocardial infarct size limitation. New York: Raven Press, 1983:17-41.
4. Yellon DM, Latchman DS. Stress proteins and myocardial protection. J Mol Cell Cardiol 1992; 24:113-24.
5. Yellon DM, Latchman DS, Marber MS. Stress proteins—an endogenous route to myocardial protection: Fact or fiction? Cardiovasc-Res 1993; 27(2):158-61.
6. Black S, Lucchesi BR. Heat shock proteins and the ischemic heart. An endogenous protective mechanism. Circulation 1993; 87:1048-1051.
7. Gerner E, Scheider MJ. Induced thermal resistance in HeLa cells. Nature 1975;256:500-502.
8. Sugahara T, Saito M. Hyperthermic Oncology. London: Taylor and Francis, 1988.
9. Li G, Li L, Liu Y, et al. Thermal response of rat fibroblasts stably transfected with the human 70KDa heat protein-encoding gene. Proc Natl Acad Sci 1991; 88:1681-1685.
10. Li G, Li L, Liu RY,et al. Heat shock protein hsp70 protects cells from thermal stress even after deletion of its ATP-binding domain. Proc Natl Acad Sci 1992; 89:2036-2040.
11. Riabowal K, Mizzan, LA, Welch, WJ. Heat shock is lethal to fibroblasts micro injected with antibodies against hsp70. Science 1988; 242:433-436.
12. Johnston R, Kucey, BL. Competitive inhibition of hsp70 gene expression causes thermosensitivity. Science 1988; 242:1551-1554.
13. Li C, Laszlo A. Amino acid analogues whilst inducing heat shock proteins sensitize cells to thermal damage. J Cell Physiol 1985; 115:116-122.
14. Landry J, Chretien P, Lambert H, et al. Heat shock resistance conferred by expression of the human HSP27 gene in rodent cells. J Cell Biol 1989; 109(1):7-15.
15. Sanchez Y, Lindquist SL. Hsp 104 required for induced thermotolerance. Science 1990; 248:1112-1115.
16. Bansal G, Norton PM, Latchman DS. The 90kd heat shock protein protects cells from stress but not from viral infection. Exp Cell Res 1991;195:303-306.
17. Laszlo A. The thermoresistant state: Protection from initial damage or better repair? Exp Cell Res 1992; 202:519-531.
18. Burgman P, Konings AWT. Heat induced protein denaturation in the particular fraction of HeLa S3 cells: Effect of thermotolerance. J Cell Physiol 1992; 153:88-94.
19. Li G, Hahn GM. Ethanol-Induced tolerance to heat and adriamycin. Nature 1978; 274:699-701.
20. Barbe M, Tytell M, Gower DJ, et al. Htperthermia protects against light damage in the rat retina. Science 1988; 241:1871-1820.
21. Christman M, Morgan RW, Jacobson FS, et al. Positive control of a regulon for defences against oxidative stress and some heat shock proteins in *Salmonella typhimurium*. Cell 1985; 41:753-762.
22. Polla B, Mili N, Kantengwa S. Heat shock and oxidative injury in human cells. Berlin: Springer-Verlag, 1991.
23. Ciocca DR, Fuqua SA, Lock-Lim S, et al. Response of human breast cancer cells to heat shock and chemotherapeutic drugs. Cancer Res 1992; 52(13):3648-54.
24. Lowenstein D, Chan PH, Miles MF. The stress protein response in cultured neurones: characterization and evidence for a protective role in excitotoxicity. Neuron 1991; 7:1053-1060.
25. Rordorf G, Koroshetz WJ, Bonventre JV. Heat shock protects cultured neurons from glutamate toxicity. Neuron 1991; 7:1043-1051.

26. Westwood J, Wu C. Stress induced oligomerization and chromosomal relocalization of heat shock factor. Nature 1991; 353:822-827.
27. Cotto J, Kline M, Morimoto R. Activation of heat shock factor 1 DNA precedes stress induced serine phosphorylation. J Biol Chem 1996; 271:3355-3358.
28. Iwaki K, Chi SH, Dillmann WH, et al. Induction of HSP70 in cultured rat neonatal cardiomyocytes by hypoxia and metabolic stress. Circulation 1993; 87:2023-2032.
29. Ananthan J, Goldberg A, Voellmy R. Abnormal proteins serve as eukaryotic signals and trigger the activation of heat shock genes. Science 1986; 232:522-524.
30. Theodorakis N, Morimoto R. Post transcriptional regulation of Hsp70 expression in human cells. Effects of heat shock, inhibition of protein synthesis, and adenovirus infection on translation and mRNA stability. Moll Cell Biol 1987; 8:393-405.
31. Petersen R, Lindquist S. The drosophila Hsp70 message is rapidly degraded at normal temperatures and stabilized by heat shock. Gene 1988; 72:161-168.
32. Currie RW, Ross BM, Davis TA. Induction of the heat shock response in rats modulates heart rate, creatine kinase and protein synthesis after a subsequent hyperthermic treatment. Cardiovasc-Res 1990; 24(2):87-93.
33. Currie RW, White FP. Characterization of the synthesis and accumulation of a 71-kilodalton protein induced in rat tissues after hyperthermia. Can-J-Biochem-Cell-Biol 1983; 61(6):438-46.
34. Currie R. Effects of ischemia and perfusion temperature on the synthesis of stress induced (heat shock) proteins in isolated and perfused rat hearts. J Mol Cardiol 1987; 19:795-808.
35. Mehta HB, Popovich BK, Dillmann WH. Ischemia induces changes in the level of mRNAs coding for stress protein 71 and creatine kinase M. Circ-Res 1988; 63(3):512-7.
36. Knowlton A, Brecher P, Apstein CS. Rapid expression of heat shock protein in the rabbit after brief cardiac ischemia. J Clin Invest 1990; 87:139-147.
37. Tuijl M, van Bergan en Henegouwen PM, van Wijk R, et al. The isolated neonatal rat-cardiomyocyte used as an in vitro model for "ischemia".II. Induction of the 68kDa heat shock protein. Biochim Biophys Acta 1991; 1091:278-284.
38. Howard G, Geoghegan TE. Altered cardiac tissue gene expression during acute hypoxia exposure. Mol Cell Biochem 1986; 69:155-160.
39. Delcayre C, Samuel JL, Marotte F, et al. Synthesis of stress proteins in rat cardiac myocytes 2-4 days after imposition of hemodynamic overload. J-Clin-Invest 1988; 82(2):460-8.
40. Knowlton AA, Eberli FR, Brecher P, et al. A single myocardial stretch or decreased systolic fiber shortening stimulates the expression of heat shock protein 70 in the isolated, erythrocyte-perfused rabbit heart. J-Clin-Invest 1991;88(6):2018-25.
41. Low Friedrich I, Weisensee D, Mitrou P, et al. Cytokines induce stress protein formation in cultured cardiac myocytes. Basic-Res-Cardiol 1992; 87(1):12-8 issn: 0300-8428.
42. Moalic JM, Bauters C, Himbert D, et al. Phenylephrine, vasopressin and angiotensin II as determinants of proto-oncogene and heat-shock protein gene expression in adult rat heart and aorta. J-Hypertens 1989; 7(3):195-201.
43. White FP, White SR. Isoproterenol induced myocardial necrosis is associated with stress protein synthesis in rat heart and thoracic aorta. Cardiovasc-Res 1986; 20(7):512-5.
44. Low Friedrich I, Schoeppe W. Synthesis of shock proteins in cultured fetal mouse myocardial cells. Exp-Cell-Res 1989; 180(2):451-9.
45. Low Friedrich I, Schoeppe W. Effects of calcium channel blockers on stress protein synthesis in cardiac myocytes. J-Cardiovasc-Pharmacol 1991; 17(5):800-6.
46. Low Friedrich I, von Bredow F, Schoeppe W. A cell culture assay for the detection of cardiotoxicity. J-Pharmacol-Methods 1991; 25(2):133-45.
47. Morris SD, Cumming DV, Latchman DS, et al. Specific induction of the 70-kD heat stress proteins by the tyrosine kinase inhibitor herbimycin-A protects rat neonatal cardiomyocytes. A new pharmacological route to stress protein expression? J-Clin-Invest 1996; 97(3):706-712.
48. Currie RW, Karmazyn M, Kloc M, et al. Heat-shock response is associated with enhanced postischemic ventricular recovery. Circ Res 1988; 63:543-9.
49. Donnelly TJ, Sievers RE, Vissern FL, et al. Heat shock protein induction in rat hearts. A role for improved myocardial salvage after ischemia and reperfusion? Circulation 1992; 85(2):769-78.

50. Yellon DM, Pasini E, Cargnoni A, et al. The protective role of heat stress in the ischemic and reperfused rabbit myocardium. J Mol Cell Cardiol 1992; 24:895-907.
51. Currie RW, Tanguay RM, Kingma JG. Heat-shock response and limitation of tissue necrosis during occlusion/reperfusion in rabbit hearts. Circulation 1993; 87:963-71.
52. Pasini E, Cargnoni, A, Ferrari, R, et al. Heat stress and oxidative damage following ischemia and reperfusion in the isolated rat heart. J Mol Cell Cardiol 1991; 23(Suppl 5): S70.
53. Currie R, Karmazyn M. Improved post-ischemic ventricular recovery in the absence of changes in energy metabolism in working rat hearts following heat shock. J Mol Cell Cardiol 1990; 22:631-636.
54. Cornelussen R, Spiering W, Webers JH, et al. Heat shock improves ischemic tolerance of hypertrophied rat hearts. Am J Physiol 1994;267(5 Pt 2):H1941-7.
55. Joyeux M, Baxter GF, Thomas DL, et al. Protein kinase C is involved in resistance to myocardial infarction induced by heat stress. J Mol Cell Cardiol 1997; 29(12):3311-9.
56. Walker DM, Pasini E, Kucukoglu S, et al. Heat stress limits infarct size in the isolated perfused rabbit heart. Cardiovasc-Res 1993; 27(6):962-7 issn: 0008-6363.
57. Marber MS, Latchman DS, Walker JM, et al. Cardiac stress protein elevation 24 hours after brief ischemia or heat stress is associated with resistance to myocardial infarction. Circulation 1993; 88:1264-72.
58. Yellon DM, Iliodromitis E, Latchman DS, et al. Whole body heat stress fails to limit infarct size in the reperfused rabbit heart. Cardiovasc-Res 1992; 26(4):342-6.
59. Donnelly TJ, Sievers RE, Vissern FL, et al. Heat shock protein induction in rat hearts. A role for improved myocardial salvage after ischemia and reperfusion? Circulation 1992; 85:769-78.
60. Hutter MM, Sievers RE, Barbosa V, et al. Heat-shock protein induction in rat hearts. A direct correlation between the amount of heat-shock protein induced and the degree of myocardial protection. Circulation 1994; 89:355-60.
61. Miura T, Ogawa T, Iwamoto T, et al. Dipyridamole potentiates the myocardial infarct size-limiting effect of ischemic preconditioning. Circulation 1992; 86(3):979-85.
62. Liu X, Engelman RM, Moraru H, et al. Heat shock. A new approach for myocardial preservation in cardiac surgery. Circulation 1992; 86(5 Suppl):358-63.
63. Schott R, Nao, B, Strieter, R, et al. Heat shock does not precondition canine myocardium (abstract). Circulation 1990; 82(Suppl III):III-464.
64. Walker DM, Pasini E, Kucukoglu S, et al. Heat stress limits infarct size in the isolated perfused rabbit heart. Cardiovasc-Res 1993; 27(6):962-967.
65. Huber SA. Heat-shock protein induction in adriamycin and picornavirus-infected cardiocytes. Lab-Invest 1992; 67(2):218-24.
66. Kukreja RC, Kontos MC, Loesser KE, et al. Oxidant stress increases heat shock protein 70 mRNA in isolated perfused rat heart. Am-J-Physiol 1994; 267(6 Pt 2):H2213-9.
67. Van Winkle DM, Thornton J, Downey JM. Cardioprotection from ischemic preconditioning is lost following prolonged reperfusion in the rabbit. Coronary Artery Dis 1991; 2:613-19.
68. Thornton J, Striplin S, Liu GS, et al. Inhibition of protein synthesis does not block myocardial protection afforded by preconditioning. Am J Physiol 1990; 259:H1822-5.
69. Kuzuya T, Hoshida S, Yamashita N, et al. Delayed effects of sublethal ischemia on the acquisition of tolerance to ischemia. Circ Res 1993; 72:1293-9.
70. Kitagawa K, Matsumoto M, Tagaya M, et al. "Ischemic tolerance" phenomenon found in the brain. Brain Res 1990; 528:21-24.
71. Kitagawa K, Matsumoto M, Kuwabara K, et al. Ischemic tolerance phenomenon detected in various brain regions. Brain Res 1991; 561:203-211.
72. Liu Y, Kato H, Nakata N, et al. Protection of rat hippocampus against ischemic neuronal damage by pretreatment with sublethal ischemia. Brain Res 1992;586:121-4.
73. Nowak TS, Jr. Protein synthesis and the heart shock/stress response after ischemia. Cerebrovasc-Brain-Metab-Rev 1990; 2(4):345-66.
74. Muller D, Topol EJ, Califf RM, et al. Relationship between antcedent angina pectoris and short-term prognosis after thrombolytic therapy for acute myocardial infarction. Thrombolysis and angioplasty in myocardial infarction (TAMI) study group. Am Heart J 1990; 119:224-231.
75. Meerson F, Malyshev IY. Adaption to stress increases the heart resistance to ischemic and reperfusion arrhythmias. J Mol Cell Cardiol 1989; 21:299-303.

76. Meerson FZ, Malyshev I, Zamotrinsky AV. Differences in adaptive stabilization of structures in response to stress and hypoxia relate with the accumulation of hsp70 isoforms. Mol-Cell-Biochem 1992; 111(1-2):87-95.
77. Meerson F, Malyshev I, Arkhipenko Y, et al. Adaptive increase in the resistance of the heart to the calcium paradox (abstract). J Moll Cell Cardiol 1991; 23(suppl V):S162.
78. Meerson FZ, Malyshev I, Shneider AB. Phenomenon of the adaptive stabilization of sarcoplasmic and nuclear structures in myocardium. Basic Res Cardiol 1991; 3:205-14.
79. Marber MS, Walker JM, Latchman DS, et al. Attenuation by heat stress of a submaximal calcium paradox in the rabbit heart. J-Mol-Cell-Cardiol 1993; 25(9):1119-26.
80. Su CY, Chong KY, Owen OE, et al. Constitutive and inducible hsp70s are involved in oxidative resistance evoked by heat shock or ethanol. J Mol Cell Cardiol 1998; 30(3):587-98.
81. Marber MS, Walker JM, Latchman DS, et al. Myocardial protection after whole body heat stress in the rabbit is dependent on metabolic substrate and is related to the amount of the inducible 70-kD heat stress protein. J Clin Invest 1994; 93:1087-94.
82. Marber MS, Mestril R, Chi SH, et al. Overexpression of the rat inducible 70-kD heat stress protein in a transgenic mouse increases the resistance of the heart to ischemic injury. J Clin Invest 1995; 95:1446-56.
83. Plumier JC, Ross BM, Currie RW, et al. Transgenic mice expressing the human heat shock protein 70 have improved post-ischemic myocardial recovery. J Clin Invest 1995; 95:1854-60.
84. Heads RJ, Latchman DS, Yellon DM. Stable high level expression of a transfected human HSP70 gene protects a heart-derived muscle cell line against thermal stress. J Mol Cell Cardiol 1994; 26:695-9.
85. Mestril R, Chi SH, Sayen MR, et al. Expression of inducible stress protein 70 in rat heart myogenic cells confers protection against simulated ischemia-induced injury. J Clin Invest 1994; 93:759-67.
86. Heads RJ, Yellon DM, Latchman DS. Differential cytoprotection against heat stress or hypoxia following expression of specific stress protein genes in myogenic cells. J Mol Cell Cardiol 1995; 27(8):1669-78.
87. Cumming DV, Heads RJ, Watson A, et al. Differential protection of primary rat cardiocytes by transfection of specific heat stress proteins. J-Mol-Cell-Cardiol 1996; 28(12):2343-9.
88. Karmazyn M, Mailer K, Currie RW. Acquisition and decay of heat-shock-enhanced postischemic ventricular recovery. Am J Physiol 1990; 259:H424-31.
89. Ceconi C, Curello S, Cargnoni A, et al. The role of glutathione status in the protection against ischaemic and reperfusion damage: effects of N-acetyl cysteine. J-Mol-Cell-Cardiol 1988; 20(1):5-13.
90. Currie RW, Tanguay RM. Analysis of RNA for transcripts for catalase and Hsp71 in rat hearts after in vivo hyperthermia. Biochem-Cell-Biol 1991; 69(5-6):375-82.
91. Kukreja RC, Hess ML. The oxygen free radical system: from equations through membrane-protein interactions to cardiovascular injury and protection. Cardiovasc-Res 1992; 26(7):641-55.
92. Ferrari R, Ceconi C, Curello A, et al. No evidence of oxygen free radicals-mediated damage during the calcium paradox. Basic Res Cardiol 1989; 84:396-403.
93. Morimoto R, Milarski KL. Expression and function of vertebrate Hsp70 genes. In: Morimoto R, Tissieres A, Georgopoulos C, eds. Stress proteins in biology and medicine. New York: Cold Spring Harbour Laboratory Press, 1990:223-278.
94. Hartl FU. Molecular chaperones in cellular protein folding. Nature 1996 ;381(6583):571-9.
95. Gething MJ, Sambrook J. Protein folding in the cell. Nature 1992; 1995; 95:185460.
96. Kampinga HH, Brunsting JF, Stege GJ, et al. Thermal protein denaturation and protein aggregation in cells made thermotolerant by various chemicals: role of heat shock proteins. Exp Cell Res 1995; 219(2):536-46.
97. Kabakov AE, Gabai VL. Heat shock-induced accumulation of 70-kDa stress protein (HSP70) can protect ATP-depleted tumor cells from necrosis. Exp Cell Res 1995; 217(1):15-21.
98. Kampinga HH. Thermotolerance in mammalian cells. Protein denaturation and aggregation, and stress proteins. J Cell Sci 1993; 104(Pt 1):11-7.
99. Patriarca EJ, Maresca B. Acquired thermotolerance following heat shock protein synthesis prevents impairment of mitochondrial ATPase activity at elevated temperatures in *Saccharomyces cerevisiae.* Exp Cell Res 1990; 190(1):57-64.

100. Ciavarra RP, Goldman C, Wen KK, et al. Heat stress induces hsc70/nuclear topoisomerase I complex formation in vivo: Evidence for hsc70-mediated, ATP-independent reactivation in vitro. Proc Natl Acad Sci USA 1994; 91(5):1751-5.
101. Beckmann RP, Mizzen LE, Welch WJ. Interaction of Hsp 70 with newly synthesized proteins: implications for protein folding and assembly. Science 1990; 1995; 95:185460.
102. Gabai VL, Meriin AB, Mosser DD, et al. Hsp70 Prevents Activation of Stress Kinases. Journal of Biological Chemistry 1997; 272(July 1995; 95:185460.
103. Altschuld R, Ganote CE, Nayler WG. Editoral Comment: What constitutes the calcium paradox? J Mol Cell Cardiol 1991; 23:765-767.
104. Steenberg C, Hill ML, Jennings RB. Cytoskeletal damage during myocardial ischemia: Changes in Vinculin immunofluorescence staining during total in vitro ischemia in canine heart. Circ Res 1987; 60:478-486.
105. Bennardini F, Wrzosek A, Chiesi M. Alpha β-crystallin in cardiac tissue. Association with actin and desmin filaments. Circ-Res 1992; 71(2):288-94.
106. Green L, Liem, RK. Beta-internexin is a microtubule-associated protein identical to the heat-shock cognate protein and the clathrin uncoating ATPase. J Biol Chem 1989; 1995; 95:185460.
107. Havre PA, Hammond GL. Isolation of a translation-inhibiting peptide from myocardium. Am-J-Physiol 1988; 255(5 Pt 2):H1024-31.
108. Kato K, Shinohara H, Goto S, et al. Copurification of small heat shock protein with aβ-crystallin from human skeletal muscle. J Biol Chem 1992; 267:7718-7725.
109. Arrigo AP, Landry J. Expression and function of the low molecular weight heat shock proteins: Cold Spring Harbour Laboratory Press, 1994.
110. Lutsch G, Stahl J, Offhaub U, et al. Localization of Hsp27 and β-crystallin in heart and kidney tissue by immunofluoresence and immunoelectron microscopy. Euro J Cell Biol 1995; 67(suppl.41):25.
111. Hoch B, Lutsch G, Schlegel WP, et al. HSP25 in isolated perfused rat hearts: localization and response to hyperthermia. Mol Cell Biochem 1996; 161:231-9.
112. Guay J, Lambert H, Gingras Breton G, et al. Regulation of actin filament dynamics by p38 map kinase-mediated phosphorylation of heat shock protein 27. J-Cell-Sci 1997; 110(Pt 3):357-68.
113. Huot J, Houle F, Spitz DR, et al. HSP27 phosphorylation-mediated resistance against actin fragmentation and cell death induced by oxidative stress. Cancer Res 1996; 56(2):273-9.
114. Inaguma Y, Hasegawa K, Goto S, et al. Induction of the synthesis of hsp27 and alpha β crystallin in tissues of heat-stressed rats and its suppression by ethanol or an alpha 1- adrenergic antagonist. J Biochem (Tokyo) 1995;117(6):1238-43.
115. Lindquist S. The heat shock response. Ann Rev Biochem 1986; 55:1151-1191.
116. Lau S, Patnaik N, Sayen R, et al. Simultaneous Overexpression of Two Stress Proteins in Rat Cardiomyocytes and Myogenic Cells Confers Protection Against Ischaemia induced Injury. Circulation 1997; 96:2287-2294.
117. Pauly D, Kirk, KA, McMillan, JB. Carnitine palmitoyltransferase in cardiac ischemia. A potential site for altered fatty acid metabolism. Circ Res 1991:68.

CHAPTER 2

Heat Stress Proteins:
A Possible Route to Myocardial Protection

Mohamed Amrani, Caroline C. Gray and Magdi H. Yacoub

Heat stress proteins (hsp) are induced by a variety of stimuli including elevated temperature,[1] ischemia,[2] hypoxia,[3] pressure overload[4] and some chemicals. They help to maintain the metabolic and structural integrity of the cell, as a protective response to external stresses.[5] They are known to protect the myocardium from the damaging effects of ischemia and reperfusion.[6] The heat stress response results in accumulation of heat stress proteins, elevated catalase activity[7] and preservation of high energy phosphates.[8] The beneficial effects associated with these metabolic changes include improved endothelial and mechanical recovery of the ischemic heart.[9] In addition, increased antioxidant capacity,[10] lower incidence of dysrhthymias[11] and reduction in infarct size.[12] It has also been shown that critical amounts of hsp70 are necessary to ensure protection of the myocardium.[13] However, questions remain regarding the biochemical mechanisms underlying this protective effect. Alterations in the cell metabolism and chaperone function[5] of cells expressing heat shock proteins are thought to be responsible.

Despite the obvious clinical benefits related to the heat stress response in a clinical setting, the application of this phenomena remains limited. Heat, both quantitatively and qualitatively, is one of the best inducers of heat stress proteins. However, the effects of heat stress are nonspecific and intracellular damage is a common occurrence. The search for alternative stimuli, particularly within the fields of pharmacotherapy or genetic manipulation, may offer more viable options, if the heat stress response is to take its place as an established strategy for myocardial protection.

Introduction

The outcome of open heart surgery and heart transplantation depends not only on surgical technique but also on adequate myocardial protection against ischemia. Although extensive work has been performed over the past 30 years, the safe ischemic time still remains four hours. This represents a major drawback and obstacle to the use of a larger number of organs. The main focus of research in the field of myocardial protection has been the ischemic period with a view to prolonging the time course for organ procurement and transplantation.

Over the last 10 years, studies have revealed that the pre-ischemic period could also be targeted as a strategy for protection against ischemia, by stimulating the intrinsic cellular mechanisms of the heart. Candidates for the role of "endogenous myocardial protectant" are numerous. However, none have been studied more extensively than the heat stress proteins. Major efforts have been made to elucidate the underlying mechanisms surrounding their expression and hence the clinical implications of their potential benefits.

Heat Shock Proteins in Myocardial Protection, edited by Rakesh C. Kukreja and Michael L. Hess.

What Are Heat Stress Proteins?

In 1963, Ritossa et al reported observations of chromosomal puffing of the salivary glands of the fruit fly, *Drosophila busckii*, following exposure to hyperthermia. Ritossa recognized that the pattern of chromosmal puffing corresponded to the switching on and off of specific genes in response to heat stress.[14] He also noted that induction of gene expression was not exclusive to heat but compounds such as salicylate and 2,4-DNP were also effective. Ten years later, Tissieres et al demonstrated that increased protein synthesis in response to heat was the same in all organs tested, not just the salivary glands of the fruit fly. He observed an upregulation of distinct gene products.[15] It would be a few years before these proteins were identified and characterized by molecular biologists as heat stress proteins. However the findings of these early studies established the heat stress response as a general adaptation mechanism. Over the years, scientists have gained a greater understanding of this phenomena and recognition of the potential benefits of utility in many areas of therapeutic medicine, mainly organ preservation against ischemia.

Heat stress proteins are a small family of gene products which are expressed as an intracellular response to stress.[16] This is classically termed the heat shock response and is characterized by a temporary change in cell metabolism in response to a brief sublethal exposure to a noxious stimulus.[17] As such, it is a universal response which is used by all known organisms to minimize the harmful effects caused by alterations in their cellular environment.[18] The high conservation of hsp's throughout the evolutionary ladder suggests that these proteins must have a vital role in attenuating cell injury.[19]

Many agents and conditions are known to initiate the heat stress response. These stimulants include elevated temperature,[20] ischemia,[2] hypoxia,[21] depletion of ATP,[22] free radicals[23] and hypothermia.[24] Cells and tissues which accumulate heat shock proteins develop a transient resistance to subsequent episodes of that particular stress or a 'cross tolerance' to a different stress.[25] The accumulation of hsp's in cardiac cells enhances myocardial resistance to ischemia/reperfusion injury and improves post-ischemic recovery of cardiac function.[26]

Introducing the Major Cardiac Heat Stress Proteins

The gene members of this family are numerous and diverse in nature; they are characterized by molecular weight. The inducible forms are expressed exclusively in response to intracellular stress, to help facilitate survival of the cell due to their cytoprotective properties. They are also expressed constitutively in the unstresssed cell and referred to as heat shock cognates. Their role is to bind reversibly to denaturing or immature polypeptides to deter inappropriate interactions which may lead to misfolding, aggregation and loss of function.[27] Therefore, hsp's are often referred to as 'molecular chaperones'.[5] The underlying mechanisms surrounding the protective effects of hsp's in the stressed cell have yet to be fully elucidated. However, it is believed that by acting as molecular chaperones this may contribute to their cytoprotective properties. This section will give a brief overview of those family members which are thought to be important cardiac hsp genes.

The Hsp90 Class

Hsp90 is one of the most abundant constitutively expressed stress protein and is located in the nucleus and cytoplasm of the eukaryotic cell. This stress protein contains a ATP-binding site necessary for autophorylation and substrate specificity for protein kinases.[28] Although hsp90 is heat-inducible,[29] hsp90 mRNA levels are more strongly induced by ischemia/reperfusion than heat stress.[30] Hsp90 shows a high degree of specificity for binding to steroid receptor complexes in association with hsp56 and hsp70. The binding of hsp90 to the erb-A gene family (glucocorticoid, estrogen, androgen and progestrone receptor) exerts a negative effect on their activity.[31] Recently it has been demonstrated that the interaction of hsp90 with endothelial nitric oxide synthase activates production of agonist-stimulated release of nitric oxide and subsequent endothelium- dependent relaxation of blood vessels.[32] This may have important implications as low-coronary reflow, following prolonged cardioplegic arrest is thought to be result of an attenuation in nitric oxide release.[33,34] In addition, hsp90 has the ability to associate with transcription factors which modulate transcriptional activity and the expression of other heat stress proteins.[35] Hsp90 can also function as a molecular chaperone, with the assistance of proteins from the prolyl isomerase family, to help direct intracellular protein folding.[36] The 90kDa stress protein is also able to bind to actin and tublin, major constituents of the cell cytoskeleton. It is thought that hsp90 crosslinks with actin filaments in a Ca^{2+} and ATP dependent manner.[37] Therefore, hsp90 may regulate actin-myosin interactions which may contribute to modulation of the cytoskeletal dynamics, particularly in the stressed cell. This could be of particular relevance in myocardial protection in that integrity of the cytoskeleton is known to be affected during myocardial necrosis.

The Hsp70 Class

The 70kDa stress protein is the most closely studied of all the hsp's. Hsp70 is constitutively expressed and located in the cytosol. It is heat-inducible and can be induced by a whole variety of stimuli which cause accumulation in the nucleus.[38] The structure of hsp70 consists of two domains; a highly conserved amino-terminal ATPase and a carboxy-terminal peptide-binding domain.[39] Hsp70 is the main chaperone molecule of all eukaryotic cells and plays a major role in facilitating the folding of newly synthesized proteins.

In the unstressed cell, hsp70 interacts with immature or denaturing proteins via a K^{+}ATP-dependent mechanism to ensure the proper folding of the protein into its native three dimensional structure.[40] Hydrophobic regions which become exposed during protein synthesis or denaturation are the target sites for hsp70 interaction.[41] The association of hsp70 with unstable proteins prevents the formation of unfavorable protein interactions which could result in cellular dysfunction and cell death especially during intracellular stress. The cytoprotective role of hsp70 is thought to be an extension of its ability to chaperone damaged proteins in response to intracellular stress. The accumulation of hsp70 in cardiac cells by heat stress is known to protect the myocardium from ischemic injury.[8,9,42] The precise mechanism of this effect as yet to be revealed. This stress protein is also involved in the translocation of polypeptides between compartments of the cell. They facilitate the unfolding of proteins to allow them entry through nuclear pores or across cellular membranes. Once the protein has transversed the membrane, hsp70 assists in the refolding of the protein.[43]

The Hsp60 Class

This stress protein is constitutively expressed in the cytoplasm and translocated to the mitochondria. The structure of hsp60 consists of a ring-like oligomeric structure with seven subunits which exhibits a weak K^{+}-dependent ATPase activity. This stress protein is also heat inducible; however ischemia has been shown to be a potent inducer.[44] Hsp60 is the major molecular chaperone of the mitchondria. Nuclear encoded mitochondrial proteins are imported from the cytoplasm, it is the role of hsp60 and hsp70 to facilitate their refolding as they translocate the outer and inner membranes of the mitochondria.[45,46]

The Hsp27 Class

Hsp27 is found in all eukaryotic cells and contains a highly conserved α-crystallin domain. Hsp27 is constitutively expressed and induction by heat stress is well-known.[47] Phosphorylation of human hsp27 occurs at the serine residues 78 and 82,[48] by either MAPKAP kinase-2,[49]

MAP or protein kinase C,[50] in response to stress factors which renders this stress protein active. This heat stress protein appears to be involved in the regulation of actin microfilament dynamics or actin filament stability as activation of hsp27 increases its affinity for actin filament.[51] Although there is a lack of evidence to suggest that hsp27 plays a direct role in preservation of cardiac tissue, it would appear that conservation of cytoskeleton during heat stress may contribute to myocardial protection. Overexpression of hsp27 following gene transfection of Chinese hamster cells has been shown to confer thermotolerance.[52]

Dynamics of Heat Stress Protein Gene Expression and Regulation

For the molecular biologist, the example of the heat stress response represents the epitome of inducible gene expression. Activation of the heat stress gene is rapid in response to heat stress or any other physiological stimuli. For transcription to occur, the heat shock transcription factor (HSF) must assemble to form a trimer. Human HSF is a multi-zipper protein with a high affinity for DNA. Formation of HSF trimers are thought to be dependent on the a interaction of hydrophobic repeats contained in the amino-terminal region. The carboxyl terminal end contains a leucine motif which helps to maintain the protein in its monomeric form. In the unstressed cell, HSF is found in a nonactive monomer state, which is devoid of any DNA-binding activity. There is evidence to suggest that the carboxyl-terminal zipper inhibits trimerization by forming intramolecular coil interactions with the zipper containing the amino-terminal of the HSF. These coil interactions are thought to be sensitive to heat stress.[53] In the stressed cell, HSF becomes phosphorylated and assembles from the cytoplasm and nucleus to form activated trimers, which accumulate in the nucleus.[54] Phosphorylation of serine and threonine residues contained within the HSF may also contribute to the regulation of heat shock gene activation.[54] The HSF trimers associate with specific target sequences on the DNA promoter region of the heat-inducible gene. These regions are commonly termed the heat shock elements (HSE), which consist of a motif of inverted repeats, with the sequence 5′-nGAAn-3′.[55] The binding of the HSF trimer to the HSE results in transcription of hsp mRNA. The activation of HSF is transient and only lasts for a few hours; however once transcription is initiated, the appearance of hsp mRNA occurs within minutes and can be increased 20-fold within 20 minutes.[17]

Transcription of the hsp genes are also modulated by other transcription factors, namely the TATA-binding factor (TBP) and the GAGA factor. These transcription factors recognize other promoter sequences besides the HSE, of the heat shock gene. The target sequence of TBP is the TATA box and the GAGA factor associates with the GAGA sequence. The binding of these factors are critical for the preactivation of transcription. When the GAGA factor attaches itself to the GAGA box, the nucleosome undergoes structural alterations which cause the promoters to open ready for transcription. The association of TBP to the TATA box sequence is crucial for the modulation of RNA polymerase II activity.[55]

The next level of regulation occurs at translation of the hsp mRNA. The heat shock genes are unusual in structure, as they do not contain any introns or intervening sequences; subsequently this gives rise to RNA lacking intervening sequences. The lack of introns in eukaryotic genes are very rare and it appears to be a feature of all heat shock genes. If present, these introns would have to be removed during RNA processing prior to the transcript being used as a template for protein synthesis. However, the absence of any introns allows for rapid transcription of the gene and mRNA processing.

An early response to intracellular stress, is the loss of splicing function within the cell, which stops the synthesis of genes which contain introns. Therefore the cells replicating machinery is free to make active mRNA of genes i.e., hsp's which lack introns. As a result the response time to hsp expression is quick and efficient. Heat stress causes the accumulation of hsp mRNA in the cytoplasm, ribosomes bind to the template and hsp's are the product of protein synthesis.[17] Another factor which contributes to the selective synthesis of hsp70 during heat stress, is the 10-fold increase in mRNA half-life as demonstrated in Hela cells which ensures rapid synthesis and expression of hsp70 in the heat-stressed cell.[56]

Relevance to Myocardial Protection

Dillman et al was the first to show that hearts subjected to prolonged ischemia and subsequent necrosis, expressed increased levels of hsp70.[57] In 1988, Currie et al introduced the concept of stress preconditioning as a strategy for myocardial protection. They subjected rats to whole body hyperthermia at 42°C for at least 15 minutes and left to recover for 24 hours before excising the heart for perfusion as described by Langendorff. They observed an increase in both hsp70 and catalase activity which correlated with improved myocardial function.[1] These findings were confirmed by Yellon et al using the rabbit isolated perfusion model. They also demonstrated a significant improvement in post-ischemic ventricular function as well as a reduction in creatine phosphokinase release, and better preservation of high energy phosphates.[6] It was therefore proposed that the heat stress "preconditioning" has a number of beneficial effects on the ischemic myocardium and has since been investigated using many animal models.

Experimental Models

Using the isolated perfused heart and global ischemia, many studies have observed additional parameters of protection afforded by heat stress. These include better preservation of postischemic mitochondrial function associated with reduced levels of oxidised glutathione which suggests that there is an attenuation of oxidative stress in the heat stressed heart.[6] Induction of hsp70 in the hypertrophied rat heart 24 hours following whole body hyperthermia enhances cardiac function whilst there is a lower incidence of dysrhythmias.[11] It is known that ischemic dysrhythmias are diminished in the presence of exogenous free radical scavengers, which suggests that heat stress is capable of limiting free radical damage in the ischemic myocardium.[58] Heat stress induction could also be a major benefit in the setting of myocardial infarction. Indeed, there is evidence to suggest that heat stress limits infarct size in the myocardium.[59] Steare et al have demonstrated that whole body hyperthermia renders the isolated rat heart resistant to dysrhythmias caused by coronary ligation and reperfusion. With this experimental model using 45 minutes of regional ischemia in a isolated rabbit heart perfused with either buffer or blood from a control support rabbit, heat stress was shown to reduce infarct size by approximately 15%. However this protection was lost when the support animal was heat stressed. These findings suggest that heat stress can activate certain "blood elements" which are carried in the blood and are capable of deactivating the beneficial effects of hsp70 induction.[60]

Models which explore the potential benefits of heat stress on infarct size in the in situ heart have been used. In this model, a portion of the heart is rendered ischemic by ligation of the coronary artery and infract size is evaluated. Yellon et al have demonstrated that heat stress after 24 hours was not able to reduce infract size in the rabbit following a 45 minute occlusion.[61] These findings were substantiated by other investigators in the rat heart. A study by Donnelly et al demonstrated the effective reduction of infract size in the heat-stressed rat heart following 35 minutes of occlusion but not 45 minutes.[62] The discrepancy between these results is not obvious; however the observed reduction in infarct size is directly proportional to the amount of hsp expression. This suggests that the degree of myocardial protection afforded by heat stress is related to a critical level of ischemic insult which induces the optimal amount of hsp expression. In addition, species specificity of these findings demonstrates the complex nature of heat stress phenomenon.

In vitro models of simulated ischemia, mimicking substrate deprivation and metabolite accumulation known to occur during ischemia are useful in that they explore the cytoprotective effects of hsp induction.[63] Conditions such as ATP depletion can stimulate hsp expression. When myocyte-derived cell lines (H9c2) are transfected with the human hsp70 gene and subjected to oxygen deprivation and limited extracellular volume, the cells overexpressing hsp70 were shown to be more resistant to simulated ischemia than control myogenic cells.[64]

The role of stress proteins in ischemic preconditioning has been a source of speculation for many years. Ischemic preconditioning is an endogenous defence mechanism of the heart to ischemia/reperfusion injury.[65] Brief episodes of ischemia and reperfusion render the myocardium less vulnerable to cellular injury following a prolonged period of ischemia. Marber et al used a preconditioning model which subjected the in vivo rabbit myocardium to four cycles of 5-minute periods of regional ischemia followed by 10 minutes of reperfusion. After 24 hours the level of hsp70 was found to have increased 2- to 3-fold. The degree of hsp accumulation was found to be similar to that observed 24 hours post heat stress. Infarct size after both preconditioning treatment and heat stress were shown to be reduced to 50% of the respective control value.[44] Following the discovery of this second period of myocardial protection which is observed 24 hours later, after the original transient ischemic preconditioning, this phase was termed the 'second window of protection' or SWOP.[66]

Heat Stress and Models Mimicking Cardiac Surgery

The use of cardioplegic arrest and hypothermia are the standard tools for cardiac preservation. The beneficial effects produced by hypothermia are due to a decrease in ATP hydrolysis,[67] an attenuation in loss of mitochondrial function, mainly calcium content and oxygen consumption.[68] The principal component of cardioplegia solution is potassium which causes hyper-polarization and increases the resting potential of the cardiac membrane and raises the threshold level necessary for action potential.[69] The use of cardioplegia and hypothermia for myocardial protection provides a safe period of ischemia, covering four hours for surgical intervention to the ischemic myocardium. Strategies for prolonging the safe ischemic period include heat stress preconditioning, which has been viewed as a possible answer to this problem.

Over the years, we have continued to investigate the role of heat stress proteins in the recovery of cardiac and endothelial function in a protocol mimicking the conditions of cardiac transplantation and routine cardiac surgery. In 1994, we demonstrated that heat stress improved the post-ischemic recovery of cardiac output and endothelial function following cardioplegic arrest for 4 hours at 4°C.[9] To assess the role of catalase in the protective effect of heat stress, we subjected working heat stressed and control rat hearts to ischemic cardioplegic arrest for 4 hours at 4°C with and without the presence of 3-aminotriazole, a catalase inhibitor. We concluded that heat stress enhanced endothelial recovery following prolonged cardioplegic arrest which is dependent on catalase activity, but does not apply to recovery of cardiac mechanical function.[26]

The time course and induction of heat stress proteins following cardioplegic arrest was demonstrated using the working rat heart model and Western blotting. We observed that both cardiac output and endothelial function were improved when the time interval between heat stress and the onset of ischemia ranged from 24-30 hours. Levels of hsp70 fell to virtually zero by 96 hours. Analysis of hsp70 expression showed maximal levels at 24 hours, which correlated with improved mechanical function. These findings emphasized the need for a critical amount of hsp70 to be present in the heart for sufficient protection of the ischemic myocardium.[13]

We have also demonstrated that coronary endothelial cells are the main site of hsp70 induction in the heart and not the cardiomyocytes. Western immunoblotting revealed a tentative amount of hsp70 in endothelial cells and immunocytochemistry showed similar results, which correlated with improved mechanical function from those heat-stressed rat hearts with their endothelium intact.[70] This finding has important implications for preservation of the myocardium following ischemia and reperfusion as endothelial damage is known to play a role in low coronary reflow and myocardial dysfunction following cardioplegic arrest.[9]

Transgenic Animal Models: The Answer to Heat Shock Associated Damage?

Although heat stress proteins can be induced by a variety of stimulants, including ischemia,[71,72] heavy metals,[73] oxidative stress[74] and hypoxia,[75] hyperthermia[76] remains the gold standard. Heat, both quantitatively and qualitatively, is the best inducer of the heat stress response. The main disadvantage are the heat-related effects which cause disruption to the cytoskeleton of the cell. The heat-related damage includes the collapse of the cytoplasmic filaments, swelling of the mitochondria and fragmentation of the Golgi apparatus.[77] In addition, unwanted changes in cellular metabolism also accompany hsp expression and include a switch from aerobic respiration to anaerobic glycolysis[78,79] the activity of glycosyltransferases[80] and polyamine enzymes are altered.[81] Furthermore, heat shock stimulates the release of prostaglandins, arachidonic acid metabolites, and LTB_4 from the cell membrane.[82] Stress conditioning protocols used to induce the synthesis of hsp consist of heating at 42.5°C for 15-20 minutes. This temperature is the standard parameter for many aspects of thermal biology; however for cells this temperature is severe and approaches cytotoxicity.

With the development and introduction of transgenic animals which overexpress hsp70, many of the problems associated with thermal induction of hsp70 have been abolished. For many years, the effects of heat stress protein accumulation via hyperthermia has been difficult to interpret. Induction of hsp70, the major hsp to confer myocardial protection via heat stress, is also associated with increased catalase,[83,84] superoxide dismutase activity[85] and changes in energy metabolism.[86,87] In addition, increased expression of other heat stress proteins have also been reported.[44] The true nature and function of hsp70 has been difficult to assess due to the contributing factors of the above metabolic alterations associated with thermal induction of hsp70. The major advantage of using genetically engineered animals, is that it is now possible to induce and increase hsp70 levels in the myocardium without the introduction of other metabolic changes. Studies also suggest that cardiac levels of hsp70 in transgenic animals are higher than those of heat-stressed animals by 2-fold. Therefore the cytoprotective effects may be enhanced as suggested.[88]

Marber et al were the first to show the myocardial protective effects of hsp70 using transgenic mice. They developed a transgenic mouse cell line using a chimeric transgene encoding rat inducible hsp70 with a cytomegalovirus enhancer and β-actin promotor. Hearts from both transgene negative and positive mice were subjected to Langendorff perfusion, 20 minutes of normothermic ischemia and 120 minutes of reperfusion. In the transgene positive hearts there was a 40% reduction in infarct size, a 2-fold increase in cardiac function at 30 minutes of reperfusion and a 50% reduction in creatine kinase efflux compared to transgene negative hearts.[59] Transgenic mice expressing human hsp70 also showed improved post-ischemic myocardial recovery following 30 minutes of normothermic ischemia compared to control hearts.[89] This also correlated with a decrease in creatine kinase release, an indicator of cell injury. Another study using a similar transgenic mouse line and ^{31}P nuclear magnetic resonance observed enhanced preservation of ATP and phosphocreatine within the initial stages of ischemia. This effect was lost as the ischemic episode lasted for 20 minutes and beyond. This finding suggests that overexpression of the hsp70 may have a detrimental effect on the intact heart with regard to recovery of metabolic pathways.[90]

Suzuki et al using a novel gene transfection method demonstrated improved myocardial tolerance to ischemia/reperfusion injury in rat hearts overexpressing human hsp70. Rat hearts were transfected with human hsp70 by coronary infusion of hemagglutinating virus of Japan, (HVJ) liposome containing the human hsp70 gene. These hearts were then heterotopically transplanted into the abdomens of recipient rats of the same strain. On the fourth day following gene transfection the hearts were excised for Langendorff perfusion and functional assessment. After 30 minutes of normothermic ischemia, better functional recovery was observed, which correlated with a reduction in creatine phosphokinase leakage in hsp70 gene transfected hearts compared to non-treated hearts. Those hearts which were transfected with the hsp70 gene also displayed improved functional recovery compared to heat stressed animals.[88] The results suggest that in vivo gene transfection may be a novel strategy for myocardial protection and appears to be more effective than traditional heat-stress procedures.

Proposed Mechanisms for HSP-Mediated Protection

Molecular Chaperone Functions

Heat stress proteins have been implicated as mediators of myocardial protection. The precise mechanism of their cytoprotective effects remains unknown. However, most hsp's exhibit chaperoning properties and are believed to extend and potentiate this role in the stressed cell to attenuate cellular damage.

A common feature of all toxic agents which accounts for cross-tolerance is their ability to cause proteotoxicity and hence protein denaturation.[91] This is thought to trigger activation of hsp genes and subsequently transcription.[92] It has been speculated that hsp's may negatively regulate their own transcription by means of a autoregulatory loop.[93,94] Hsp70 and perhaps hsp90 are normally present in the cell already bound to newly synthesized polypeptides acting as molecular chaperones. Under the influence of a noxious stimulus, proteins contained within the cell undergo denaturation and aggregation. During this process, the proteins become unstable and lose their structural configuration leading to the exposure of hydrophobic regions. The uncovered hydrophobic sites essentially are target sequences for 'Hsp chaperone attack'.[95] This event causes a decrease in the amount of free Hsp70 available in the cytosol. The inhibitory effect of hsp70 on HSF is removed, activated HSF binds to DNA and the transcriptional response is initiated. This subsequently leads to the synthesis of new hsp70. Newly synthesized hsp70 deactivates HSF and switches off the transcriptional signal.[96-98]

The newly generated hsp's bind to denaturing proteins to avert structural disruption of the cell. hsp's can repair and salvage unfolded proteins to restore their functional structure. Hsp's are also able to target denatured and dysfunctional proteins for degradation by the lyosomes.[99] This prevents the obstruction and disarrangement of metabolic pathways by denatured proteins which have been overlooked by other protective mechanisms.

The acquisition of normal protein synthesis and mitochondrial function in heat-stressed cells 2 hours (5 hours of recovery for control cells to resume normal cell function) after hyperthermia[100] suggests that hsp's can rapidly restore the structural integrity and metabolic functions of the cell following a period of intracellular stress such as ischemia and reperfusion.

Elevated Catalase Activity

Early studies showed that heat stress, not only increases myocardial hsp levels but is also accompanied by an elevation in catalase activity. Currie et al were the first to show an approximate 2-fold increase in catalase activity which was not associated with any changes in mRNA levels encoding catalase which suggests an alteration in translational control processes.[1]

Catalase is a redox enzyme which is thought to potentially reduce the extent of free radical injury in the ischemic myocardium.

The restoration of blood flow to the ischemic myocardium results in the generation of reactive oxygen species or free radicals. This type of injury is termed reperfusion injury. These free radicals cause lipid peroxidation and enzyme dysfunction. Potential sources of reactive oxygen metabolites in the reperfused heart are the mitochondrial redox chain and endothelial enzymes such as NO synthase and xanthine oxidase.[101] The leakage of electrons to oxygen in the mitochondria results in the formation of the O^{2-} anion which is directly related to the early stages of ischemia/reperfusion injury of the heart.[102] It has been demonstrated that xanthine oxidase contributes to the reperfusion injury of the ischemic isolated rat heart.[103] The breakdown of adenosine triphosphate (ATP) during ischemia leads to end products like xanthine and hypoxanthine. These catabolites, together with oxygen supplied during reperfusion, are utilized as substrates by endothelial xanthine oxidase to generate O^{2-} anion.[104] Moreover, the normally present xanthine dehydrogenase is converted to xanthine oxidase. Thus, at the very onset of reperfusion, superoxide anions are generated. Xanthine oxidase is the catalyst, hypoxanthine produced during ischemia and oxygen supplied by reperfusion are the substrates. The fairly innocuous superoxide anion (O^{2-}) can react with H_2O_2 in a Haber-Weiss reaction or through the Fenton reaction to produce a highly harmful hydroxyl radical (OH^-).[104] Under pathological conditions of NO, a vasodilator, released from the endothelium, can combine with superoxide radicals to produce peroxynitrite a very strong oxidizing species, which is implicated in the process of ischemia/reperfusion injury.[105]

We have shown that inhibition of catalase release by 3-amino-1,2,4-triazole abolishes the enhanced endothelial recovery[26] normally observed in the heat-stressed heart. Elevated catalase activity is an important component of the heat stress response and is essential for the protection of the myocardium from the free radical damage which is a major component of ischemia/reperfusion injury.[7]

Preservation of High Energy Phosphates

ATP-depletion is known to have a detrimental effect on cell homeostasis. These effects range from protein aggregation, collapse of the cytoskeleton to loss of ionic balance. Heat stress and subsequent hsp accumulation give rise to an 'ATP-sparing' effect.[22] We have demonstrated using ^{31}P nuclear magnetic resonance that heat stress causes beneficial changes in high energy phosphate metabolism during cardioplegic arrest and reperfusion. Evaluation using High performance liquid chromatography showed increased concentrations of ATP and phosphocreatine levels in heat-stressed hearts compared to control hearts. These changes correlated with an attenuation in purine catabolite release and improved functional recovery.[8]

We have also observed, that heat stress induces increases in myocardial GTP, UTP, CTP and NADPH concentration compared to baseline values in the rat myocardium following 5 min of normoxic Langendorff perfusion.[106] GTP is involved in the signalling pathways of major hormones and metabolites regulating heart function as a ligand of G-proteins.[107] Elevated UTP levels in the heat-stressed heart may facilitate better glycogen turnover[108] which may enhance the resistance of the heart to ischemia.[109] CTP plays an important role in phospholipid synthesis, a constituent of signalling pathways.[110] NADPH contributes to the protection of the myocardium against oxidative stress,[111] increases in the NADP pool provide evidence that heat stress not only increases antioxidant enzyme activity but also alterations to pathways which support antioxidant mechanisms. The changes in energy metabolism may facilitate the cardioprotective effects of heat stress by minimizing the harmful effects of ATP-depletion and improving regulatory processes and metabolism during myocardial ischemic stress.

Activation of Potassium Channels

The second window of protection observed following ischemic preconditioning has been proposed by many investigators to be mediated via synthesis of heat-stress proteins.[44,66] Other forms of cardioprotection following acute ischemic preconditioning are known to be associated with ATP-sensitive potassium (K_{ATP}) channel opening and hence the question, whether K_{ATP} channels play a role in the heat shock response? When heat-resistant cells from radiation-induced fibrosaroma and heat-resistant variants (TR-4, TR-5) were heated at 45°C for 3-30 minutes, induction of voltage-dependent currents were observed following heating. Tetraethyl-ammonium cations blocked this current from activated K_{ATP} channels, suggesting that K^+ voltage-dependent currents play a role in the heat-stress response.[112] Several studies have demonstrated that blockade of ATP-sensitive potassium channels via glibenclamide and sodium 5-hydroxydecanoate abolished reduction of infarct size in heat-stressed hearts when given at the onset of ischemia and reperfusion.[113,114] The results suggest that K_{ATP} channel activation contributes to the cytoprotective effect induced by the heat-stress response.

Protection Against Apoptosis

Apoptosis, programmed cell death, is a highly regulated process[115] involved in ischemic injury[116] and heart disease.[117] Synthesis of heat-stress proteins is thought to increase resistance to apoptosis. The cell surface receptor Fas/APO-1 and its ligand are important mediators of apoptosis. Mehlan et al demonstrated that hsp27 blocks apoptotic cell death preventing anti-APO-1 induced DNA fragmentation and morphological changes and may thus act as novel regulators of apoptosis.[118] Overexpression of human hsp70 gene protects against heat-induced apoptosis, whereas c-myc proto-oncogene expression enhances this effect.[119] Samali et al demonstrated that heat stress treatment of U937 and Wehi-s cells exposed to apoptotic inducing agents actinomycin-D, camptothecin and etoposide showed resistance to cell death (determined by DNA fragmentation and flow cytometric analysis) as compared to control cells.[120] These results suggest that expression of heat stress proteins exhibit a anti-apoptotic role in the mechanism of cardioprotection.

Conclusion: Is There a Role for Heat Stress in the Armamentarium of Myocardial Protection?

Our understanding of the heat-stress proteins has come along way since Ritossa's original discovery of the heat-stress response. However, there still remain elusive areas within our present knowledge of this subject. We do know that expression of heat stress proteins are a cellular response to stress and subsequently leads to an acquired protected state. This state of protection confers resistance to further episodes of exposure to the same stress or a different harmful stimulus. Acquired cellular protection is also known to be transitional, depends on a critical concentration of hsp accumulation for maximal protection[121] and is accompanied by other metabolic alterations. In the myocardium, hsp accumulation improves functional recovery and is associated with increased catalase activity,[83] preservation of high energy phosphates[8] and reduction in infarct size,[12] activation of ATP- sensitive potassium channels[112] and anti-apoptotic effects.[118] However, the precise details of cytoprotective mechanisms of these proteins have yet to be fully elucidated.

From a wide variety of models, we have gained a basic understanding of how hsp's may be used as a strategy for attenuating ischemia/reperfusion injury. However the findings of various animal models alone cannot tell us how the human heart will respond to stress conditioning. There still remains the ever present problem of inducing heat-stress proteins in the human myocardium, as heat stress is not a viable option in a clinical setting. Should an alternative method of inducing hsp's be established and the mechanism of protection elucidated, then heat stress could become an important component in the general strategy of myocardial protection.

References

1. Currie RW, Karmazyn M, Kloc M et al. Heat-shock response is associated with enhanced post-ischemic ventricular recovery. Circ Res 1988; 63:543-549.
2. Richard V, Kaeffer N, Thuillez C. Delayed protection of the ischemic heart—from pathophysiology to therapeutic applications. Fundam Clin Pharmacol 1996; 10:409-415.
3. Heads RJ, Yellon DM, Latchman DS. Differential cytoprotection against heat stress or hypoxia following expression of specific stress protein genes in myogenic cells. J Mol Cell Cardiol 1995; 27:1669-1678.
4. Katayose D, Isoyama S, Fujita H et al. Separate regulation of heme oxygenase and heat shock protein 70 mRNA expression in the rat heart by hemodynamic stress. Biochem Biophys Res Commun 1993; 191:587-594.
5. Macario AJ. Heat-shock proteins and molecular chaperones: implications for pathogenesis, diagnostics, and therapeutics. Int J Clin Lab Res 1995; 25:59-70.
6. Yellon DM, Pasini E, Cargnoni A et al. The protective role of heat stress in the ischaemic and reperfused rabbit myocardium. J Mol Cell Cardiol 24.(1992) pp.895-907.
7. SE Steare and DM Yellon. The potential for endogenous myocardial antioxidants to protect the myocardium against ischaemia-reperfusion injury: refreshing the parts exogenous antioxidants cannot reach? J Mol Cell Cardiol 1995; 27:65-74.
8. Jayakumar J, Smolenski RT, Gray CC et al. Influence of heat stress on myocardial metabolism and functional recovery after cardioplegic arrest: a 31P N.M.R. study. Eur J Cardiothorac Surg 1998; 12:467-474.
9. Amrani M, Corbett J, Allen NJ et al. Induction of heat-shock proteins enhances myocardial and endothelial functional recovery after prolonged cardioplegic arrest. Ann Thorac Surg 1994; 7:157-160.
10. Das DK, Maulik N, Moraru II. Gene expression in acute myocardial stress. Induction by hypoxia, ischemia, reperfusion, hyperthermia and oxidative stress. J Mol Cell Cardiol 1995; 27:181-193.
11. Cornelussen RN, Snoeckx LH, de Bruin LG et al. Hyperthermic preconditioning improves ischemia tolerance in the hyperthrophied and non-hyperthropied rat heart. (Abstract) J Mol Cell Card 1987; 19:795-808.
12. Currie RW, Tanguay RM, Kingma JG, Jr. Heat-shock response and limitation of tissue necrosis during occlusion/reperfusion in rabbit hearts see comments. Circulation 1993; 87:963-971.
13. Amrani M, Corbett J, Boateng SY et al. Kinetics of induction and protective effect of heat-shock proteins after cardioplegic arrest. Ann Thorac Surg 1996; 61:1407-1411.
14. Ritossa F. New puffs induced by temperature shock, DNP and salicylate in salivary chromosomes of D. melanogaster. Drosophila Information Service 1963; 37:122-123.
15. Tissieres A, Mitchell HK, Tracy UM. Protein synthesis in salivary glands of *Drosophila* melanogaster: Relation to chromosome puffs. J Mol Biol 85.(1974) pp.389-398.
16. Lindquist S, Craig EA. The heat-shock proteins. Annu Rev Genet 1988; 22:631-677.
17. Perdrizet GA. The heat shock response. In: Heat shock response and organ preservation: Models of stress conditioning. Springer 1997:27-69.
18. Becker J, Craig EA. Heat shock proteins as molecular chaperones. Eur J Biochem 1994; 219:11-23.
19. Ang D, Liberek K, Skowyra D et al. Biological role and regulation of the universally conserved heat shock proteins. J Biol Chem 1991; 266:24233-24236.
20. Slakey DP, Roza AM, Pieper GM et al. Delayed cardiac allograft rejection due to combined cyclosporine and antioxidant therapy. Transplantation 1993; 56:1305-1309.
21. Patel B, Khaliq A, Jarvis J et al. Hypoxia induces HSP 70 gene expression in human hepatoma (HEP G2) cells. Biochem Mol Biol Int 1995; 36:907-912.
22. Kabakov AE, Gabai VL. Heat Shock Proteins and Cytoprotection: ATP-Deprived Mammalian Cells. In: Springer-Verlag, Heidelberg 1997:85-119.
23. Kukreja RC, Kontos MC, Loesser KE et al. Oxidant stress increases heat shock protein 70 mRNA in isolated perfused rat heart. Am J Physiol 1994; 267:H2213-9.
24 Yang XM, Baxter GF, Heads RJ et al. Infarct limitation of the second window of protection in a conscious rabbit model. Cardiovasc Res 1996; 31:777-783.

25. Heads RJ, Latchman DS, Yellon DM. Stable high level expression of a transfected human HSP70 gene protects a heart-derived muscle cell line against thermal stress. J Mol Cell Cardiol 1994; 26:695-699.
26. Amrani M, Allen NJ, O'Shea J et al. Role of catalase and heat shock protein on recovery of cardiac endothelial and mechanical function after ischemia. Cardioscience 1993; 4:193-198.
27. Wynn RM, Davie JR, Cox RP et al. Molecular chaperones: Heat-shock proteins, foldases, and matchmakers. J Lab Clin Med 1994; 124:31-36.
28. T. Scheibel, Neuhofen S, Weikl T et al. ATP-binding properties of human hsp90. J Biol Chem 1997; 272:18608-18613.
29. Ketis NV, Lawler J, Bendena WG. Extracellular matrix components affect the pattern of protein synthesis of endothelial cells responding to hyperthermia. In Vitro Cell Dev Biol Anim 1993; 29A:768-772.
30. Nishizawa J, Nakai A, Higashi T et al. Reperfusion causes significant activation of heat shock transcription factor 1 in ischemic rat heart. Circulation 1996; 94:2185-2192.
31. Baulieu EE, Binart N, Cadepond F et al. Receptor-associated nuclear proteins and steroid/antisteroid action. Ann NY Acad Sci 1990; 595:300-315.
32. Garcia-Cardena G, Fan R, Shah V et al. Dynamic activation of endothelial nitric oxide synthase by hsp90. Nature 1998; 92:821-824.
33. Amrani M, Chester AH, Jayakumar J et al. L-arginine reverses low coronary reflow and enhances post-ischemic recovery of cardiac mechanical function. Cardiovasc Res 1995; 30:200-204.
34. Amrani M, O'Shea J, Allen NJ et al. Role of basal release of nitric oxide on coronary flow and mechanical performance of the isolated rat heart. J Physiol Lond 1992; 456:681-687.
35. Nadeau K, Das A, Walsh CT. Hsp90 chaperonins possess ATPase activity and bind heat shock transcription factors and peptidyl prolyl isomerases. J Biol Chem 1993; 268:1479-1487.
36. Bose S, Weikl T, Bugl H et al. Chaperone function of hsp90-associated proteins. Science 1996; 274:1715-1717.
37. Nishida E, Koyasu S, Sakai H et al. Calmodulin-regulated binding of the 90-kDa heat shock protein to actin filaments. J Biol Chem 1986; 261:16033-16036.
38. Lewis MJ, Pelham HR. Involvement of ATP in the nuclear and nucleolar functions of the 70 kd heat shock protein. EMBO J. 1985; 4:3137-3143.
39. Minowada G, Welch WJ. Clinical implications of the stress response. J Clin Invest 1995:3-12.
40. Fung KL, Hilgenberg L, Wang NM et al. Conformations of the nucleotide and polypeptide binding domains of a cytosolic hsp70 molecular chaperone are coupled. J Biol Chem 1996; 271:21559-21565.
41. Blond Elguindi S, Cwirla SE, Dower WJ et al. Affinity panning of a library of peptides displayed on bacteriophages reveals the binding specificity of BiP. Cell 1993; 75:717-728.
42. Schelbert HR. Cardiac PET: Microcirculation and substrate transport in normal and diseased human myocardium. Ann Nucl Med 1994; 8:91-100.
43. Hartl FU. Heat shock proteins in protein folding and membrane translocation. Semin Immunol 1991; 3:5-16.
44. Marber MS, Latchman DS, Walker JM et al. Cardiac stress protein elevation 24 hours after brief ischemia or heat stress is associated with resistance to myocardial infarction. Circulation 1993; 88:1264-1272.
45. Ostermann J, Horwich AL, Neupert W et al. Protein folding in mitochondria requires complex formation with hsp60 and ATP hydrolysis. Nature 1989; 341:125-130.
46. Endo T. Cooperative binding of hsp60 may promote transfer from hsp70 and correct folding of imported proteins in mitochondria corrected published erratum appears in FEBS Lett Jan 20 1992; 296(2):235. FEBS Lett 1991; 293:1-3.
47. Kontos MC, Shipley JB, Kukreja RC. Heat stress improves functional recovery and induces synthesis of 27- and 70-kDa heat shock proteins without preserving sarcoplasmic reticulum function in the ischemic rat heart. J Mol Cell Cardiol 1996; 28:1885-1894.
48. Landry J, Lambert H, Zhou M et al. Human HSP27 is phosphorylated at serines 78 and 82 by heat shock and mitogen-activated kinases that recognize the same amino acid motif as S6 kinase II. J Biol Chem 1992; 267:794-803.

49. Rouse J, Cohen P, Trigon S et al. A novel kinase cascade triggered by stress and heat shock that stimulates MAPKAP kinase-2 and phosphorylation of the small heat shock proteins. Cell 1994; 78:1027-1037.
50. Santell L, Bartfeld NS, Levin EG. Identification of a protein transiently phosphorylated by activators of endothelial cell function as the heat-shock protein HSP27. A possible role for protein kinase C Biochem J 1992; 284:705-710.
51. Lavoie JN, Lambert H, Hickey E et al. Modulation of cellular thermoresistance and actin filament stability accompanies phosphorylation-induced changes in the oligomeric structure of heat shock protein 27. Mol Cell Biol 1995; 15:505-516.
52. Lavoie JN, Gingras Breton G, Tanguay RM et al. Induction of Chinese hamster HSP27 gene expression in mouse cells confers resistance to heat shock. HSP27 stabilization of the microfilament organization. J Biol Chem 1993; 268:3420-3429.
53. Rabindran SK, Haroun RI, Clos J et al. Regulation of heat shock factor trimer formation: Role of a conserved leucine zipper. Science. 1993; 259:230-234.
54. Morimoto RI. Cells in stress: Transcriptional activation of heat shock genes. Science. 1993; 259:1409-1410.
55. Fernandes M, O'Brien T, Lis JT. Structure and regulation of heat shock gene promoters. In: The biology of heat shock proteins and molecular chaperones. 1994:417-455. Morimoto RI, Tissieres A, Georgopoulos C. (eds.), Cold Spring Harbor, NY. Cold Spring Harbor Laboratory Press.
56. Theodorakis NG, Morimoto RI. Posttranscriptional regulation of hsp70 expression in human cells: Effects of heat shock, inhibition of protein synthesis, and adenovirus infection on translation and mRNA stability. Mol Cell Biol 1987; 7:4357-4368.
57. Dillmann WH, Mehta HB, Barrieux A et al. Ischemia of the dog heart induces the appearance of a cardiac mRNA coding for a protein with migration characteristics similar to heat-shock/stress protein 71. Circ Res 1986; 59:110-114.R.N.
58. Mocanu MM, Steare SE, Evans MC et al. Heat stress attenuates free radical release in the isolated perfused rat heart. Free Radic Biol Med 1993; 15:459-463.
59. Marber MS, Mestril R, Chi SH et al. Overexpression of the rat inducible 70-kD heat stress protein in a transgenic mouse increases the resistance of the heart to ischemic injury. J Clin Invest 1995; 95:1446-1456.
60. Steare SE, Yellon DM. The protective effect of heat stress against reperfusion arrhythmias in the rat. J Mol Cell Cardiol 1993; 25:1471-1481.
61. Yellon DM, Iliodromitis E, Latchman DS et al. Whole body heat stress fails to limit infarct size in the reperfused rabbit heart. Cardiovasc Res 1992; 26:342-346.
62. Donnelly TJ, Sievers RE, Vissern FL et al. Heat shock protein induction in rat hearts. A role for improved myocardial salvage after ischemia and reperfusion? Circulation 1992; 85:769-778.
63. Yellon DM, Marber MS. Hsp70 in myocardial ischaemia. Experientia. 1994; 50:1075-1084.
64. Williams RS, Thomas JA, Fina M et al. Human heat shock protein 70 (hsp70) protects murine cells from injury during metabolic stress. J Clin Invest 1993; 92:503-508.
65. Murry CE, Jennings RB, Reimer KA. Preconditioning with ischemia: A delay of lethal cell injury in ischemic myocardium. Circulation 1986; 74:1124-1136.
66. Yellon DM, Baxter GF. A "second window of protection" or delayed preconditioning phenomenon: Future horizons for myocardial protection? J Thorac Cardiovasc Surg 1995; 115:200-209.
67. Popovic V, Popovic P. Hypothermia in Biology and Medicine. In:AnonymousGrune and Stratton, New York 1974.
68. Ferrari R, Raddino R, Di Lisa F et al. Effects of temperature on myocardial calcium homeostasis and mitochondrial function during ischemia and respefusion. J Thorac Cardiovasc Surg 1990; 99:919-928.
69. Hearse DJ, Stewart DA, Braimbridge MV. Cellular protection during myocardial ischemia: the development and characterization of a procedure for the induction of reversible ischemic arrest. Circulation 1976; 54:193-202.
70. Amrani M, Latif N, Morrison K et al. Relative Induction of haet shock protein in coronary endothelial cells and cardiomyocytes: Implications for myocardial protection. J Thorac Cardiovasc Surg 1998:200-209.

71. Knowlton AA, Brecher P, Apstein CS. Rapid expression of heat shock protein in the rabbit after brief cardiac ischemia. J Clin Invest 1991; 87:139-147.
72. Mehta HB, Popovich BK, Dillmann WH. Ischemia induces changes in the level of mRNA coding for stress protein 71 and creatine kinase M Circ Res 1988; 63:512-517.
73. Whelan SA, Hightower LE. Induction of stress proteins in chicken embryo cells by low level zinc contamination in amino acid free media. J Cell Physiol 1985:205-209.
74. Burdon RH, Gill VM, Rice Evans C. Oxidatve stress and heat shock protein induction in human cells. Free Rad Res Comms 1987:129-39.
75. Howard G, Geoghegan TE. Altered cardiac tissue gene expression during acute hypoxic exposure. Mol Cell Biochem 1986:155-160.
76. Hutter MM, Sievers RE, Barbosa V et al. Heat-shock protein induction in rat hearts. A direct correlation between the amount of heat-shock protein induced and the degree of myocardial protection. Circulation 1994; 89:355-360.
77. Shyy T, Asch BB, Asch HL. Concurrent collapse of keratin filaments, aggregation of organelles, and inhibition of protein synthesis during heat shock response in mammary epithelial cells. J Cell Biol 1989:997-1008.
78. Lanks KW. Modulators of the eukaryotic heat shock response. Exp Cell Res 1986:1-10.
79. Nickells RW, Wang TI, Browder LW. Heat shock-induced changes in energy metabolism of *Xenopus laevis* embryos. J Cell Biol 1986; 26th meeting Abstract #913.
80. Henle KJ, Stone A. Effect of hyperthermia on activity of three glycosyltransferases in Chinese hamster ovary cells. Cancer Res 1988:5717-5721.
81. Harari PM, Tome ME, Gerner EW. Heat shock-induced polyamine oxidation in mammalian cells. J Cell Biol 1986:175a.
82. Calderwood SK, Bornstein B, Farnum EK et al. Heat shock stimulates the release of arachidonic acid and the synthesis of prostaglandins and leukotriene B4 in mammalian cells. J Cell Physiol 1998:325-333.
83. Currie RW, Tanguay RM. Analysis of RNA for transcripts for catalase and SP71 in rat hearts after in vivo hyperthermia. Biochem Cell Biol 1991; 69:375-382.
84. Wall SR, Fliss H, Korecky B. Role of catalase in myocardial protection against ischemia in heat shocked rats. Mol Cell Biochem 1993:187-194.
85. Liu X, Engelman RM, Moraru II et al. Heat shock. A new approach for myocardial preservation in cardiac surgery. Circulation 1992; 86:II358-63.
86. Amrani M, Smolenski RT, Gray C et al. Heat shock induces increase in NADP, GTP and pyrimidine nucleotides in the heart. J Mol Cell Cardiol 1996; 28:A47
87. Smolenski RT, Gray C, Amrani M et al. Nucleotide metabolism in the heart subjected to heat stress. Clin Biochem 1997; 30:15
88. Suzuki K, Sawa Y, Kaneda Y et al. In vivo gene transfection with heat shock protein 70 enhances myocardial tolerance to ischemia-reperfusion injury in rat. J Clin Invest 1997; 99:1645-1650.
89. Plumier JC, Ross BM, Currie RW et al. Transgenic mice expressing the human heat shock protein 70 have improved post-ischemic myocardial recovery. J Clin Invest 1995; 95:1854-1860.
90. Radford NB, Fina M, Benjamin IJ et al. Cardioprotective effects of 70-kDa heat shock protein in transgenic mice. Proc Natl Acad Sci USA 1996; 93:2339-2342.
91. Chang JP, Kiehl DE, Kennington A. Separation and characterization of the tryptic peptide mapping of recombinant bovine growth hormone by reversed-phase high-performance liquid chromatography electrospray mass spectrometry. Rapid Commun Mass Spectrom 1997; 11:1266-1270.
92. Anathan J, Goldberg AL, Voellmy R. Abnormal proteins serve as eukaryotic stress signals and trigger the activation of heat shock genes. Science 1986; 232:252-254.
93. Abravaya K, Myers MP, Murphy SP et al. The human heat shock protein hsp70 interacts with HSF, the transcription factor that regulates heat shock gene expression. Genes Dev. 1992; 6:1153-1164.
94. Craig EA, Gross C. Is hsp70 the cellular thermometer? Trends Biochem Sci 1991; 16:135-140.
95. Pelham HR. Speculations on the functions of major heat shock and glucose regulated proteins. Cell 1986; 46:959-961.
96. Baler R, Welch WJ, Voellmy R. Heat shock regulation by nascent polypeptides and denaturated proteins: hsp70 as a potential autoregulatory factor. J Cell Biol 1992; 117:1151-1159.

97. Mosser DD, Duchaine J, Massie B. The DNA- binding activity of the human heat shock transcription factor is regulated in vivo by hsp70. Mol Cell Biol 1993; 13:5427-5438.
98. Mifflin LC, Cohen R. hsc70 moderates the heat shock (stress) response in *Xenopus laevis* oocytes and binds to denatured protein inducers. J Biol Chem 1994; 269:15718-15723.
99. Agarraberes FA, Terlecky SR, Dice JF. An intralysosomal hsp70 is required for a selective pathway of lysosomal protein degradation. J Cell Biol 1997; 137:825-834.
100. Kim D, Ouyang H, Li GC. Heat shock protein hsp70 accelerates the recovery of heat shocked mammalian cells through the modulation of heat shock transcription factor HSF1. Proc Natl Acad Sci USA 1995; 92:2126-2130.
101. Becker AE, Massoudy P, Permanetter B et al. Possible significance of free oxygen radicals for reperfusion injury. Z Kardiol 1993; 82:49-58.
102. Liu S, Jiao X, Wang X et al. Interaction of electron leak and proton leak in respiratory chain of mitochondria proton leak induced by superoxide from an electron leak pathway of univalent reduction of oxygen. Sci China C 1996; 39:168-178.
103. Brown JM, Terada LS, Grosso MA et al. Xanthine oxidase produces hydrogen peroxide which contributes to reperfusion injury of ischemic, isolated, perfused rat hearts. J Clin Invest 1988; 81:1297-1301.
104. Thompson J, Hess ML. The oxygen free radical system: A fundamental mechanism in the production of myocardial necrosis. Prog Cardiovasc Dis 1986; 28:449-462.
105. Schulz R, Wambolt R. Inhibition of nitric oxide synthesis protects the isolated working rabbit heart from ischaemia-reperfusion injury. Cardiovasc Res 1995; 30:432-439.
106. Smolenski RT, Gray C, Amrani M et al. Nucleotide metabolism in the heart subjected to heat stress. Adv Exp Med Biol 1998; 431:373-376.
107. Insel PA, Ransnas LA. G proteins and cardiovascular disease. Circulation 1988; 78:1511-1513.
108. Songu E, Haugaard ES, Wildey G et al. The relationship between uracil nucleotide concentrations and glycogen synthesis in hepatocytes from fed and fasted rats. Metabolism. 1981; 30:119-122.
109. Jeremy RW, Ambrosio G, Pike MM et al. The functional recovery of post-ischemic myocardium requires glycolysis during early reperfusion. J Mol Cell Cardiol 1993; 25:261-276.
110. Choy PC, Chan M, Hatch G et al. Phosphatidylcholine metabolism in ischemic and hypoxic hearts. Mol Cell Biochem 1992; 116:53-58.
111. Janero DR, Hreniuk D, Sharif HM et al. Hydroperoxide-induced oxidative stress alters pyridine nucleotide metabolism in neonatal heart muscle cells. Am J Physiol 1993; 264:C1401-10.
112. Saad AH, Hahn GM. Activation of potassium channels: Relationship to the heat shock response. Proc Natl Acad Sci USA 1992; 89:9396-9399.
113. Joyeux M, Godin-Ribuot D, Ribuot C. Resistance to myocardial infarction induced by heat stress and the effect of ATP-sensitive potassium channel blockade in the isolated heart. Br J Pharmacol 1998; 123:1085-1088.
114. Pell TJ, Yellon DM, Goodwin RW et al. Myocardial ischemic tolerance following heat stress is abolished by ATP-sensitive potassium channel blockade. Cardiovasc Drugs Ther 1997; 11:676-686.
115. McConkey DJ, Orrenius S. Signal transduction pathways to apoptosis. Trends Cell Biol 1994; 4:370-375.
116. Fliss H, Gattinger D. Apoptosis in ischemic and reperfused rat myocardium. Circ Res 1996; 79:949-956.
117. Knowlton AA, Kapadia S, Torre-Amione G et al. Differential expression of heat shock proteins in normal and failing human hearts. J Mol Cell Cardiol 1998; 30:811-818.
118. Mehlen P, Schulze-Osthoff K, Arrigo AP. Small stress proteins as novel regulators of apoptosis: Heat shock protein 27 blocks FAS/APO-1 and Staurosporine-induced cell death. J Biol Chem 1996; 271:16510-16514.
119. Li WX, Chen CH, Ling CC et al. Apoptosis in heat-induced cell killing: The protective role of hsp-70 and the sensitization effect of the c-myc gene. Radiat Res 1996; 145:324-330
120. Samali A, Cotter TG. Heat shock proteins increases resistance to apoptosis. Exp Cell Res 1996; 223:163-170.
121. Fuller BJ, Busza AL, Proctor E. Possible resuscitation of liver function by hypothermic reperfusion in vitro after prolonged (24-hour) cold preservation—a 31P NMR study. Transplantation 1990; 50:511-513.

CHAPTER 3

Cardioprotection by Stress Proteins

Ruben Mestril and Wolfgang H. Dillmann

Myocardial ischemia causes a series of changes at the intracellular level within the cardiomyocyte. These intracellular changes include changes in calcium levels, altered osmotic control, membrane damage, generation of free radicals, a decrease in intracellular pH, depressed intracellular ATP levels, oxygen depravation and decreased glucose levels.[1] These changes produce a form of stress which leads to protein denaturation within the cell. An increase in denatured proteins in the cell has been previously reported to trigger the stress or heat shock response which increases the synthesis of the stress or heat shock proteins (Hsp's).[2] This stress response produces a transient rearrangement of cellular activities in order to cope with the stress period by protecting essential components within the cell so as to permit it to resume normal activity during recovery from the stress.[3] This ability of the cell for self-preservation has attracted the attention of many investigators in the field of cardiovascular research. We will, presently, attempt to cover what is known about these stress proteins and, in particular, recent studies related to the expression of these stress proteins and their involvement in cardioprotection.

The Mammalian Stress Proteins

The mammalian stress proteins can be divided into two closely related families of proteins. One family of stress proteins is made up of proteins that are induced by glucose deprivation, Ca^{2+} influx, prolonged hypoxia and so forth.[4] This family of stress proteins is known as the glucose-regulated proteins (GRP) which are known to be involved in the stabilization and formation of intracellular protein complexes. Among the glucose-regulated proteins, the best known are the GRP94 and GRP78 or BIP (immunoglobulin heavy-chain binding protein) which are both located in the endoplasmic reticulum. Another member of this family of proteins is the GRP75 or, also known as, the mitochondrial Hsp70 which is involved in the translocation and folding of proteins within the mitochondria.[5]

The other family of stress proteins is that of the heat-shock proteins (Hsp). These proteins are induced by stresses such as an increase in temperature (heat shock), exposure to transition metals, arsenite, ethanol, immediate release from hypoxia and ischemia/reperfusion. The heat-shock proteins are usually grouped by their molecular mass. Among the high molecular mass stress proteins, we find three major members namely Hsp110, Hsp90-α, and Hsp90-β. The Hsp90s have attracted much attention due to their association to the steroid hormone receptors and their involvement in steroid hormone action.[6] The largest and most abundant group of stress proteins is that of the Hsp70 family. This group includes several isoforms of the Hsp70 proteins and the mitochondrial Hsp60. It has been reported that there are at least three to four isoforms of Hsp70 in mammalian cells.[7,8] One isoform of Hsp70 is expressed constitutively and is only slightly increased in expression by heat stress or other oxidative stresses. Another three Hsp70 isoforms are the highly inducible forms which are expressed when the cell is under stress, although in primate cells, these proteins are constitutively expressed

Heat Shock Proteins in Myocardial Protection, edited by Rakesh C. Kukreja and Michael L. Hess.

even under normal conditions to a certain extent[9] Two other stress proteins, closely related to the Hsp70s, are the previously mentioned GRP78 and GRP75 (or mitochondrial Hsp70) proteins which are located in the endoplasmic reticulum and mitochondria, respectively. Although the last two proteins are glucose-regulated proteins, they exhibit high homology to Hsp70 and perform similar functions in the ER and mitochondria. Hsp60, although encoded in the nucleus, resides in the mitochondria where it is believed to be involved in the assembly of macromolecular complexes, together with Hsp10 and ATP hydrolysis.[10] Among the small molecular mass stress proteins, we have Hsp47, Hsp40, Hsp27, αβ-crystallin (20 kD), heme oxygenase (32 kD), Hsp10 and ubiquitin (8 kD). Hsp47 is a resident of the endoplasmic reticulum with high binding affinity for collagen[11] and which has been recently postulated to serve as a molecular chaperone.[12] Hsp40 is found in close association with Hsp70 and is believed to be involved in the same processes as Hsp70.[13,14] Hsp27 has been shown to be involved in the development of thermotolerance[15] Interestingly, Hsp27 is also a major target for phosphorylation in the presence of mitogens and tumor promoters.[16] The αβ-crystallin protein has been reported to be heat shock inducible[17] and has been found to be highly homologous to the small heat-shock protein Hsp27.[18,19] Interestingly, αβ-crystallin is an abundant protein in cardiac tissue.[20] Hsp32 or heme oxygenase-1 is not only induced by several common stressors (heat shock in rodents, hypoxia, hydrogen peroxide, cadmium) as are other Hsp's, but is also induced by hemin.[21] The Hsp10, still another mitochondrial Hsp, is closely associated with the Hsp60. The combination of Hsp60 and Hsp10 form the chaperonin complex which is responsible for protein folding within the mitochondria. Ubiquitin, the smallest of the stress proteins, is induced by similar stresses as the major Hsp's (heat shock, amino acid analogues, denatured proteins) and performs a vital role in the process of protein degradation.[22]

The most abundant among the Hsp's are the members of the Hsp70 group. The constitutively expressed Hsp70 (apparent molecular weight 73 kd) is found mostly in the cytoplasm under nonstress conditions, while the inducible Hsp70 (apparent molecular weight 72 kd) is found in the nucleus and more precisely in the nucleolus during a heat shock. The heat-shock proteins, besides having the common feature of being induced by stress, have been found to bind denatured and nascent polypeptides in the different compartments of the cell. This characteristic of heat-shock proteins has made them a good candidate to be involved in an endogenous cellular defense mechanism.

The protective nature of heat-shock proteins has been documented mainly by the observation that a mild heat shock (42°C) confers resistance to the cell against a subsequent lethal heat shock (45°C).[23] This phenomenon usually referred to as thermotolerance is a transient resistance to the cytotoxic effects of a subsequent lethal hyperthermic treatment which is induced by a nonlethal heat treatment. The synthesis and degradation of heat-shock proteins directly correlates with the development and decay of thermotolerance.[24] This fact has been taken as evidence that these proteins are involved in the acquisition, maintenance, and decay of thermotolerance.

Hsp70 has also been found to be an "unfoldase" which functions to facilitate the transport of proteins through the membranes of the endoplasmic reticulum (ER) and mitochondria.[25,26] Due to this property of facilitating the translocation of other proteins through the membranes of the different intracellular compartments; Hsp70 has been classified as a molecular chaperone. Other investigators have found that the mammalian constitutive Hsp70 (73 kd) is involved in a mechanism that targets intracellular proteins for lysosomal degradation during periods of serum withdrawal. According to their findings, Hsp70 recognizes and binds a short peptide sequence found in certain intracellular proteins which are preferentially degraded when cells are deprived of serum.[27] These findings suggest that Hsp's have vital functions within the cell even under nonstress conditions.

The increased synthesis of Hsp's during cellular stress may reflect the need for these proteins to protect different structures within the diverse cellular compartments. Evidence that seems to support this hypothesis comes from two reports that show when Hsp70 is depleted in cells either by microinjection of antibodies specific to Hsp70[28] or by reducing the expression of Hsp70 by genetic means (promoter competition),[29] cells are rendered sensitive to a subsequent heat shock. Although the most convincing evidence for the protective role of Hsp70 against heat stress has been reported in two more recent studies. In these studies, the constitutive expression of a stably transfected Hsp70 gene, either in a rat fibroblast cell line[30] or in simian CV cells,[31] resulted in a higher resistance to thermal stress. It would then seem that Hsp70 is involved in vital functions within the cell and that its presence is of crucial importance for cell survival during a heat shock. In addition, numerous studies have shown that increased levels of Hsp's by a heat shock will also protect against others stresses and vice versa.[32-34] This phenomenon of cross-protection or cross-tolerance has attracted the attention of many investigators especially those interested in finding new means of protecting the heart against ischemia-induced injury.

Myocardial Ischemia

Myocardial ischemia is best defined in relative rather than in absolute terms.[35,36] Ischemia results in an imbalance between the supply of oxygenated blood and the oxygen requirement. Complete and sudden occlusion of a large epicardial artery results in a wave front of myocardial necrosis starting at the subendocardial region and extending towards the epicardial part of the myocardium.[37] In experimental animals such as dogs after 20 minutes of coronary occlusion, increasing numbers of myocytes become irreversibly damaged in the subendocardial zone and by 40 minutes the majority of the myocytes are destined to necrose.[38] In small rodents (mice and rats), infarct size is primarily determined by the size of the occluded vessel, because no significant collateral vessels exist.[39] It is important to note that ischemic myocytes do not die within a few minutes after the onset of complete ischemia, while some myocytes die simultaneously other myocytes remain viable in the ischemic region for a long time or indefinitely.[37,40] In addition, it appears that myocytes exposed to a milder ischemia can survive for longer times.[41] These are then important considerations to keep in mind when setting strategies aimed at protecting the ischemic myocardium.

Ischemia, at the cellular level, leads within 8 to 10 seconds to a cessation of oxidative phosphorylation and a switch to anaerobic glycolysis.[42,43] Anaerobic glycolysis results in much less efficient production of high energy phosphates, and the demand for high energy phosphates quickly outpaces supply. Reduction of ATP concentrations below 20% of normal levels leads to the cell's inability to regenerate high energy phosphates, to maintain ion gradients, and to control their volume.[44] Metabolic products, especially lactate accumulation, contributes to pH lowering and increases the osmotic load to the cell.[45] Loss of volume control, increasing osmotic load, and intracellular volume expansion stretches the fragile sarcolemma which together with mechanical forces provided by a myocardial contraction lead to a disruption of the sarcolemma.[46] The ruptured sarcolemma presents a hallmark of irreversible myocardial damage resulting in cell death.[46,47] Rupture of the sarcolemma is evidenced by the release of cytosolic proteins including creatine phosphokinase (CPK) and lactate dehydrogenase (LDH). Severe ischemia markedly depresses protein synthesis due to decreased translational initiation and elongation.[48-50] This leads to the synthesis of incomplete polypeptides which cannot fold properly and form complexes of denatured proteins. The acidic pH, abnormal ionic milieu, and formation of oxygen radicals during reperfusion will further contribute to protein malfolding and denaturation. The presence of denatured proteins in myocytes presents probably one of the major triggering mechanisms for the induction of the heat-shock protein gene expression. Renaturation of malfolded proteins, removal of irreversibly denatured proteins, and the resumption of protein synthesis present important cell functions especially in myocytes recovering from ischemic injury after reperfusion. Brief episodes of severe ischemia can lead to prolonged contractile dysfunction in the absence of severe myocyte damage as determined by histological changes. This condition has been termed myocardial stunning.[51] Its cellular basis is currently incompletely explored, but a recent report has shown that Hsp70 may also play a protective role during this condition.[52] In addition, severe chronic ischemia can lead to myocardial dysfunction which can be ameliorated by relief of ischemia and has been termed myocardial hibernation.[53] An interesting phenomenon known as preconditioning refers to the exposure of the myocardium to brief episodes of ischemia and appears to exert a protective effect against subsequent more prolonged ischemia.[54] Ischemic preconditioning is one of the most reproducible experimental protocols in protecting the heart against ischemic injury. The possible role of stress proteins in the ischemic preconditioning phenomenon is presently the subject of much controversy. Most studies have shown that adenosine receptors and protein kinase C are involved in the early period of ischemic preconditioning.[55] Presently, there is no evidence that stress proteins are involved in the protective effect against ischemic injury during the early periods of preconditioning. However, it is unclear, at present, if stress proteins play a protective role in the late period of ischemic preconditioning.[56-58] Nonetheless, if stress proteins are or are not involved in the protective effect against ischemic injury during ischemic preconditioning, the fact remains that expression of heat-shock proteins does protect against ischemic injury is discussed later in this chapter.

Early in the course of severe ischemia, a large number of jeopardized, but not irreversibly injured myocytes exist especially at the border of the wave front progressing from the subendocardial to the epicardial portion of the myocardium. These myocytes can be salvaged by timely reperfusion.[59,60] Early recanalization of an occluded coronary artery by pharmacological or mechanical means has led to a significant improvement in short- and long-term outcomes of acute myocardial infarcts.[61] Reperfusion leads to myocardial salvage, but can also result in damage.[62] The timing of reperfusion appears to make the crucial difference for the development and the extent of reperfusion injury. In reversibly injured myocytes, reperfusion leads only to temporary changes like cell swelling.[63] In contrast in irreversibly injured myocytes, reperfusion leads to explosive cell swelling and accelerated cell death.[64] In isolated myocytes, reoxygenation leads also to cell death which may result from oxygen radicals and calcium influx.[65-67] The findings indicate the importance of salvaging the myocardium by early reperfusion. It has then been hypothesized that increased levels of Hsp's in cardiomyocytes contribute to a protective effect and accelerate recovery from ischemic damage by promoting normal protein folding. The normal folding state of proteins is a crucial requirement for proper cell function.

Interestingly, recent studies have found that a portion of cardiomyocyte death following ischemia/reperfusion is due to programmed cell death or apoptosis.[68,69] Some studies, in particular, have shown that during myocardial infarction in humans approximately 12% of the cardiomyocytes in the peri-infarct border zone are undergoing apoptosis.[68,70] In contrast, studies in rat hearts have shown that a much higher amount of cardiomyocytes undergo apoptosis following ischemia/reperfusion injury.[69,71] Presently, it is unclear if apoptosis is deleterious to cardiac tissue undergoing ischemia/reperfusion injury, as thought by some,[72] or if programmed cell death following ischemia/reperfusion is designed to sacrifice jeopardized cardiomyocytes instead of leaving these cells to the accidental process of necrosis with the subsequent loss of cell membrane integrity, enhanced membrane action permeability, and exaggerated arrhythmogenicity endangering the entire cardiac function as thought by others.[73] Nonetheless, the general consensus seems to indicate that prevention or protection against apoptotic death in the myocardium is an aim worth pursuing. Interestingly, studies have demonstrated that several members of the stress protein family are capable of increasing the cell's resistance to apoptosis.[74,75] In addition, investigators have shown that before cells exhibit common signs of nuclear apoptosis (chromatin condensation and endonuclease-mediated DNA fragmentation) cells undergo a reduction of mitochondrial transmembrane potential.[76] This finding seems to imply a mitochondrial control of nuclear apoptosis. Therefore, preservation of mitochondrial function and integrity during ischemia/reperfusion injury may be a means of blocking or reducing the onset of apoptotic death in the heart. This leads us to examine the potential protective role of stress proteins and especially the mitochondrial stress proteins during ischemia/reperfusion injury.

Cardioprotection by the Stress Proteins

Studies have shown that heat-shock proteins are readily synthesized in cardiac cells during tissue trauma,[77] aortic banding and hyperthermia.[78] Further studies have shown that Hsp70 is induced to high levels of expression following conditions similar to those encountered during myocardial ischemia. Ligation of the left anterior descending coronary artery in the heart of experimental animals for several hours produces acute myocardial ischemia which was found to increase expression of the Hsp70 inducible gene.[79,80] Although Hsp70 is the main Hsp exhibiting increased expression following in vivo experimental ischemia, it is important to point out that other Hsp's are also induced by the ischemic event. Hsp70 is also induced in cultured rat neonatal myocytes during stresses similar to those encountered in ischemia. Neonatal rat myocytes exposed to ATP depletion, using metabolic inhibitors or oxygen depletion, exhibit high levels of Hsp70 mRNA and protein.[81] The rapid induction of Hsp70 in cardiac tissue during oxidative stress has prompted interest in investigating the possible protective role that it may play in the heart during myocardial ischemia. Currie and co-workers have found that isolated perfused hearts from rats that had received a 15 minute heat treatment at 42°C 24 hours previously exhibited an improved contractile recovery after a 30 minute period of low-flow ischemia followed by reperfusion as compared to hearts from nonheat-treated animals.[82] In addition, these investigators found that the pre-heat treatment of animals produced less ultra-structure disruption of the mitochondria and a decrease in creatine kinase release in rat heart tissue following ischemia/reperfusion injury. Upon examination of the changes in the rat heart after the heat treatment, they found increased levels of Hsp70 protein and an increase in enzymatic activity for the anti-oxidative enzyme: catalase. The increase in catalase activity following whole-body heat stress remains unclear and subsequent studies have shown that it does not involve any changes in transcription activation of the gene coding for catalase.[83] In addition, it has been suggested that the heat-induced increase in catalase activity may be secondary to a direct heat-shock protein interaction which modulates the activity of the enzyme.[84] Although, recent studies indicate that catalase may not play a role in the myocardial protection conferred by a whole body heat stress, either in isolated perfused rat hearts[85] or in vivo rat hearts.[86] In addition, other studies have confirmed that a hyperthermic treatment of experimental animals can result in a significantly improved myocardial salvage following coronary occlusion and reperfusion in vivo,[87,88] as well as, in an isolated perfused heart model.[89]

It is obvious that a whole-body heat stress results in many cellular changes in an organism besides an increase in the expression of heat-shock proteins which could be responsible for the observed protection against myocardial ischemia. Nonetheless, several studies have shown that Hsp's and, in particular, the amount of Hsp70 present following whole-body heat shock is directly related to the degree of myocardial protection obtained.[90,91] Further direct evidence that Hsp70 is able to cross-protect against ischemic injury has recently been obtained using myogenic cell lines. It was found that when myogenic cells that had previously received a mild heat shock were submitted to conditions mimicking ischemia in vitro (hypoxia, glucose deprivation, hypotonicity, restricted intercellular volume) or simulated ischemia these cells were then able to survive significantly better than cells that had not been pre-heat shocked.[92]

Similar results were obtained when a stably transfected human Hsp70 was overexpressed in myogenic cells. Overexpression of human Hsp70 in rodent myogenic cell lines either by transient or stable transfection has shown to confer a protective effect against metabolic stress[93] and simulated ischemia.[92] Interestingly, this myogenic stably transfected cell line overexpressing the Hsp70 has recently been found to also be resistant to endotoxemia.[94]

These results indicate that Hsp70, if not solely responsible, must play an important role in the myocardial protection obtained following a whole body heat stress. Conclusive evidence that Hsp70 plays this protective role in vitro has been shown using neonatal rat cardiomyocytes where the delivery of exogenous copies of Hsp70 using recombinant adenoviral vectors (e.g., human adenovirus 5) results in a marked tolerance of the cardiomyocyte to simulated ischemic conditions.[95] In addition, transgenic mice that overexpress the Hsp70 in cardiac muscle have now been shown using an isolated perfused heart preparation that the hearts of these mice have a significantly marked recovery in contractile function, as well as, a reduction in infarct size and creatine release after ischemia and reperfusion.[96] Similar results using an independently generated transgenic mouse strain was found by other investigators.[97,98] These results have been further confirmed by the finding that the hearts of these transgenic mice overexpressing the Hsp70 gene show a marked reduction in infarct size in an in vivo model of ischemia and reperfusion.[99]

Obviously following a heat or oxidative stress, Hsp70 is not the only Hsp induced which raises the possibility that other Hsp's may also possess cardioprotective properties. Two of the small Hsp's, Hsp27 and αβ-crystallin, have been shown to be protective against several noxious stresses such as hyperthermia, hypertonic stress, and various cytotoxic agents including cytoskeletal disruptors. Hsp27 expression by transfection in rodent and Chinese hamster cell lines correlates directly with improved survival after hyperthermia[100-102] while ectopic expression of αβ-crystallin renders NIH 3T3 cells and glioma cells thermoresistant.[103-105] Interestingly, both small Hsp's are closely associated with cytoskeletal structures and stabilization of these structures may contribute to the observed increased tolerance to stress. Hsp27 is known to act as an inhibitor of actin filament turnover in smooth muscle cells and seems to stabilize the actin filament.[106,107] Stable overexpression of Hsp27 in Chinese hamster lung cells confers resistance to F-actin fragmentation induced by H_2O_2 and menadione.[108] αβ-crystallin stabilizes cytoskeletal structures in glioma cells.[105] In cardiomyocytes, αβ-crystallin also associates with intermediate filaments, especially desmin, an association that is strengthened under ischemic conditions.[109,110] Presently, a recent study has shown that increased expression of these two small Hsp's, αβ-crystallin and Hsp27, in adult rat cardiomyocytes through an adenovirus vector-based approach leads to increased protection against injury mediated by ischemia.[111]

Another study has now shown that the mitochondrially located stress proteins, Hsp60 and Hsp10, when expressed simultaneously using recombinant deficient adenoviral vectors in both myogenic cells and neonatal rat cardiomyocytes confer protection against ischemia-induced injury.[112] Interestingly, expression of just Hsp60 or Hsp10 alone does not render the cardiomyocyte resistant to ischemia. This finding implies that the interaction of Hsp60 and Hsp10 within the mitochondria where these proteins form the chaperonin complex is a requirement for the observed increased tolerance to ischemia induced injury.

While it might seem that all stress proteins are potentially cardioprotective, studies in our laboratory as well as by other investigators have shown that this is not necessarily the case. This difference in cardioprotective capacity among stress proteins may be related to the intracellular location and function within the cell of each particular stress protein. Much work still remains to be done to completely elucidate the mechanism in which stress proteins protect against ischemia/reperfusion induced injury.

Conclusion

In summary, the evidence presently available indicates that several of the Hsp's play an important role in myocardial protection against ischemic and reperfusion injury. The future challenge will be to fully understand the precise mechanism in which heat-shock proteins confer myocardial protection and eventually to discover possible pharmacological means of increasing the expression of the endogenous heat-shock proteins to protect the heart of patients undergoing cardiopulmonary by-pass and thrombolytic or coronary angioplastic therapies.

References

1. Bonventre JV. Mediators of ischemic renal injury. Ann Rev Med 1988; 39:531-544.
2. Ananthan J, Goldberg AL, Voellmy R. Abnormal proteins serve as eukaryotic stress signals and trigger the activation of heat shock genes. Science 1986; 232:522-524.
3. Lindquist S. The heat shock response. Ann Rev Biochem 1986; 55:1151-1191.
4. Lee AS. Coordinated regulation of a set of genes by glucose and calcium ionophores in mammalian cells. Trends Biochem Sci 1987; 12:20-23.
5. Martin J. Molecular chaperones and mitochondrial protein folding. J Bioenerg Biomemb 1997; 29:35-43.
6. Pratt WB. The role of heat shock proteins in regulating the function, folding, and trafficking of the glucocorticoid receptor. J Biol Chem 1993; 268:21455-21458.
7. Lowe DG, Moran LA. Molecular cloning and analysis of DNA complementary to three mouse Mr=68,000 heat shock protein mRNAs. J Biol Chem 1986; 261:2102-2112.
8. Harrison GS, Drabkin HA, Kao FT et al. Chromosomal location of human genes encoding major heat shock protein Hsp70. Som Cell Mol Gen 1987; 13:119-130.
9. Welch WJ, Garrels JI, Thomas GP et al. Biochemical characterization of the mammalian stress proteins and identification of two stress proteins as glucose and calcium ionophore regulated proteins. J Biol Chem 1983; 258:7102-7111.
10. Ostermann J, Horwich AL, Neupert W et al. Protein folding in mitochondria requires complex formation with Hsp60 and ATP hydrolysis. Nature 1989; 341:125-130.
11. Nagata K, Nakai A, Hosokawa N et al. "Interaction of Hsp47 with newly synthesized procollagen and regulation of Hsp expression." In: Heat Shock, Maresca B, Lindquist S, eds. Berlin, Springer-Verlag, 1991.
12. Sauk JJ, Smith T, Norris K et al. Hsp47 and the translation-translocation machinery cooperate in the production of alpha1(I) chains of type I procollagen. J Biol Chem 1994; 269:3941-3946.
13. Hattori H, Kaneda T, Lokeshwar B et al. A stress-inducible 40 kDa protein (Hsp40): Purification by modified two-dimensional gel electrophoresis and co-localization with hsc70 (p73) in heat-shocked Hela cells. J Cell Sci 1993; 104:629-638.
14. Frydman J, Nimmesgern E, Ohtsuka K et al. Folding of nascent polypeptide chains in a high molecular mass assembly with molecular chaperones. Nature 1994; 370:111-117.
15. Kampinga HH, Brunsting JF, Stege GJ et al. Cells overexpressing Hsp27 show accelerated recovery from heat-induced nuclear protein aggregation. Biochem Biophy Res Comm 1994; 204:1170-1177.
16. Welch WJ. Phorbol ester, calcium ionophore, or serum added to quiescent rat fibroblast cells all result in the elevated phosphorylation of two 28,000 dalton mammalian stress proteins. J Biol Chem 1985; 260:3058-3062.
17. Klemenz R, Frohli E, Steiger RH et al. Alpha B-crystallin is a small heat shock protein. Proc Natl Acad Sci USA 1991; 88:3652-3656.
18. Ingolia TD, Craig EA. Four small *Drosophila* heat shock proteins are related to each other and to mammalian a-crystallin. Proc Natl Acad Sci USA 1982; 79:2360-2364.
19. Southgate R, Ayme A, Voellmy RW. Nucleotide sequence analysis of the *Drosophila* small heat shock gene cluster at locus 67B. J Mol Biol 1983; 165:35-57.
20. Bennardini F, Wrzosek A, Chiesi M. αβ-crystallin in cardiac tissue, association with actin and desmin filaments. Circ Res 1992; 71:288-294.
21. Sistonen L, Sarge KD, Phillips B et al. Activation of heat shock factor-2 during hemin induced differentiation of human erythroleukemia cells. Mol Cell Biol 1992; 12:4104-4111.

22. Mayer RJ, Lowe J, Landon M et al. "Ubiquitin and the lysosomal system: Molecular pathological and experimental findings." In: Heat Shock, Maresca B and Lindquist S, eds. Berlin, Springer-Verlag, 1991.
23. Li GC, Werb Z. Correlation between synthesis of heat shock proteins and development of thermotolerance in Chinese hamster fibroblasts. Proc Natl Acad Sci USA 1982; 79:3218-3222.
24. Li GC, Mak JY. Induction of heat shock protein synthesis in murine tumors during the development of thermotolerance. Cancer Res 1985; 45:3816-3824.
25. Deshaies RJ, Koch BD, Werner-Washburne M et al. A subfamily of stress proteins facilitates translocation of secretory and mitochondrial precursor polypeptides. Nature 1988; 332:800-805.
26. Chirico WJ, Walters MG, Blobel G. 70 K heat shock related proteins stimulate protein translocation into microsomes. Nature 1988; 332:805-810.
27. Chiang HL, Terlecky SR, Plant CP et al. A role for a 70 kilodalton heat shock protein in lysosomal degradation of intracellular proteins. Science 1989; 246:382-385.
28. Riabowol KT, Mizzen LA, Welch WJ. Heat shock is lethal to fibroblasts microinjected with antibodies against Hsp70. Science 1988; 242:433-436.
29. Johnston RN, Kucey BL. Competitive inhibition of Hsp70 gene expression causes thermosensitivity. Science 1988; 242:1551-1554.
30. Li GC, Li L, Liu YK et al. Thermal response of rat fibroblasts stably transfected with the human 70 kD heat shock protein encoding gene. Proc Natl Acad Sci USA 1991; 88:1681-1685.
31. Angelidis CE, Lazaridis I, Pagoulatos GN. Constitutive expression of heat shock protein 70 in mammalian cells confers thermoresistance. Eur J Biochem 1991; 199:35-39.
32. Mizzen LA, Welch WJ. Characterization of the thermotolerant cell. I. Effects on protein synthesis activity and the regulation of heat shock protein 70 expression. J Cell Biol 1988; 106:1105-1116.
33. Hahn GM, Li GC. "Thermotolerance, thermoresistance and thermosensitization." In: Morimoto RI, Tissieres A, Georgopoulos C, eds. Stress Proteins in Biology and Medicine, Cold Spring Harbor Laboratory Press, New York, 1990.
34. Polla BS, Mili N, Kantengwa S, 1991. "Heat shock and oxidative injury in human cells." In: Maresca B, Lindquist S, eds. Heat Shock. Berlin, Springer-Verlag, 1991.
35. Braunwald E, Sobel BE. "Coronary blood flow and myocardial ischemia." In: Braunwald E, ed. Heart Disease. WB. Saunders Co., 1992.
36. Reimer KA, Jennings RB. Myocardial ischemia, hypoxia and infarction. In: Fozzard HA, Jennings RB, Haber E, Katz AM, Morgan HE, eds. "The Heart and Cardiovascular System." New York, Raven Press, 1986.
37. Reimer KA, Lowe JE, Rasmussen MM et al. Myocardial infarct size vs duration of coronary occlusion in dogs. Circulation 1977; 56:786-794.
38. Jennings RB, Sommers HM, Smyth GA et al. Myocardial necrosis induced by temporary occlusion of a coronary artery in the dog. Arch Pathol 1960; 70:68-78.
39. Fishbein MC, Maclean DM, Maroko PR. Experimental myocardial infarction in the rat: Qualitative and quantitative changes during pathologic evaluation. Am J Pathol 1978; 90:57-70.
40. Reimer KA, Jennings RB. Transmural progression of necrosis within the framework of ischemic bed size (myocardium at risk) and collateral flow. Lab Invest 1979; 40:633-644.
41. Reimer KA. Myocardial infarct size. Measurements and predictions. Arch Pathol Lab Med 1980; 104:225-230.
42. Kubler W, Spieckermann PG. Regulation of glycolysis in the ischemic and the anoxic myocardium. J Mol Cell Cardiol 1970; 1:351-377.
43. Neely JR, Morgan HE. Relation between carbohydrate and lipid metabolism and the energy balance of heart muscle. Ann Rev Physiol 1974; 36:413-459.
44. Jennings RB, Hawkins HK, Lowe JE et al Relation between high energy phosphate and lethal injury in myocardial ischemia in the dog. Am J Pathol 1978; 92:187-214.
45. Rovetto MJ, Lamberton WF, Neely JR. Mechanisms of glycolytic inhibition in ischemic rat hearts. Circ Res 1975; 37:742-751.
46. Jennings RB, Reimer KA, Steenbergen C, Jr. Myocardial ischemia revisited. The osmolar load, membrane damage and reperfusion. J Mol Cell Cardiol 1986; 18:769-780.
47. Jennings RB, Murry CE, Steenbergen C, Jr et al. Development of cell injury in sustained acute ischemia. Circulation 1990; 82(3):II2-II12.

48. Schreiber SS, Rothschild MA, Evans C et al. The effect of pressure or flow stress on right ventricular protein synthesis in the face of constant and restricted coronary perfusion. J Clin Invest 1975; 55:1-11.
49. Kao R, Rannels DE, Morgan HE. Effects of anoxia and ischemia on protein synthesis in perfused rat hearts. Circ Res 1976; 38:I125-I130.
50. Williams EH, Kao RL, Morgan HE. Protein degradation and synthesis during recovery from myocardial ischemia. Am J Physiol 1981; 240:E268-E273.
51. Heyndrickx GR, Millard RW, McRitchie RJ et al Regional myocardial functional and electrophysiological alterations after brief coronary artery occlusion in conscious dogs. J Clin Invest 1975; 56:978-985.
52. Sun JZ, Tang XL, Knowlton AA et al. Late preconditioning against myocardial stunning. An endogenous protective mechanism that confers resistance to postischemic dysfunction 24 h after brief ischemia in conscious pigs. J Clin Invest 1995; 95:388-403.
53. Rahimtoola SH. The hibernating myocardium. Am Heart J 1989; 117:211-221.
54. Murry CE, Jennings RB, Reimer KA. Preconditioning with ischemia: A delay of lethal cell injury in ischemic myocardium. Circulation 1986; 74:1124-1136.
55. Downey JM, Cohen MV, Ytrehus K et al. Cellular mechanisms in ischemic preconditioning: The role of adenosine and protein kinase C. Ann NY Acad Sci 1994; 723:82-98.
56. Tang XL, Qiu Y, Park SW et al. Time course of late preconditioning against myocardial stunning in conscious pigs. Circ Res 1996; 79:424-434.
57. Yang XM, Baxter GF, Heads RJ et al. Infarct limitation of the second window of protection in a conscious rabbit model. Cardiovasc Res 1996; 31:777-783.
58. Schwarz ER, Whyte WS, Kloner RA. Ischemic preconditioning. Curr Opin Cardiol 1997; 12:475-481.
59. Jennings RB, Murry CE, Reimer KA. Myocardial effects of brief periods of ischemia followed by reperfusion. Adv Cardiol 1990b; 37:7-31.
60. Ellis SG, Henschke CI, Sandor T et al. Time course of functional and biochemical recovery of myocardium salvaged by reperfusion. J Am Coll Cardiol 1983;1:1047-1055.
61. Lavie CJ, Gersh BJ, Chesebro JH. Reperfusion in acute myocardial infarction. Mayo Clin Proc 1990; 65:549-564.
62. Braunwald E, Kloner RA. Myocardial reperfusion: A double-edged sword? J Clin Invest 1985; 76:1713-1719.
63. Jennings RB, Schaper J, Hill ML et al Effect of reperfusion late in the phase of reversible ischemic injury. Changes in cell volume, electrolytes, metabolytes and ultrastructure. Circ Res 1985;5 6:262-278.
64. Jennings RB, Reimer KA. Lethal myocardial ischemic injury. Am J Pathol 1981;102:241-255.
65. Josephson RA, Silverman HS, Lakatta EG et al. Study of the mechanisms of hydrogen peroxide and hydroxyl free radical-induced cellular injury and calcium overload in cardiac myocytes. J Biol Chem 1991; 266:2354-2361.
66. Quaife RA, Kohmoto O, Barry WH. Mechanisms of reoxygenation injury in cultured ventricular myocytes. Circulation 1991; 83:566-577.
67. Hohl C, Ansel A, Altshuld R et al. Contracture of isolated rat heart cells on anaerobic to aerobic transition. Am J Physiol 1982; 242:H1022-H1030.
68. Itoh G, Tamura J, Suzuki M et al. DNA fragmentation of human infarcted myocardial cells demonstrated by the nick end labeling method and DNA agarose gel electrophoresis. Am J Pathol 1995; 146:1325-1331.
69. Kajstura J, Cheng W, Reiss K et al. Apoptotic and necrotic myocyte cell deaths are independent contributing variables of infarct size in rats. Lab Invest 1996; 74:86-107.
70. Bardales RH, Hailey LS, Xie SS et al. In situ apoptosis assay for the detection of early acute myocardial infarction. Am J Pathol 1996; 149:821-829.
71. Buerke M, Murohara T, Skurk C et al. Cardioprotective effect of insulin-like growth factor I in myocardial ischemia followed by reperfusion. Proc Natl Acad Sci USA 1995; 92:8031-8035.
72. MacLellan WR, Schneider MD. Death by design. Programmed cell death in cardiovascular biology and disease. Circ Res 1997; 81:137-144.
73. Bromme HJ, Holtz J. Apoptosis in the heart: When and why? Mol Cell Biochem 1996; 163/164:261-275.

74. Samali A, Cotter TG. Heat shock proteins increase resistance to apoptosis. Exp Cell Res 1996; 223:163-170.
75. Mehlen P, Schulze-Osthoff K, Arrigo A-P. Small stress proteins as novel regulators of apoptosis. J Biol Chem 1996; 271:16510-16514.
76. Zamzami N, Susin SA, Marchetti P et al. Mitochondrial control of nuclear apoptosis. J Exp Med 1996; 183:1533-1544.
77. Currie RW, White FP. Trauma induced protein in rat tissues: A physiological role for a "heat shock" protein? Science 1981; 214:72-73.
78. Hammond GL, Lai YK, Markert CL. Diverse forms of stress lead to new patterns of gene expression through a common and essential metabolic pathway. Proc Natl Acad Sci USA 1982; 79:3485-3488.
79. Dillmann WH, Mehta HB, Barrieux A et al. Ischemia of the dog heart induces the appearance of a cardiac mRNA coding for a protein with migration characteristics similar to heat shock/stress protein 71. Circ Res 1986; 59:110-114.
80. Mehta HB, Popovich BK, Dillmann WH. Ischemia induces changes in the level of mRNAs coding for stress protein 71 and creatine kinase M. Circ Res 1988; 63:512-517.
81. Iwaki K, Chi SH, Dillmann WH et al. Induction of Hsp70 in cultured rat neonatal cardiomyocytes by hypoxia and metabolic stress. Circulation 1993; 87:2023-2032.
82. Currie RW, Karmazyn M, Kloc M et al. Heat shock response is associated with enhanced post-ischemic ventricular recovery. Circ Res 1988b; 63:543-549.
83. Currie RW, Tanguay RM. Analysis of RNA for transcripts for catalase and SP71 in rat hearts after in vivo hyperthermia. Biochem Cell Biol 1991; 69:375-382.
84. Kukreja RC, Hess ML. The oxygen free radical system: From equations through membrane protein interactions to cardiovascular injury and protection. Cardiovasc Res 1992; 26:641-655.
85. Wall SR, Fliss H, Korecky B. Role of catalase in myocardial protection against ischemia in heavy shocked rats. Mol Cell Biochem 1993; 129:187-194.
86. Auyeung Y, Sievers RE, Weng D et al. Catalase inhibition with 3-amino-1,2,4-triazole does not abolish infarct size reduction in heat-shocked rats. Circulation 1995; 92:3318-3322.
87. Donnelly TJ, Sievers RE, Vissern FLJ et al. Heat shock protein induction in rat hearts. Circulation. 1992; 85:769-778.
88. Currie RW, Tanguay RM, Kingma Jr JG. Heat shock response and limitation of tissue necrosis during occlusion/reperfusion in rabbit hearts. Circulation 1993; 87:963-971.
89. Walker DM, Pasini E, Kucukoglu S et al. Heat stress limits infarct size in the isolated perfused rabbit heart. Cardiovasc Res 1993; 27:962-967.
90. Hutter MM, Sievers RE, Barbosa V et al. Heat shock protein induction in rat hearts: A direct correlation between the amount of heat shock protein induced and the degree of myocardial protection. Circulation 1994; 89:355-360.
91. Marber MS, Walker JM, Latchman DS et al. Myocardial protection after whole body heat stress in the rabbit is dependent on metabolic substrate and is related to the amount of the inducible 70kD heat stress protein. J Clin Invest 1994; 93:1087-1094.
92. Mestril R, Chi SH, Sayen MR et al. Expression of inducible stress protein 70 in rat heart myogenic cells confers protection against simulated ischemia induced injury. J Clin Invest 1994b; 93:759-767.
93. Williams RS, Thomas JA, Fina M et al. Human heat shock protein 70 (Hsp70) protects murine cells from injury during metabolic stress. J Clin Invest 1993; 92:503-508.
94. Chi SH, Mestril R. Stable expression of a human Hsp70 gene in a rat myogenic cell line confers protection against endotoxin. Amer J Physiol 1996; 39:C1017-C1021.
95. Mestril R, Giordano FJ, Conde AG et al. Adenovirus mediated gene transfer of a heat shock protein 70 (Hsp70i) protects against simulated ischemia. J Mol Cell Cardiol 1996; 26:2351-2358.
96. Marber MS, Mestril R, Chi SH et al. Overexpression of the rat inducible 70 kD heat stress protein in a transgenic mouse increases the resistance of the heart to ischemic injury. J Clin Invest 1995; 95:1446-1456.
97. Plumier JC, Ross BM, Currie RW et al. Transgenic mice expressing the human heat shock protein 70 have improved post-ischemic myocardial recovery. J Clin Invest 1995; 95:1854-1860.
98. Radford NB, Fina M, Benjamin IJ et al. Cardioprotective effects of 70-kDa heat shock protein in transgenic mice. Proc Natl Acad Sci USA 1996; 93:2339-2342.

99. Hutter JJ, Mestril R, Tam EKW et al. Overexpression of heat shock protein 72 in transgenic mice decreases infarct size in vivo. Circulation 1996; 94:1408-1411.
100. Landry J, Chretien P, Lambert H et al. Heat shock resistance conferred by expression of the human Hsp27 gene in rodent cells. J Cell Biol 1989; 109:7-15.
101. Chretien P, Landry J. Enhanced constitutive expression of the 27-kDa heat shock protein in heat-resistant variants from Chinese hamster cells. J Cell Physiol 1988; 137:157-166.
102. Lavoie JN, Gingras-Breton G, Tanguay RM et al. Induction of Chinese hamster Hsp27 gene expression in mouse cells confers resistance to heat shock. J Biol Chem 1993; 268:3420-3429.
103. Aoyama A, Frohli E, Schafer R et al. Crystallin expression in mouse NIH 3T3 fibroblasts: Glucocorticoid responsiveness and involvement in thermal protection. Mol Cell Biol 1993; 13:1824-1835.
104. Blackburn R, Galoforo S, Berns CM et al. Thermal response in murine L929 cells lacking αβ crystallin expressing L929 transfectants. Mol Cell Biochem 1996; 55:51-60.
105. Iwaki A, Iwaki T, Tateishi J et al. Sense and antisense modification of glial αβ-crystallin production results in alterations of stress fiber formation and thermoresistance. J Cell Biol 1994; 125:1385-1393.
106. Miron T, Wilchek M, Geiger B. Characterization of an actin polymerization in vinculis-rich fraction of turkey gizzard smooth muscle. Eur J Biochem 1988; 178:543-553.
107. Lavoie JN, Hickey E, Weber L et al. Modulation of actin microfilaments and fluid phase pinocytosis by phosphorylation of heat shock protein 27. J Biol Chem 1993; 268:24210-24214.
108. Huot J, Houle F, Spitz DR et al. Hsp27 phosphorylation-mediated resistance against actin fragmentation and cell death induced by oxidative stress. Cancer Res 1996; 56:273-279.
109. Bennardini F, Wrzosek A, Chiesi M. αβ-crystallin in cardiac tissue: Association with actin and desmin filaments. Circ Res 1992; 71:288-294.
110. Barbato R, Menabo R, Dainese P et al. Binding of cytosolic proteins to myofibrils in ischemic rat hearts. Circ Res 1996; 78:821-828.
111. Martin JL, Mestril R, Hilal-Dandan R et al. Small heat shock proteins and protection against ischemic injury in cardiac myocytes. Circulation 1997; 96:4343-4348.
112. Lau SS, Patnaik N, Sayen RM et al. Simultaneous overexpression of two stress proteins in rat cardiomyocytes and myogenic cells confers protection against ischemia induced injury. Circulation 1997; 96:2287-2294.

CHAPTER 4

Role of Heat Shock Proteins, Protein Kinase C and ATP-Sensitive Potassium Channel in Delayed Myocardial Protection

Rakesh C. Kukreja, Yong-Zhen Qian and Jeffery B. Hoag

Heat shock proteins (Hsp's) are one of the highly conserved proteins in existence, found in every organism.[1] These proteins are synthesized quickly and intensely in response to stressors and are known to protect the cells from the toxic effects of heat and other stresses.[2] There has been a tremendous interest in the role of Hsp's to understand their function under stress conditions as well as homeostatic states. Exactly how Hsp's protect cells is unclear; however, several explanations have been offered. These include the renaturation of damaged proteins, or facilitation of the folding and targeting of newly synthesized proteins to organelles.[2,3] Hsp's may also maintain newly synthesized proteins in a translocational configuration (linear or unfolded).[4] After heat stress the cytoplasmic Hsp 72 is found to localize in and around the nucleus but move back out to the cytoplasm during the recovery phase. Hsp 72 and 73 bind transiently to nascent proteins acting as intracellular chaperones and help stabilize these proteins until they achieve their final conformation.[5]

Stress and Ischemic Protection

Sublethal ischemia or nonlethal whole body heat stress (HS) activate a powerful endogenous protective mechanism which has been shown to significantly improve myocardial salvage following prolonged ischemia in in vivo and in vitro models.[4,6] Heat stress has been shown to enhance the post-ischemic contractile function in vitro[7] and reduce infarct size in vivo.[8] The induction of Hsp's following whole body hyperthermia or sublethal ischemia has been suggested as the mechanism of myocardial protection against ischemia/reperfusion injury.[7,9] More recently, it has been shown that overexpression of Hsp70 transgene in the mouse heart protects the myocardium against ischemia/reperfusion injury in vitro[10,11] as well as in vivo.[12] Despite the distinct correlation observed between the Hsp70 and cardiac resistance, their cause and effect relationship in inducing stress response following heat shock or ischemic preconditioning continues to be an area of investigation and debate. The results from transgenic mice studies may not necessarily be applicable in elucidating the mechanism of cardiac protection in a physiological model of heat stress or ischemic preconditioning. This is because the acquisition of cardiac resistance to ischemia by heat shock or ischemic preconditioning is a multi-factorial process that includes several other mechanisms besides the induction of one or more members of the Hsp family.[13] These include the activation of antioxidant defense systems such as increased activities of SOD,[14,15] stress-activated MAPKAP kinase[2,16] or possibly other unknown mechanisms. The stress-activated protein kinases or C-Jun NH_2-terminal protein kinases are

Heat Shock Proteins in Myocardial Protection, edited by Rakesh C. Kukreja and Michael L. Hess.

believed to be the transducers between stress stimuli and genetic responses in vitro and in vivo.[17] The following review describes studies which suggest that delayed ischemic protection following whole body heat stress or ischemic preconditioning may be mediated by other factors in addition to the expression of Hsp's.

Whole-Body Hyperthermia and Delayed Ischemic Protection

In order to examine the role of Hsp's in ischemic protection following heat shock, we performed studies to correlate the expression of these proteins with the reduction in infarct size in vivo.[18] Animals were randomly assigned into one of six subgroups and subjected to heat stress by raising whole body temperature to 42°C for 15 minutes. At 2, 4, 12, 24 and 30 hrs after heat shock, the expression of Hsp 72 and Hsp 27 were measured. Sham animals were not subjected to heat shock. A separate subset of animals was subjected to infarct-producing prolonged ischemia and reperfusion. The synthesis of Hsp 72 was minimal in sham anesthetized rats although its level increased rapidly to >80% of maximum by 4 hrs after heat shock. The peak expression of the protein was observed at 12 hrs post heat shock HS (12) and remained at significantly higher levels up to 24-30 hrs (Fig. 4.1A). A similar trend in the expression of Hsp 27 was observed (Fig. 4.1B). Infarct size in the ischemic/reperfused rat hearts was 39.2 ± 2.75 % 24 hours after sham anesthetization (Fig. 4.2). Heat shock failed to reduce infarct size after 2, 4 and 12 hours later although the expression of Hsp 72 and Hsp 27 were high at these time points. A significant but transient protective effect of heat shock was observed after 24 hours of heat shock, HS (24), which was lost by 30 hrs post heat shock. These data suggest the infarct-limiting effect of hyperthermia was not entirely correlated with the amount of Hsp's accumulated following heat stress stimulus in the heart.

Delayed Ischemic Preconditioning—Role of Hsp 72

It is well established that preconditioning immediately and markedly elevates cardiac tolerance against ischemia.[6,19] However, this tolerance wanes abruptly within 2 hours.[20] It has been proposed that preconditioning induces a slower form of tolerance resulting in the restoration of cardio-protection after the rapid preconditioning effect has worn off. This slower form of protection was designated as the delayed preconditioning or second window of protection (SWOP).[21] Marber et al[21] showed a 45% reduction in infarct size in the preconditioned as compared to sham hearts. A number of studies from our laboratory[22,23] have also showed significant reduction in the infarct size in rabbit supporting the existence of SWOP in this species. Kuzuya et al[24] were able to demonstrate approximately 62% reduction in infarct size 24 hours following ischemic preconditioning in dog using four episodes of preconditioning. On the other hand, Tanaka et al[25] could not observe SWOP in the rabbit despite increased expression of Hsp 72 in the heart. Two additional reports failed to demonstrate SWOP against myocardial infarction in the porcine heart.[26,27] Marber et al proposed a role of Hsp 72 in SWOP because this protein was found to be elevated 24 hours following ischemic preconditioning and heat shock.[21] In order to further resolve the relationship of Hsp 72 expression and induction of myocardial protection, we performed studies[29] in the rat model where SWOP was not conclusively demonstrated.

To confirm early preconditioning in the rat, the hearts were subjected to ischemic preconditioning with one or three 5-minute occlusions of the left coronary artery (LCA) followed by a 10-minute reperfusion period prior to sustained ischemia and reperfusion. For late preconditioning, the animals underwent 1 to 3 cycles of preconditioning (PCX1, PCx2 and PCx3) with a 5-minute of LCA occlusion followed by 10 min of recovery period prior to 30 min of sustained ischemia and 90 min of reperfusion, which was carried out 24 hrs later. The infarct size was 47.5 ± 3.8 % in the control hearts subjected to sustained ischemia and reperfusion. Precon-

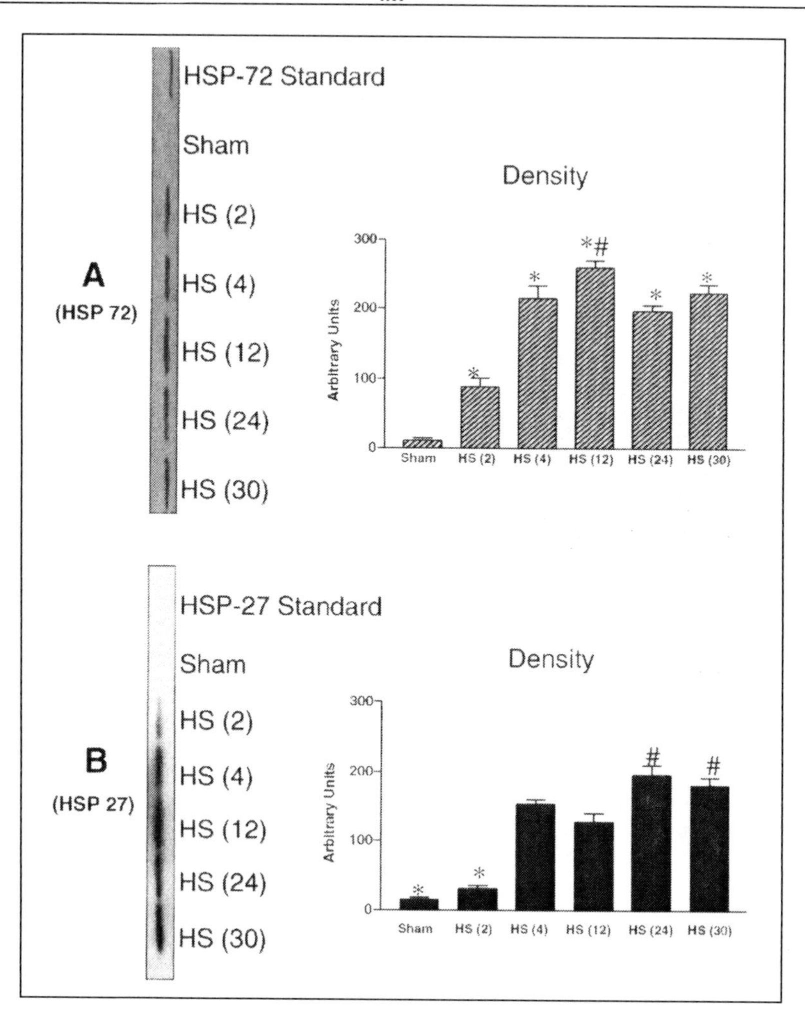

Fig. 4.1. Time course of expression of inducible forms of Hsp72 (A) and Hsp27 (B) in the left ventricle following 2 (HS 2), 4 (HS 4), 12 (HS 12), 24 (HS 24) and 30 (HS 30) hrs post-heat shock. Hearts were harvested post-heat shock without the infarct-producing sustained ischemia. Sham controls were not subjected to heat shock.

ditioning resulted in significant reduction of infarct size with PCx1 and PCx3 respectively (Fig. 4.3). These studies confirmed the reproducibility of early preconditioning in the rat model of myocardial infarction. Pilot experiments using PCx3 stimulus (5 rats in each of the sham and preconditioned groups) failed to demonstrate reduction in infarct size 12 hours after sustained ischemia (data not shown). We therefore performed delayed preconditioning 24 and 48 hours later, the time windows that have been shown to reduce infarct size in the rabbit heart.[21-24] The infarct size in the ischemia/reperfused hearts was not significantly different from the sham and preconditioned hearts (Fig. 4.4). Also, the infarct size was not significantly different as compared to the corresponding sham after 48 hrs of preconditioning (48.4 ± 4.0 sham versus 50.0 ± 4.2 in preconditioned hearts).

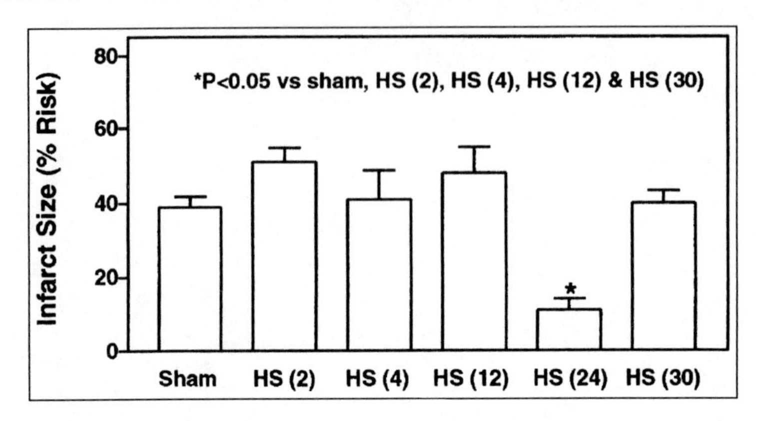

Fig. 4.2. Time course of changes in myocardial infarct size following whole body heat shock. Infarct sizes are expressed as % risk area. The animals were subjected to sustained ischemia by LAD occlusion following 2 (HS 2), 4 (HS 4), 12 (HS 12), 24 (HS 24) nd 30 (HS 30) hrs of heat shock. Sham controls were not subjected to heat shock treatment.[18]

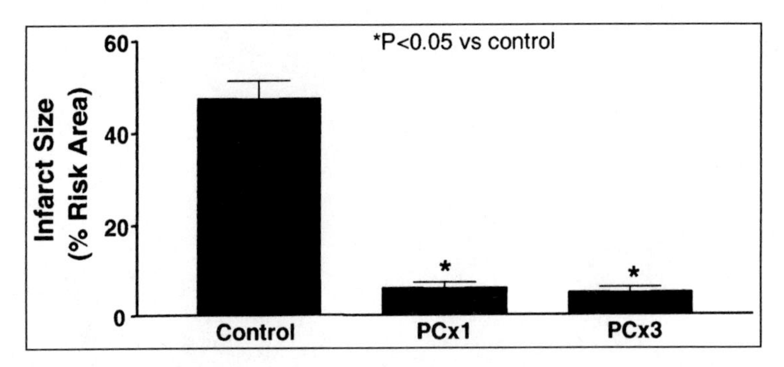

Fig. 4.3. Reduction in infarct size (expressed as % area at risk) following early preconditioning with one or three cycles of 5 min ischemia and 10 min of reperfusion. PCx1—one cycle of 5 min ischemia and 10 min of reperfusion, PCx3—three cycles of 5 min ischemia followed by 10 min of reperfusion. [29]

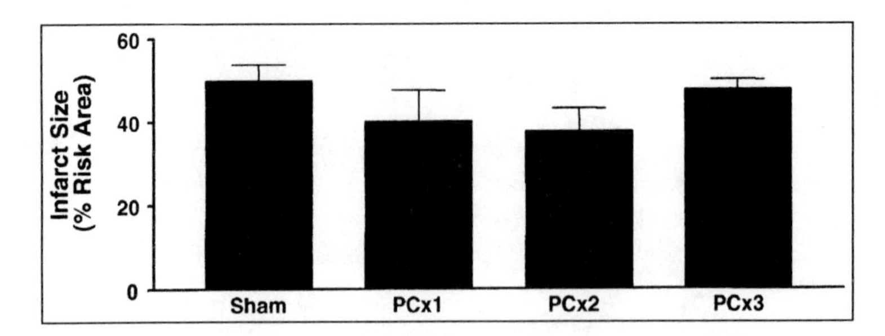

Fig. 4.4 Myocardial infarct size (expressed as % of area at risk) in the ischemic/reperfused hearts 24 hours after preconditioning with one to three cycles (PCx1 to PCx3) of 5 minute ischemia and 10 minute of reperfusion.[29]

Expression of Heat Shock Protein

No expression of Hsp70 mRNA was observed in the control hearts. The hearts subjected to preconditioning cycles demonstrated increased synthesis of Hsp70 mRNA (Fig. 4.5A). Normalization of Hsp70 mRNA with respect to the housekeeping gene, β-actin, revealed an over 3-fold increase in the Hsp70 mRNA (Fig. 4.5B). A similar 3-fold increase in Hsp70 mRNA has been shown in the rabbit heart following four cycles of 5 min ischemia and 5 minute of reperfusion.[28] Das et al 14 showed induction of several inducible genes for Hsp's and antioxidant enzymes following four episodes of preconditioning in the heart. We did not find significant differences in the levels of Hsp70 mRNA between PCx1 and PCx3 groups. This discrepancy may be attributed to the differences of experimental models. Our studies were performed in the in situ model of regional ischemia as opposed to the globally ischemic isolated perfused rat heart used by Das and coworkers.[14] Western blot analysis showed significantly increased expression of Hsp 72 in the preconditioned hearts as compared to sham operated rats (Fig. 4.6A). Heat shock also induced significantly higher expression of Hsp 72 as compared to the corresponding sham group (Fig. 4.6B). The overall expression of Hsp 72 between PCx3 and heat shocked rats was not significantly different. Thus it is quite obvious that rat hearts do not respond to delayed ischemic preconditioning despite enhanced expression of Hsp 72. On the other hand, heat shock stimulus was able to cause ischemic protection in the identical model. These studies suggest that delayed preconditioning induced by heat shock or sublethal ischemia may have distinct mechanisms of protection that may not be exclusively related to enhanced Hsp 72 expression. Also, it is possible that rodents behave differently when it comes to delayed cardiac preconditioning. In support of this argument, we and others have observed that rat and mouse required at least 10-fold higher concentration of a cardioprotective drug, monophosphoryl lipid A for pharmacological preconditioning[30-31] as compared to rabbit and dogs.[32-34]

Hsp 72 and Ischemic Protection—Controversies

Although Hsp 72 has been shown to be associated with ischemic protection, there are several studies that could not find such a correlation. Currie et al[4] reported that the cardioprotection by heat shock was lost even though Hsp 72 was still present in the rabbit heart. Wall et al[35] could not demonstrate significant improvement in ventricular functional recovery in the heat shocked rats following 20, 25, or 30 min of no-flow global ischemia in the isolated "working" heart preparation despite the enhanced synthesis of Hsp. In addition, isolated perfused mouse heart failed to respond to heat-shock induced functional recovery, despite the enhanced expression of Hsp72.[36] There is evidence that expression of Hsp72 is not always related to the tissue protection in other organs also. Joannidis et al[37] reported that whole body heat shock failed to prevent the ischemic injury of rat renal tubules despite significant induction of Hsp's. Similarly Narasimhan et al[38] demonstrated that heat shock and acid treatment increased the vulnerability of cultured astrocytes to acidosis 24 hr later despite significant induction of Hsp72. In heart, the infarct size was correlated with protection only after 24 hrs, but not at other time points when the expression of these proteins was high.

Role of Protein Kinase C

As discussed above, the increase in Hsp production peaked around 4 hrs after HS whereas protection was not seen until after 12-24 hrs of HS.[39] This study suggested that the mere presence of Hsp's was not enough to produce protection in the ischemic myocardium. We therefore hypothesized that there must be an 'unknown' downstream event that must be completed before heat shock could induce protection in the ischemic heart.[40] Recent studies suggest that protein kinase C (PKC), a ubiquitous intracellular mediator, may play a role in the protective effects of ischemic preconditioning while the activators such as phorbol 12-myristate

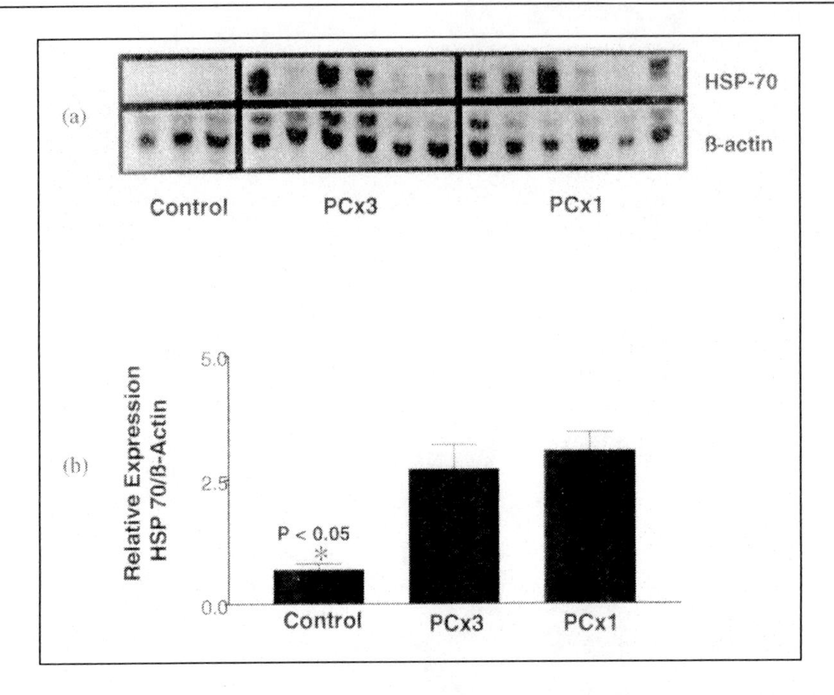

Fig. 4.5. (A) Northern blot analysis showing increase in Hsp70 mRNA following one or three cycles of ischemic preconditioning in rat heart. Total cellular RNA was prepared from myocardial risk region, electrophoresed, transferred to nytran membrane and hybridized with ^{32}PHsp 70 probe. Blots were stripped and rehybridized with β-actin cDNA probe. Each band represents Hsp70 mRNA from separate heart. (B) Transcript levels of Hsp70/β-actin measured by densitometer scanning of autoradiogram bands. From reference 29.

acetate (PMA) mimic the protective effect via phosphorylation of unknown effector protein. PKC plays a crucial role in the signal transduction for the activation of many cellular functions. Many oncogenes and transcription factors are activated by various PKC subtypes.[41] These include heat shock protein transcription factors and/or antioxidant enzyme genes that are suspected to play a crucial role in delayed protection. PKC inhibitors administered at the end of the ischemic preconditioning period in rabbit hearts[42,43] or to the metabolically preconditioned isolated cardiomyocytes[44] blocked the protective effect of preconditioning. Baxter et al[45] suggested that a PKC signaling pathway links the activation of adenosine receptor to the observed cytoprotection many hours later. Their data also demonstrated that chelerythrine, a specific PKC inhibitor, blocked delayed cardiac protection induced by ischemia in rabbit heart.

The synthesis of Hsp's requires phosphorylation of heat shock transcription factor (HSF) prior to the subsequent transcription and translation of the protein. It has been suggested that the activation of HSF occurs in two steps. The first step involves an ATP-independent heat induced alteration of HSF that allows it to bind the heat shock element, and the second involves phosphorylation of the HSF protein.[46-48] Activation of HSF1, the primary component of the HSF-DNA-binding activity in cells exposed to HS, requires oligomerization, acquisition of DNA-binding activity and localization to the nucleus.[49] HSF1 exists as two closely sized forms in normal or stressed conditions, although HS causes a marked increase in the size of HSF1 owing to its hyperphosphorylation.[50] We hypothesized that inhibiting PKC might block the expression of Hsp 72 as well as ischemic tolerance in heat shocked hearts. Therefore our

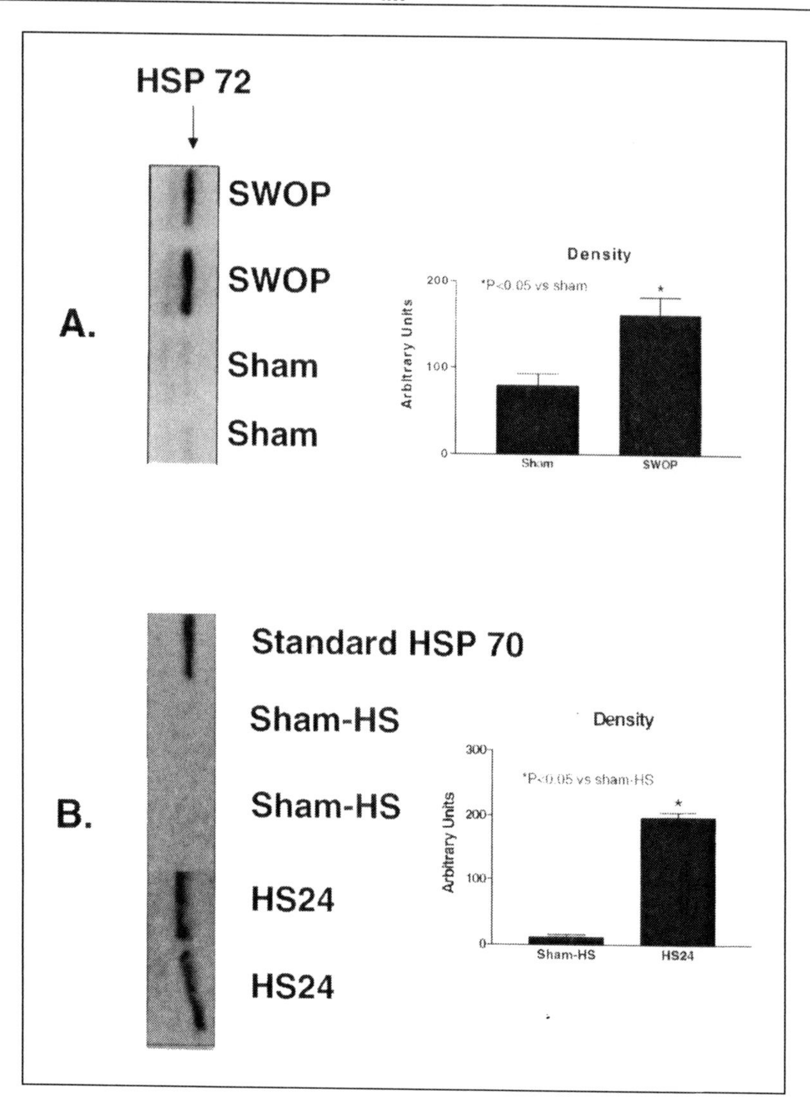

Fig. 4.6. Western blot analysis showing the expression of inducible form of Hsp 72 in the left ventricle. A: SWOP 24 hours, B: Heat shock preconditioning, group.[29]

first goal was to demonstrate if PKC acts as a trigger for inducing delayed myocardial protection following HS in rat hearts. A second goal was to show if the expression of Hsp 72 is also inhibited as a result of pharmacological inhibition of PKC by chelerytherine, a specific antagonist of the enzyme.

Animals were randomly assigned into one of the 5 subgroups: Group I (sham); group II (heat stressed); group III (vehicle pretreated heat stressed rats); group IV (chelerythrine-pretreated heat stressed) and group V (chelerythrine treated ischemic/reperfused hearts). Chelerythrine (5 mg/kg, ip) or equivalent volume of the vehicle which consisted of 50% dimethylsulfoxide (DMSO) were given 30 minutes prior to the initiation of HS (groups II-IV) or ischemia/reperfusion in group V. Infarct size (% area at risk) reduced significantly from 49.4 ± 2.3% in sham to 10.0 ± 2.5% and 9.1 ± 3.1% in HS and vehicle treated HS groups respectively (Fig. 4.7). Infarct size in chelerythrine-treated non-HS ischemic/reperfused heart was 40.7 ±5.4%, which did not differ significantly from vehicle-treated sham group. However, treatment with chelerythrine prior to HS increased infarct size to 49.4 ±2.3%. The expression of Hsp72 was minimal in sham anesthetized rats although its synthesis increased after heat shock in the heat shock as well as the vehicle treated rat hearts. Chelerythrine treatment 30 min prior to heat stress did not inhibit the synthesis of Hsp72 (Fig. 4.8). These data strongly indicate that PKC activation plays an important role in the signaling mechanisms leading to HS-dependent delayed cardiac protection in the rat heart.

PKC is a ubiquitous serine-threonine kinase with multiple isoforms that are associated with a variety of receptors and physiological effects.[51] PKC can activate cardiac gene transcription[52,53] and nuclear factor kB[54] which in turn could initiate transcription of a variety of genes. The mechanism by which PKC activation may have protected the HS-induced protection is not known although it is likely that it may have done so via synthesis of certain cytoprotective proteins, which could possibly be Hsp's or antioxidative enzymes.[55,56] Phosphorylation is a fundamentally important biological control mechanism, and it is becoming apparent that protein phosphorylation may have an important function in regulating the specificity and activity of a number of transcription factors.[57,58] Transcriptional activation of heat shock genes in yeast and human cells is known to be associated with changes in phosphorylation of the HS gene transcriptional factor. Choi et al[50] investigated the importance of phosphorylation as a control mechanism by evaluating the ability of cAMP and cAMP-dependent protein kinases to regulate the basal and/or induced promoter activity of human Hsp70 gene. In the present studies, chelerythrine failed to block the expression of Hsp 72 concomitant with the HS-induced ischemic tolerance suggesting that PKC-mediated protection in the heart may have been caused by other members of the Hsp family or another cytoprotective protein. Jacquier-Sarlin et al[59] failed to show a robust expression of inducible Hsp 72 (compared with HS) in the human monocytes with PMA. They also showed that the PKC inhibitors staurosporine and H-7 failed to block HS-mediated increase in inducible Hsp70 in these cells suggesting that the expression of this protein was not dependent on activation of PKC. Whether PKC affects regulation of other stress proteins in the heart remains to be determined.

Role of K_{ATP} Channel

In our quest for the 'unknown' effector of HS-induced protection, we considered the opening of ATP-sensitive potassium channel as a possible mediator of heat shock induced protection.[60] Opening of K_{ATP} channels plays an important role in myocardial protection following ischemic preconditioning.[61] K_{ATP} channel is protective because opening of this channel increases outward potassium current resulting in the shortening of the action potential,[62] which in turn may spare ATP thereby allowing less entry of calcium into the myocyte through the voltage sensitive calcium channel. Decreased intracellular calcium overload then results in a reduction of ischemic injury and therefore leads to better preservation of myocytes. K_{ATP} channel opening has been implicated in the protection of myocardium following ischemic preconditioning as well as drug-induced protection.[63,64] Opening of K_{ATP} channel appears to play a role in the delayed ischemic[65] or pharmacological preconditioning with monophosphoryl lipid A (MLA), a nontoxic derivative of endotoxin.[66] We wanted to test if the blockers of K_{ATP} channel, glybenclamide or 5-HD abolish heat-shock induced myocardial protection in vivo. Our second goal was to show whether the channel blockers inhibit the expression of Hsp 72 in the heat-stressed rabbit hearts. Heat-shocked rabbits were treated with glibenclamide and 5-HD prior to sustained ischemia, which was carried out 24 hours following whole body

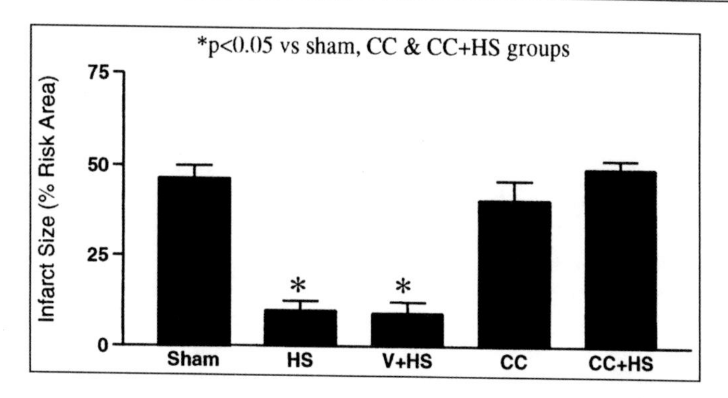

Fig. 4.7. Effect of PKC inhibitor, chelerythrine on myocardial infarct size in heat shocked hearts. Note that the infarct size following ischemia/reperfusion was significantly reduced in the heat shocked (HS) as well as vehicle-treated heat shocked animals (V + HS) group as compared to sham (nonheat shocked). Chelerythrine chloride (CC) significantly blocked the infarct reducing effect of heat shock (CC + HS), without affecting ischemic injury in the sham animals.[40]

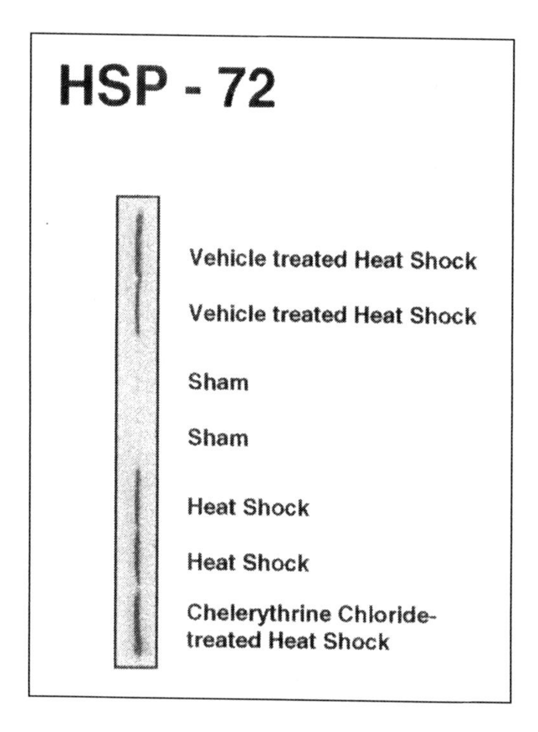

Fig. 4.8. Western blot analysis showing the expression of Hsp72 in the sham, heat shocked and chelerythrine-treated heat shocked animals. Note that the expression of Hsp 72 was not diminished in chelerythrine-treated heat shocked animals.[40]

hyperthermia. Infarct size was 39.4 ± 8.1 % in the control group; it decreased significantly in the heat shocked rabbits. Treatment with glybenclamide and 5-HD in HS rabbits resulted in a significant increase in the infarct size (Fig. 4.9). Non-HS control rabbits treated with glybenclamide or 5-HD had infarct size that was not significantly different when compared to untreated control hearts. Furthermore, glybenclamide or 5-HD did not block the protection when given prior to the institution of whole body hyperthermia, suggesting that these drugs did not interfere with the protective mechanism triggered following the heat shock. The heat shock-induced protection was accompanied by significant elevation in the expression of Hsp 72, which was not diminished by glybenclamide and 5-HD (Fig. 4.10). Taken together, it appears that induction of Hsp's is associated with the ischemic protection after 24 hours as observed in several other studies. It is possible that heat shock protein may possibly be linked to another 'effector' for inducing protective effect, which may perhaps be the K_{ATP} channel.

Hu et al[67] recently showed that PKC activated K_{ATP} channel in rabbit and human ventricular myocytes by reducing channel sensitivity to intracellular ATP. No studies are available to show the activation of K_{ATP} channel by HS or Hsp's in the myocytes. Sadd and Hahn[68] observed activation of voltage-dependent K^+ channels after heating in radiation-induced fibrosarcoma cell line, which decayed to nonmeasurable levels in 6 hours. These currents were blocked by tetraethylammonium cations as well modification of extracellular K^+ currents. Negulyaev et al[69] showed that exogenous Hsp70 resulted in an activation of outward currents through potassium-selective channel. Although these studies do not directly implicate a similar activation of K_{ATP} channel induced by HS or Hsp's, such a possibility cannot be ruled out. Further studies showing the cause and effect relationship, if any, of Hsp 72 with the activation of K_{ATP} channels in cardiac myocytes warrant investigations.

Conclusions

The above studies suggest that heat shock and ischemic preconditioning lead to the expression of Hsp's 24 hrs later. However, the protective effect was associated with the expression of Hsp's only at 24 hrs in the heat stressed rats. Interestingly such an association of heat shock protein was lacking in the ischemic preconditioning model, where the delayed anti-ischemia was not observed despite the presence of Hsp 72. These experiments suggest that quantitative accumulation of Hsp's may not be the only important factor in causing ischemic protection in the heart. The role of PKC and opening of K_{ATP} channel appear to play an important role in inducing delayed preconditioning. Whether these proteins undergo posttranslational modifications/ translocation or activate some other unknown effector of protection such as K_{ATP} channel before they can exert protection remains to be determined.

References

1. Hunt C, Morimoto RI. Conserved features of eukaryotic Hsp70 genes revealed by comparison with the nucleotide sequence of human Hsp70. Proc Natl Acad Sci USA 1985; 82:6455-6459.
2. Lindquist S, Craig EA. The heat shock proteins. Ann Rev Genet 1988; 22:631-637.
3. Morimoto RI, Mosser D, McClanahan TKet al. Stress-Induced Proteins. New York: Alan R. Liss, Inc. 1993:83-94.
4. Currie RW, Tanguay RM, Kingma Jr. JG: Heat-shock response and limitation of tissue necrosis during occlusion/reperfusion in rabbit hearts. Circulation 1993; 87:963-971.
5. Hightower LE. Heat shock, stress proteins, chaperones, and proteotoxicity. Cell 1991; 66:191-197.
6. Murry CE, Jennings RB, Reimer KA. Preconditioning with ischemia: A delay of lethal cell injury in ischemic myocardium. Circulation 1986; 74:1124-1136.
7. Currie RW, Karmazyn M. Improved post-ischemic ventricular recovery in the absence of changes in energy metabolism in working rat hearts following heat-shock. J Mol Cell Cardiol 1990; 22:631-636.

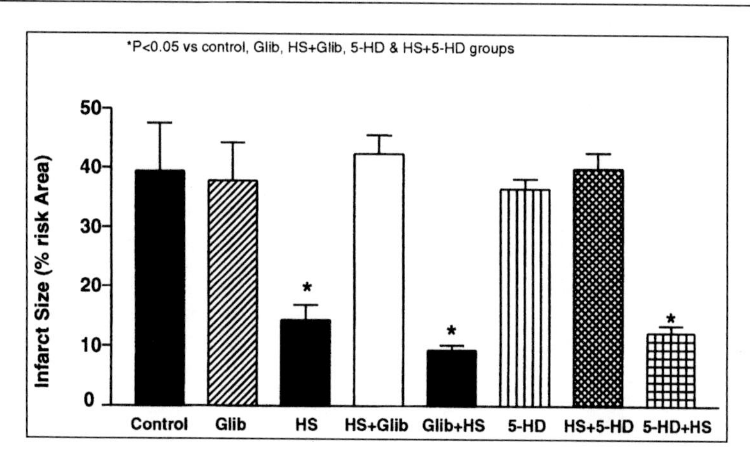

Fig. 4.9 Effect of K_{ATP} channel blockers, glibenclamide (Glib) and 5-hydroxydecanoate (5-HD) on myocardial infarct size (% of area at risk). In the heat shocked (HS) animals, infarct size was reduced. The beneficial effect of HS preconditioning was lost by glibenclamide as well as 5-HD when these agents were administered before ischemia/reperfusion in heat shocked rabbits (groups HS-Glib and HS-5-HD). Glibenclamide and 5-HD failed to block the protective effect of HS when these agents were given prior to heat shock (groups Glib-HS and 5-HD-HS). Glibenclamide and 5-HD did not change infarct size significantly as compared to non heat shocked control animals subjected to ischemia/reperfusion only (groups Glib-I/R and 5-HD-I/R.[60]

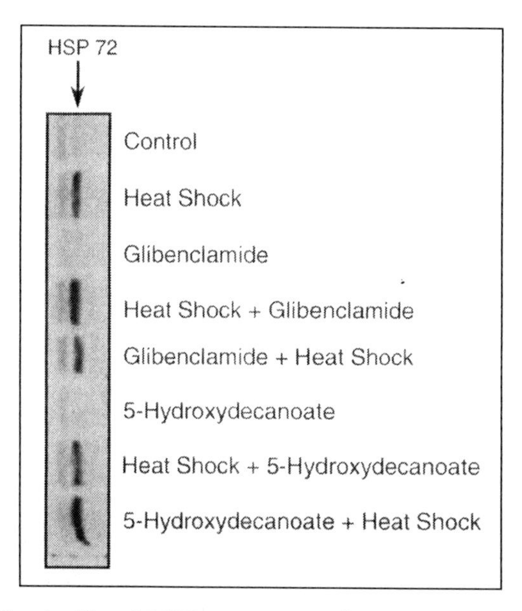

Fig. 4.10. Effect of glibenclamide and 5-HD on expression of Hsp 72 in the left ventricle. Hsp 72 was elevated in the heat shocked hearts. Glib or 5-HD did not inhibit the expression of Hsp 72. Experimental groups are same as described in the legend to Figure 7.[60]

8. Hutter MW, Sievers RE, Barbosa V, Wolfe CL: Heat-shock protein induction in rat hearts: A direct correlation between the amount of heat-shock protein induced and the degree of myocardial protection. Circulation 1994; 89:355-360.
9. Kontos MC, Shipley JS, Kukreja RC. Heat stress improves functional recovery and induces synthesis of 27- and 70-kDa heat shock proteins without preserving sarcoplasmic reticulum function in the ischemic rat heart. J Mol Cell Cardiol 1996; 28:1885-1894.
10. Marber MS, Mestril R, Chi SH, Sayen MR, Yellon DM. A heat shock protein 70 transgene results in myocardial protection. J Clin Invest 1995; 95:1446-1556.
11. Plumier J-CL, Ross BM, Currie RW et al. Transgenic mice expressing the human heat shock protein 70 have improved post-ischemic myocardial recovery. J Clin Invest 1995; 95:1854-1860.
12. Hutter JJ, Mestril R, Tam EK et al. Overexpression of heat shock protein 72 in transgenic mice decreases infarct size in vivo. Circulation 1996; 94:1408-1411.
13. Okubo S, Xi L, Yoshida K-I et al. Myocardial preconditioning: Basic concepts and mechanisms. Mol Cell Biochem 1999; 196:3-12.
14. Das DK, Engelman RM, Kimura Y. Molecular adaptation of cellular defences following preconditioning of the heart by repeated ischemia. Cardiovasc.Res. 1993; 27:578-584.
15. Kukreja RC, Hess ML. The oxygen free radical system: From equations through membrane protein-interactions to cardiovascular injury and protection. Cardiovasc Res 1992; 26:641-655.
16. Engel K, Ahlers A, Brach MA et al. MAPKAP kinase 2 is activated by heat shock and TNF-alpha: In vivo phosphorylation of small heat shock protein results from stimulation of the MAP kinase cascade. J Cell Biochem 1995; 57:321-330.
17. Bensaude O, Bellier S, Dubois MF et al. Heat-shock induced protein modifications and modulation of enzyme activities. EXS. 1996; 77:199-219.
18. Qian Y-Z, Shipley JS, Levasseur JE et al. Dissociation of the expression of 72 and 27 kDa heat shock proteins with ischemic tolerance following heat shock in rat heart. J Mol Cell Cardiol 1998; 30:1163-1172.
19. Qian Y-Z, Levasseur JE, Yoshida KI et al. K_{ATP} channels in rat heart: Blockade of ischemic and acetylcholine-mediated preconditioning by glibenclamide. Am J Physiol 1996; 271:H23-H28.
20. Murry CE, Richard VJ, Jennings RB et al. Myocardial protection is lost before contractile function recovers from ischemic preconditioning. Am J Physiol. 1991; 260:H796-H804
21. Marber MS, Latchman DS, Walker JM et al. Cardiac stress protein elevation 24 hours after brief ischemia or heat stress is associated with resistance to myocardial infarction. Circulation 1993; 88:1264-1272.
22. Okubo S, Bernardo NL, Jao AB et al. Tyrosine phosphorylation is involved in second window of preconditioning in rabbit heart. Circulation 1997; 96 Suppl.:I-313(Abstract)
23. Bernardo NL, D'Angelo M, Desai PV et al. ATP-sensitive potassium channel is involved in the second window of ischemic preconditioning. Am J Physiol.
24. Kuzuya T, Hoshida S, Yamashita N et al. Delayed effect of sublethal ischemia on the acquisition of tolerance to ischemia. Circ Res 1993; 72:1293-1299.
25. Tanaka M, Fujiwara H, Yamasaki K et al. Ischemic preconditioning elevates cardiac stress protein but does not limit infarct size 24 or 48 h later in rabbits. Am J Physiol. 1994; 267:H1476-82.
26. Strasser R, Arras M, Vogt A et al. Preconditioning of porcine myocardium: How much ischemia is required for induction? What is its duration? Is a renewal of effect possible? Circulation 1994; 90:I-109(Abstract).
27. Qiu Y, Tang X-L, Park SW et al. The early and late phases of ischemic preconditioning: A comparative analysis of their effects on infarct size, myocardial stunning, and arrhythmias in conscious pigs undergoing a 40-minute of coronary occlusion. Circ Res. 1997; 80:730-742.
28. Knowlton AA, Brecher P, Apstein CS. Rapid expression of heat shock protein in the rabbit after brief cardiac ischemia. J Clin Invest. 1991; 87:139-147.
29. Qian Y-Z, Bernardo NL et al. Induction of 72 kDa heat shock protein does not confer second window of ischemic preconditioning in rat heart. Am J Physiol 1999; 276:H224-H234.
30. Xi L, Jarrett NC, Hess ML et al. Essential role of inducible nitric oxide synthase in monophosphoryl lipid A-induced late cardioprotection: Evidence from pharmacological inhibition and gene knock-out mice. Circulation 1999; 99:2157-2163.

31. Jarrett NC, Xi L, Hess ML et al. Monophosphoryl lipid A induces delayed protection against ischemia/reperfusion injury in the mouse heart. J Mol Cell Cardiol 1998; 30:A262(Abstract)
32. Yao Z, Auchampach JA, Pieper GM et al. Cardioprotective effects of monophosphoryl lipid A, a novel endotoxin analogue, in the dog. Cardiovasc Res. 1993; 27:832-838.
33. Yoshida KI, Maaieh MM et al. Monophosphoryl lipid A induces pharmacologic 'preconditioning' in rabbit hearts without concomitant expression of 70-kDa heat shock protein. Mol.Cell Biochem. 1996; 159:73-80.
34. Elliott GT, Comerford ML, Smith JR et al. Myocardial ischemia/reperfusion protection using monophosphoryl lipid A is abrogated by the ATP-sensitive potassium channel blocker, glibenclamide. Cardiovasc Res 1996; 32:1071-1080.
35. Wall SR, Fliss H, Kako KJ et al. Heat pretreatment does not improve recovery of function after no flow ischemia in isolated working rat hearts. J Mol Cell Cardiol 1990; 22:(Suppl I): S44(Abstract)
36. Xi L, Chelliah J, Nayeem MA et al. Whole body heat shock fails to protect mouse heart against ischemia/reperfusion injury: Role of 72 kDa heat shock protein and antioxidant enzymes. J Mol Cell Cardiol 1998; 30:2213-2227.
37. Joannidis M, Cantley LG, Spokes K et al. Induction of heat-shock proteins does not prevent renal tubular injury following ischemia. Kidney Int 1995; 47:1752-1759.
38. Narasimhan P, Swanson RA, Sagar SM et al. Astrocyte survival and Hsp70 heat shock protein induction following heat shock and acidosis. Glia 1996; 17:147-159.
39. Shipley JB, Qian Y-Z, Levasseur JE et al. Expression of the stress proteins Hsp27 and Hsp72 in rat hearts does not correlate with ischemic tolerance after heat shock. Circulation 1995; 92:I-654 (Abstract)
40. Kukreja RC, Qian Y-Z, Okubo S, Role of protein kinase C and 72 kDa heat shock protein in ischemic tolerance following heat stress in the rat heart. Mol Cell Biochem 1999; 195:123-131.
41. Hug H, Sarre TF. Protein kinase C isozymes: Divergence in signal transduction. Biochem J 1993; 291:329-343.
42. Ytrehus K, Liu Y, Downey JM. Preconditioning protects the ischemic rabbit heart by protein kinase C activation. Am J Physiol 1994; 266:H1145-H1152
43. Liu Y, Ytrehus K, Downey JM. Evidence that translocation of protein kinase C is a key event during ischemic preconditioning of rabbit myocardium. J Mol Cell Cardiol. 1994; 26:661-668.
44. Armstrong SC, Hoover DB, Delacey MH et al. Translocation of PKC, protein phosphatase inhibition and preconditioning of rabbit cardiomyocytes. J Mol Cell Cardiol 1996; 28:1479-1492.
45. Baxter GF, Goma FM, Yellon DM. Involvement of PKC in the delayed cytoprotection following sublethal ischemia in rabbit myocardium. Br J Pharmacol 1995; 115:222-224.
46. Gallo GJ, Schuetz TJ, Kingston RE. Regulation of heat shock factor in *Schizosaccharomyces* pombe more closely resembles regulation in mammals than in *Saccharomyces cerevisiae.* Mol Cell Biol 1991; 11:281-288.
47. Hensold JO, Hunt CR, Calderwood SK et al. DNA binding of heat shock factor to the heat shock element is insufficient for transcriptional activation in murine erythroleukemia cells. Mol Cell Biol. 1990; 10:1600-1608.
48. Sorger PK, Pelham RB. Yeast heat shock factor is an essential DNA-binding protein that exhibits temperature-dependent phosphorylation. Cell 1988; 54:855-864.
49. Cotto JJ, Kline M, Morimoto RI. Activation of heat shock factor 1 DNA-binding precedes stress-induced serine phosphorylation. Evidence for a multistep pathway of regulation. J Biol Chem. 1996; 271:3355-3358.
50. Choi HS, Li B, Lin Z et al. cAMP and cAMP-dependent protein kinase regulate the human heat shock protein 70 gene promoter activity. J Biol Chem 1991; 266:11858-11865.
51. Mitchell MB, Meng X, Ao L et al. Preconditioning of isolated rat heart is mediated by protein kinase C Circ.Res 1995; 76:73-81.
52. Komuro I, Yamazaki T, Katoh Y et al. Protein kinase cascade activated by mechanical stress in cardiocytes: Possible involvement of angiotensin II. Eur Heart J 1995; 16 Suppl C:8-11.
53. Yao A, Takahashi T, Aoyagi T et al. Immediate-early gene induction and MAP kinase activation during recovery from metabolic inhibition in cultured cardiac myocytes. J Clin Invest 1995; 96:69-77.

54. Ghosh S, Baltimore D. Activation in vitro of NF-kappa B by phosphorylation of its inhibitor I kappa B. Nature 1990; 344:678-682.
55. Maggirwar SB, Dhanraj DN, Somani SM et al. Adenosine acts as an endogenous activator of the cellular antioxidant defense system. Biochem Biophys Res Comm. 1994; 201:508-515.
56. Kukreja RC, Hess ML. Free radicals, cardiovascular dysfunction and protection strategies. Austin, Texas. R.G. Landes Company, 1994.
57. Poteat HT, Chen FY, Kadison P et al. Protein kinase A-dependent binding of a nuclear factor to the 21- base-pair repeat of the human T-cell leukemia virus type I long terminal repeat. J Virol 1990; 64:1264-1270.
58. Manak JR, de Bisschop N, Kris RM et al. Casein kinase II enhances the DNA binding activity of serum response factor. Genes Dev 1990; 4:955-967.
59. Jacquier-Sarlin MR, Jornot L, Polla BS. Differential expression and regulation of hsp70 and hsp90 by phorbol esters and heat shock. J Biol Chem 1995; 270:14094-14099.
60. Hoag JB, Qian Y-Z, Nayeem MA et al. ATP-sensitive potassium channel mediates delayed ischemic protection by heat stress in rabbit heart. Am J Physiol 1997; 42:H861-H868
61. Gross GJ, Auchampach JA. Blockade of ATP-sensitive potassium channels prevents myocardial preconditioning in dogs. Circ Res 1992; 70:223-233.
62. Nichols CG, Ripoll C, Lederer WJ. ATP-sensitive potassium channel modulation of guinea pig ventricular action potential and contraction. Circ Res 1991; 68:280-287.
63. Yao Z, Gross GJ. Role of nitric oxide, muscarinic receptos, and the ATP-sensitive K+ channel in mediating the effects of acetylcholine to mimic preconditioning in dogs. Circ Res 1993; 73:1193-1201.
64. Qiu Y, Rizvi A, Tang X-L et al. The protective effect of late preconditioning against stunning in conscious rabbits is mediated by nitric oxide synthase: Evidence that nitric oxide acts both as a trigger and as mediator of the late phase of preconditioning. Am J Physiol 1997; 273:H2931-H2936
65. Bernardo NL, D'Angelo M, Desai PV et al. ATP-sensitive potassium (K_{ATP}) channel is involved in the second window of ischemic preconditioning in rabbit. J Mol Cell Cardiol 1997; 29:A228(Abstract)
66. Mei DA, Elliott GT, Gross GJ. ATP-sensitive K^+ channels mediate the cardioprotective effect of monophophoryl lipid A. Circulation 1995; 92:I-388(Abstract)
67. Hu KL, Duan DY, Li GR et al. Protein kinase C activates ATP-sensitive K^+ current in human and rabbit ventricular myocytes. Circ Res 1996; 78:492-498.
68. Saad AH, Hahn GM. Activation of potassium channels: Relationship to the heat shock response. Proc Natl Acad Sci USA 1992; 89:9396-9399.
69. Negulyaev YA, Vedernikova EA, Kinev AV et al. Exogenous heat shock protein hsp70 activates potassium channels in U937 cells. Biochim Biophys Acta Bio-Membr 1996; 1282:156-162.

Chapter 5

Hsp70 and Ischemia Tolerance in the Compromised Heart

Luc H.E.H. Snoeckx, Richard N.M. Cornelussen, Robert S. Reneman and Ger J. van der Vusse

The discovery in eukaryotic and prokaryotic organisms of a prompt and specific response to heat shock, known as the heat shock response, has stimulated the development of a complete new research domain, in which the potential protective role of stress induced proteins in organisms, tissues, individual cells and subcellular structures under life threatening circumstances became the subject of intense investigations. During the last decade our knowledge of the action of stress proteins in organs such as the heart has grown impressively.

The potential of the expression of inducible stress proteins in hearts of experimental animals has been investigated in a variety of studies. In different mammalian animal species like rat and rabbit, using different models of ischemia, the tolerance of the heart against an ischemic insult was found to be improved by the activation of a powerful endogenous protective mechanism, based upon the enhanced expression of inducible and constitutive (cognate) stress proteins.[1,2] In isolated hearts of young and adult animals, using various ischemia protocols, the expression of stress proteins as induced by whole-body heat stress 24 hours earlier, has been shown to improve postischemic functional recovery and to reduce infarct size following global or regional ischemia, respectively (for review see refs. 3 and 4). The beneficial role of these proteins was studied in even more detail in isolated cell cultures, in which individual stress proteins such as the major inducible stress protein of the 70 kDa family, i.e., Hsp70, were expressed after (viral) transfection.[5-8] Experiments on hearts of transgenic animals with a constitutive overexpression of Hsp70 and experiments in which the expression of this protein was blocked by anti-sense oligonucleotides have shown that this protein plays a key role in the protection of the organ against the deleterious effects of ischemia and reperfusion.[9-13]

More recently, the potential of stress proteins to protect myocardial tissue against ischemia has been extended in experimental pathophysiological models, such as the senescent but healthy heart[14] and the (aged) hypertrophied heart.[14,15] Whereas the protective potential of stress proteins have been demonstrated in these animal models, data on the beneficial effects of stress proteins in human diseased hearts are limited, mainly due to our incomplete knowledge of the pathways involved in the activation of the expression of inducible stress proteins and the inapplicability in the human setting of the techniques in use for stimulation of enhanced stress protein expression. In this chapter we will discuss our current knowledge of the expression of stress proteins and the potential beneficial effects of these proteins in protecting the aged and diseased animal heart and the human heart against ischemia.

Heat Shock Proteins in Myocardial Protection, edited by Rakesh C. Kukreja and Michael L. Hess.

Stress Proteins in the Aged and Diseased Animal Heart

The Aged Heart

In the senescent animal overall gene transcription and mRNA translation and protein degradation are decreased, while the number of malfunctioning proteins is increased.[16] Also the so-called heat shock response is diminished in aged animals, resulting in a decline in the synthesis of inducible stress proteins (for review see ref. 17). This reduced ability has been documented in such organs and organ systems as vascular tissue,[18-20] liver,[21,22] brain,[23] lymphoid tissue,[24] and lung and skin[25] of aged but healthy animals. This difference in expression has also been shown between cells in culture, as in hyperthermically treated cells, isolated from liver tissue from young and aged animals,[26] or in long-lasting cultures of human fibroblasts, reaching the end of their replicative life span (the so-called 'cell senescence').[27]

The overall reduced production of stress proteins in aged tissues upon stress probably reflects a common intrinsic mechanism. Heydari and colleagues showed that the diminished stress protein synthesis in aged tissues was a consequence of a reduced transcription of the heat shock genes.[21] Furthermore, it was found that this decreased transcription rate was caused by reduced binding of the heat shock factor 1 (HSF1) to the heat shock elements (HSE) in the upstream region of the heat shock gene promoter.[24,28] This reduced binding is probably not related to a diminished HSF1 protein content, since the levels of this protein factor were found not to be different between aged and adult tissues.[28] The logical suggestion that the decreased synthesis of inducible stress proteins in aged tissues is due to alterations in the signaling pathway for the phosphorylation and thus activation of the HSF1 is supported by findings in, among others, aortic tissue of aged rats.[18] Whereas the synthesis of the major inducible stress protein Hsp70 in the media of the aortic wall by α1-adrenergic receptor stimulation or by heat stress treatment is comparable in adult rats, the response to α1-adrenergic receptor stimulation seems to be much more attenuated, compared to that after hyperthermic treatment, in aged rats.[18] In aged liver, however, Hsp70 synthesis following heat stress was depressed compared to that in adult animals, but not after severe physical exercise.[29] These data indicate that the regulation of the synthesis of inducible stress proteins is more complicated and does not depend on the attenuation of the binding of HSF1 to the HSE in the promoter region of the heat shock genes alone. In the aged liver, for instance, it has been documented that Hsp70 synthesis upon stress is affected by the type of diet, since restriction of calories reverses the age-dependent decline in the induction of stress proteins.[21] In summary, it is feasible that the stress response is reduced in aged animals, but that full activation of the heat shock genes is still possible under certain circumstances, probably because the various pathways for the HSF1 activation are differentially operational in adult and aged tissues.

As in other organs, stress protein synthesis is also reduced in the aged myocardium when a stimulus such as heat stress or ischemia is applied. In an interesting study, Nitta and colleagues[30] showed that the production of Hsp70 in aged hearts, induced by short coronary occlusion, was significantly lower than in adult hearts. These authors suggested that the ischemia sensing mechanism in the aged myocardium is defective and thus, at least in part, explains the reduced ischemia tolerance of this type of heart. Indeed, several studies in humans and animals have shown that the ischemia tolerance of the aged heart is impaired.[14,31,32] A parallel observation has been made regarding the thermotolerance of the aged heart, which was found to be decreased significantly compared to the healthy adult heart.[23]

In aged hearts of healthy 18 months old Wistar-Kyoto rats, Bongrazio and colleagues[33] and Gaia and colleagues[34] found that the expression of Hsp70 24 hours after whole-body heat stress was substantially decreased compared to the hearts of young adult animals of the same strain, a finding confirmed in other rat strains.[35] In our laboratory, we investigated the synthesis of

Hsp70 in hearts of young (3 months) and aged (17 months) male Lewis rats 24 hours after whole-body heat stress (15 min; 42°C). Whereas the basal levels of Hsp70 were comparable in cardiac tissue of nonstressed young and aged rats, after heat stress they were doubled in aged hearts, while a five-fold increase was found in young hearts. These data are comparable to those found by Kregel and colleagues in heat-stressed male Fisher 344 rats of 12 and 24 months of age.[36]

Only limited information is available on the relation between the decreased ability of stress protein synthesis and the impaired ischemia tolerance in the heart of aged experimental animals. In 22 months old Fisher 344 rat hearts which were isolated from the body 24 hours after heat-stress, Locke and Tanguay found no improvement of postischemic functional recovery, although a significantly increased expression of Hsp70 was found.[35] In contrast, in isolated ejecting hearts of 17 months old Lewis rats in which Hsp70 levels were doubled 24 hours after heat treatment, we found a significantly better recovery of cardiac output, left ventricular developed pressure and contractility than in nonheated, age-matched control hearts. Concomitantly, the postischemic loss of intracellular enzymes, like creatine kinase, and the duration of postischemic arrhythmias was significantly reduced.[14] At present no satisfactory explanation is present for the discrepancy between the results of Locke and Tanguay and our group. Among others, possible differences in experimental circumstances and strain of the animals might be involved.

In conclusion, although the results on the protective effects of stress proteins on ischemia tolerance of aged hearts are controversial, the induction of the major inducible stress protein Hsp70 is still present but limited. It cannot be excluded that the general stress response coincides with a secondary protective mechanism, the activation of which is not dependent on the absolute levels of the synthesized stress proteins.

The Hypertrophied Heart of Adult and Aged Animals

The hypertrophied heart has been recognized to be more vulnerable to ischemic damage than the nonhypertrophied heart. In this type of heart, postischemic reperfusion results in a sustained poor cardiac output, prolonged duration of arrhythmias and increased loss of intracellular enzymes. These phenomena are often associated with myocardial contracture and a substantial underperfusion of subendocardial layers of the left ventricle.[37-39] These observations have been made in several experimental models of cardiac hypertrophy, as in the spontaneously hypertensive rat (SHR) and in the thoracic or abdominal aorta-banded animal. As in the normal heart, in the young adult heart in which cardiac hypertrophy is fully compensated, ischemia is better supported than in the aged hypertrophied heart, which eventually reaches the phase of decompensation.

Some information is available on the basal expression of stress proteins in the hypertrophied heart and on the ability to upregulate their synthesis. In the adult SHR, for instance, it was found that the basal cardiac Hsp70 levels were comparable with those in the age-matched normotensive control rat. Following heat stress, however, both the hsp70 mRNA and the Hsp70 protein level were significantly higher in the hypertrophied than nonhypertrophied heart.[33,40] It cannot be excluded that this overinduction in the SHR heart is caused by the increased thermosensitivity of this strain of rats, since thermoregulation seems to be abnormal in the SHR.[41] It is of interest to note that also in other SHR tissues Hsp70 expression is enhanced upon heat stress. The expression levels, however, appear to relate to the age of the animals. For instance, following whole-body heat stress in hearts of juvenile SHR the Hsp70 expression was found to be about three times higher than in the heated hearts of age-matched normotensive rats, and more than ten-fold increased compared to levels in nonheated SHR hearts.[33] In contrast, following the same heat stress in 18 month old heated SHR hearts, the Hsp70 levels were only three-fold to four-fold higher than in the nonheated SHR hearts, and were increased to comparable levels as in heated hearts from age-matched normotensive rats. Thus throughout life the ability to induce Hsp70 decreased significantly more in this type of hypertrophied heart than in the nonhypertrophied heart.

The findings in the Lewis rat heart, hypertrophied because of aortic banding, are different from those in the SHR heart. In young adult rats in which the abdominal aorta was banded suprarenally at six to seven weeks, we documented a left ventricular hypertrophy of about 40%.[15] The basal mRNA levels of Hsp70 and the cognate Hsc70 in these hearts were comparable in the hypertrophied and nonhypertrophied hearts (Fig. 5.1). Three hours after a hyperthermic stress (15 min; 42°C), the hsp70 mRNA levels increased three-fold in nonhypertrophied hearts and sevenfold in hypertrophied hearts. The hsc70 mRNA levels increased only slightly. Twenty-four hours after the hyperthermic treatment the mRNA levels were completely normalized while the Hsp70 protein levels were three-fold to four-fold higher than in the respective nonheated control hearts. Besides, a comparable increase in protein levels was documented in hyper-trophied and nonhypertrophied hearts. The data obtained for the mRNA signals probably does not reflect the maximal accumulation of the messenger signal, since they were only determined three hours after the heat stress. Besides, it has been found that the hsp70 gene is more rapidly activated and that the messenger signal also declines more rapidly in the hypertrophied than in the normal heart.[30]

In aged animals with cardiac hypertrophy due to aortic banding, Isoyama described a depressed ability to express stress proteins in various tissues.[42] In our laboratory we investigated hypertrophied hearts of 17 month old Lewis rats, which were aorta-banded at the age of 2 months.[14] Only hypertrophied hearts from animals without signs of cardiac decompensation were investigated. The basal expression levels of Hsp70 were comparable in hypertrophied and age-matched nonhypertrophied hearts. Twenty-four hours after hyperthermic treatment (15 min; 42°C) the Hsp70 protein levels had not changed significantly in the hypertrophied hearts whereas they had doubled in the nonhypertrophied hearts, supporting the observations of Isoyama and colleagues.[42]

Although Hsp70 could not be induced in the heated hypertrophied hearts, there was a significant improvement of the postischemic functional outcome.[14] The poor postischemic recovery of cardiac output (average 5% ± 8% of the preischemic cardiac output) in the nonheated hypertrophied hearts was raised to 33% ± 26% in the heated hypertrophied hearts, while the duration of postischemic arrhythmias was significantly reduced from an average of 38 min in the former group to 19 min in the latter. These results again reflect the poor quantitative relationship between the degree of functional postischemic recovery and the cardiac levels of Hsp70 in aged hearts. Such a relationship, however, was found in normal adult hearts.[2,43] In conclusion, although the ability to express stress proteins in the senescent and (aged) hypertrophied heart is impaired, it seems that both types of hearts can be protected against the deleterious effects of ischemia and subsequent reperfusion.

Stress Proteins and Cardiovascular Disease in Humans

To date, the data available on stress proteins in human cardiovascular tissues are scarce. Some detailed studies have been performed on isolated human cells in culture. All cell types brought into culture reacted to an environmental stress by the increased expression of inducible stress proteins. For instance, upon heating, increased Hsp70 expression has been documented in cultured adult and aged endothelial cells from the human umbilical vein,[44] in fibroblasts,[27,45] and in erythroleukemia cells.[46]

Investigation of the potentially beneficial properties of inducible stress proteins in the human heart is hampered by the absence of reliable control tissues and the technical difficulty of inducing the expression of stress proteins like Hsp70 in the intact human body. Under

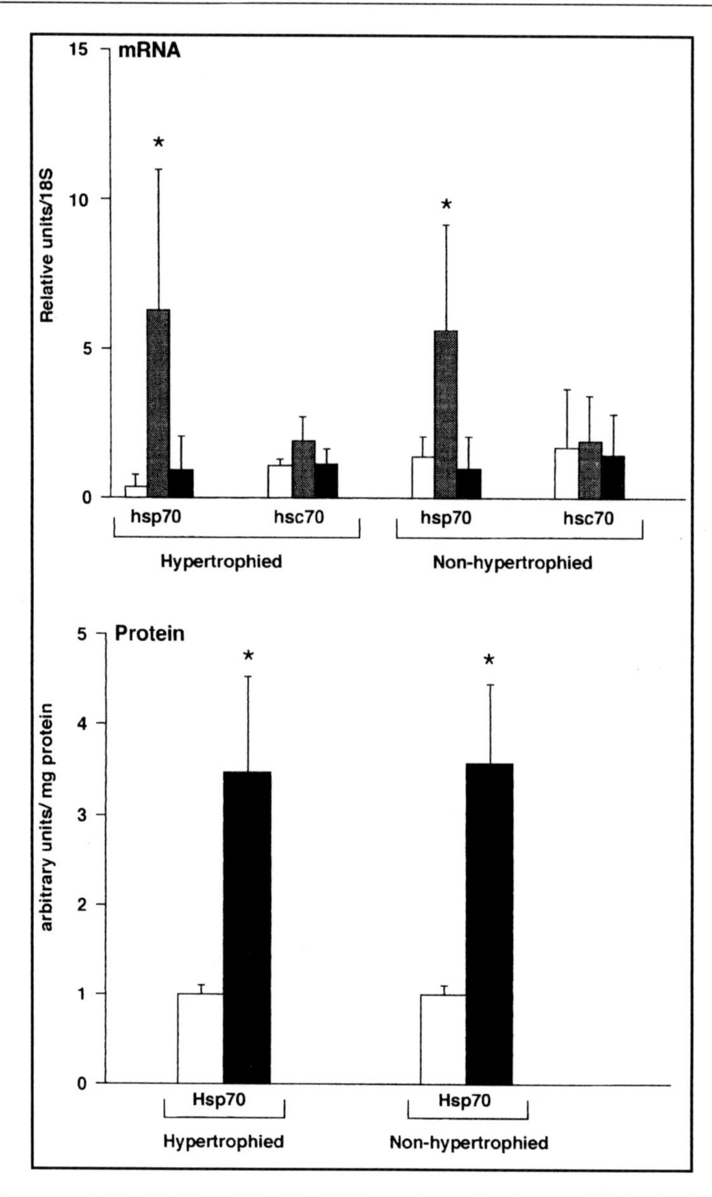

Fig. 5.1. Upper panel: The Hsp70 and Hsc70 mRNA signals, as related to the 18S signals, determined in 10 mg total RNA on Northern blots. Tissue samples were taken from non-heated control rat hearts (open bars), and from hearts 3 (hatched bars) and 24 hours (black bars) after heat treatment. At least 5 samples were determined per group. *: significantly different from the control hearts ($p<0.05$).
Lower panel: Hsp70 protein content determined in Western blots from 1% total cardiac tissue homogenates. Tissue samples were taken from non-heated control rat hearts (open bars), and from hearts twenty-four hours after heat treatment (black bars). At least 5 samples were determined per group. *: significantly different from the control hearts ($p<0.05$).

experimental conditions, one of the most potent ways of inducing the expression of inducible stress proteins has been heating or toxic stimuli such as endotoxin. These techniques, however, cannot be envisaged in humans, certainly not under life threatening circumstances in the clinical setting. The reported findings in human cardiac tissues are merely phenomenological and therefore have to be interpreted with care. The characteristics of the tissue samples and the hemodynamic circumstances and serum hormone levels at the moment of tissue preservation should be documented as detailed as possible, since several conditions can provoke the expression of inducible stress proteins.[47] For instance, in the heart and blood vessels of experimental animals it has been found that sudden changes in left ventricular loading conditions or in myocardial perfusion can induce a fast (transient) expression of Hsp70.[47-51] Furthermore, enhanced levels of circulating hormones like catecholamines, vasopressin and angiotensin II were reported to have a stimulating effect on the expression of inducible stress proteins.[52,53] Therefore, it cannot be excluded that the reported findings in human tissues under clinical conditions were confounded by circulating hormones and/or hemodynamic circumstances, and, therefore, do not reflect the basal expression level of the various stress proteins.[54,55] For instance, McGrath and colleagues investigated the expression of Hsp70 in atrial biopsies of patients undergoing cardiopulmonary bypass surgery.[56] The first biopsy was obtained before any surgical manipulation of the heart, the second one at 5 min following reperfusion after the release of the aortic crossclamp, and the last one 15 min after weaning from the cardiopulmonary bypass. Invariably, all tissue samples showed relatively high Hsp70 protein levels compared to the average values found in nonstressed animal hearts. The authors suggested that either the levels had been artificially enhanced by perioperative circumstances, like drug therapy, or that the basal expression of this particular stress protein is higher in the human than in other mammalian hearts. Otherwise, a limited number of data suggests that the expression level of Hsp70 can vary in human heart tissue. For instance, in hearts from healthy patients killed in traffic accidents, the hsp70 mRNA signal in atrial biopsies was significantly lower than in hyper-trophied ventricular tissue of patients with tetralogy of Fallot.[54] Very recently, Knowlton and colleagues investigated the expression of a number of stress proteins in hearts from transplant recipients.[57] Both dilated and ischemic cardiomyopathic hearts were investigated. Unused donor hearts were used as controls. It was found that the small stress protein Hsp27 levels were increased in dilated cardiomyopathic hearts, while Hsp60 levels were significantly increased in both dilated and ischemic cardiomyopathic hearts. In contrast, the Hsp70 levels were comparable in cardiomyopathic and control hearts. As in the above mentioned study of McGrath and colleagues,[56] the Hsp70 levels in the control hearts were higher than in animal hearts and thus probably reflect a higher basal level of this particular stress protein in the human heart.

To get a better insight into the physiological behavior of inducible stress proteins, some investigators have mimicked the conditions of surgical interventions in humans after the expression of stress proteins. For instance, Maulik and colleagues performed a study in pigs, which were treated with amphetamine, thereby provoking stress protein synthesis through a body temperature increase.[58] Forty hours later the animals were subjected to cardiopulmonary bypass, one hour occlusion of the left coronary artery, one hour of global hypothermic cardioplegic arrest and one hour of reperfusion. Cardiac biopsies were investigated 3 hours after amphetamine injection for the expression of Hsp27, Hsp70, and Hsp89 mRNA. All three messenger signals were significantly elevated compared to nontreated controls. Parameters for functional recovery during postischemic reperfusion were all significantly improved. Although this study elegantly demonstrates the effectiveness of stress proteins in protecting cardiac function during surgical interventions, it remains questionable whether amphetamine is a suitable drug for preconditioning of the heart, since body temperatures reached uncontrollable high levels (>42°C). To circumvent this problem, Liu and colleagues[59] applied warm blood cardioplegia by circulating 42°C warm blood through the coronary vascular system of the arrested pig heart immediately before two hours hypothermic cardioplegic arrest. The improved recovery of functional parameters during the subsequent one hour reperfusion was associated with an almost threefold increase of Hsp70 tissue content.

In search for an effective but acceptable technique for the expression of stress proteins, some investigators explored the delayed effects of ischemic preconditioning. Brief repetitive periods of ischemia and reperfusion not only improve transiently the tolerance towards a longer period of ischemia, i.e., within a subsequent time window between 0 and 3 hours, but also towards an ischemic insult applied one day later. This phenomenon is known as the second window of protection.[60] In studies on dog and rabbit hearts the second window of protection has been shown to be associated with a marked increase of Hsp70.[61,62] Other studies, however, have reported a lack of late protection against cardiac ischemia despite a significant increase of Hsp70 tissue content.[63,64] Methodological differences between the various studies hamper the proper interpretation of this conflicting findings.

In conclusion, studies on the beneficial properties of inducible stress proteins in the diseased human heart are still descriptive, because of the difficulties in making the technique to express these proteins operational. Furthermore, a major problem is the time-delay between the induction of stress protein synthesis, which is relatively fast (<6 hours following the stress event), and the occurrence of the beneficial effects on cardiac function during and after an ischemic insult.[65,66] The studies, in which hyperthermic treatment was used to induce stress protein synthesis, indicate that heat stress masks the beneficial effect since intracellular structures are destabilised.[67] Indeed, a cytoskeletal collapse has been documented upon heat stress treatment.[68] Moreover, the ability of the hyperthermically pretreated heart to cope with extreme hemodynamic conditions, such as an increased loading of the left ventricle, seems to be depressed during the first 24 hours following hyperthermia.[69] However, in studies using ischemic preconditioning the same long time-delay, i.e., 24 hours, is indeed necessary to make the stress protein-mediated protective mechanism fully operational.

New Research and Anticipated Developments

In experimental animals, probably the best known stress protein until now is the major inducible stress protein Hsp70. Its protective potentials have been demonstrated in the heart of the intact animal as well as in the isolated heart. Also in isolated cardiomyocytes, in which the expression of Hsp70 was induced by such measures as heat stress, endotoxin administration or hypoxia, protection against a subsequent severe stress has been demonstrated. Two approaches of experimental overexpression of Hsp70 will allow the detailed study of the physiological role in the heart and in all cardiac cell types. First, the transgenic mouse overexpressing cardiac Hsp70 has been developed in several laboratories. Hearts of these animals have been investigated for their resistance to global[9-11] or regional ischemia.[12] In all these investigations, it was shown that the postischemic functional recovery was better than in the hearts of wild type animals, and that the beneficial effects could be related to the only overexpressed stress protein Hsp70. Second, overexpression of the Hsp70 protein in the cell under experimental conditions has been achieved by the application of so-called plasmid transfection or by adenoviral infection techniques.[6,7,70] Although these are techniques 'par excellence' for the isolated cell in culture, recent developments in which a viral vector was coupled to liposomes containing foreign plasmids are very promising, since these viruses can cross the endothelial barrier and are able to infect cardiomyocytes within the intact heart.[71] Using this technique, Suzuki and colleagues have been able to transfer the human Hsp70 gene into cardiomyocytes of intact rat hearts.[8] After virus infection through coronary infusion in the excised arrested heart, the organ was heterotopically transplanted and investigated four days later in an isolated perfusion apparatus. The ischemia tolerance was significantly improved and enzyme leakage was diminished compared to heterotopically transplanted control hearts. The better recovery in these hearts was even slightly better than in hyperthermically pretreated hearts. Such experiments show that even without adaptational processes, as in the transgenic animal that overexpresses a certain stress protein, selective upregulation of the Hsp70 expression can improve the tolerance of the heart to ischemia or other threatening events. This technique could be important in endangered cardiac tissue, since any stress protein gene can be placed behind a promoter of choice so that the expression levels are independent of activation of the internal gene apparatus.

Conclusions

It has been acknowledged that myocardial hypertrophy is a major risk factor for sudden death, infarction and heart failure.[72] Under experimental circumstances, it has been shown that the hypertrophied heart, certainly when it is aged, has an extremely high vulnerability for ischemic damage.[14,32,37-39] Experimental studies have shown that hypertrophied hearts, even when there is a long-standing hypertrophic process, can be efficiently protected against the deleterious effects of ischemia and reperfusion by a preceding expression of inducible stress proteins. The potential of this endogenous protective mechanism needs to be explored in more detail. The fact that stress pretreatment prevents the deleterious effects of ischemia and reperfusion to occur in the (aged) hypertrophied heart legitimates optimism for a therapeutic application of stress proteins in the diseased human heart. Further studies will be needed to fully understand the induction routes of the various protective stress proteins and their specific protective action in the (aged) hypertrophied heart. Experiments in hearts of aging transgenic animals overexpressing Hsp70 will certainly be helpful in understanding the pathophysiology of this organ and in developing techniques to upregulate the Hsp70 synthesis in the human heart without harmful side-effects.

Acknowledgments

The authors are indebted to Dr. Michael M. Vork, Dr. Anne Garnier, Mr. Léon de Bruin, and Mr. Peter Geurten for their appreciated contribution. This study was supported by the Netherlands Heart Foundation Grant 92.057 and the European Community Grant BMH1-CT-1171

References

1. Currie RW, Karmazyn M, Kloc M et al. Heat-shock response is associated with enhanced post-ischemic recovery. Circ Res 1988; 63:543-549.
2. Marber MS, Walker JM, Latchman DS et al. Myocardial protection after whole body heat stress in the rabbit is dependent on metabolic substrate and is related to the amount of the inducible 70-kD heat stress protein. J Clin Invest 1994; 93:1087-1094.
3. Dillmann WH, Mestril R. Ischemia, infarction, and Hsp70. In: Heat shock proteins and the cardiovascular system. Ed. A.A. Knowlton. Kluwer Acad. Publish. Boston 1997:25-40.
4. Currie RW, Plumier J-CL. Heat shock proteins and antioxidative enzymes in myocardial protection. In: Heat shock proteins and the cardiovascular system. AA Knowlton, Ed. Kluwer Acad. Publish. Boston 1997:71-83.
5. Heads RJ, Latchman DS, Yellon DM. Stable high level expression of a transfected human Hsp70 gene protects a heart-derived muscle cell line against thermal stress. J Mol Cell Cardiol 1994; 26:695-699.
6. Mestril R, Chi SH, Sayen MR et al. Expression of inducible stress protein 70 in rat heart myogenic cells confers protection against simulated ischemia-induced injury. J Clin Invest 1994; 93:759-767.
7. Sanders Williams R, Thomas JA, Fina M et al. Human heat-shock protein 70 (Hsp70) protects murine cells from injury during metabolic stress. J Clin Invest 1993; 92:503-508.
8. Suzuki K, Sawa Y, Kaneda Y et al. In vivo gene transfer with heat shock protein 70 enhances myocardial tolerance to ischemia-reperfusion injury in rat. J Clin Invest 1997; 99:1645-1650.

9. Marber MS, Mestril R, Chi S-H et al. Overexpression of the rat inducible 70-kD heat stress protein in a transgenic mouse increases the resistance of the heart to ischemic injury. J Clin Invest 1995; 95:1446-1456.
10. Plumier JCL, Ross BM, Currie RW et al. Transgenic mice expressing the human heat shock protein 70 have improved post-ischemic myocardial recovery. J Clin Invest 1995; 95:1854-1860.
11. Radford NB, Fina M, Benjamin IJ et al. Cardioprotective effects of 70-kDa heat shock protein in transgenic mice. Proc Natl Acad Sci USA 1996; 93:2339-2342.
12. Hutter JJ, Mestril R, Tam EKW et al. Overexpression of heat shock protein 72 in transgenic mice decreases infarct size in vivo. Circulation 1996; 94:1408-1411.
13. Nakano M, Mann DL, Knowlton AA. Blocking the endogenous increase in Hsp72 increases the susceptibility to hypoxia and reoxygenation in isolated adult feline cardiocytes. Circulation 1997; 95:1523-1531.
14. Cornelussen RN, Garnier AV, Vork MM et al. Heat stress protects aged hypertrophied and nonhypertrophied rat hearts against ischemic damage. Am J Physiol 1997; 273:H1333-H1341.
15. Cornelussen RN, Spiering W, Webers JHG et al. Heat shock improves the ischemic tolerance of the hypertrophied rat heart. Am J Physiol 1994; 267(Heart Circ Physiol):H1941-H1947.
16. Lakatta E. Cardiovascular regulatory mechanisms in advanced age. Physiol Rev 1993; 73:413-467.
17. Richardson A, Holbrook NJ. Aging and the cellular response to stress: Reduction in the heat shock response. In: Cellular Aging and Cell Death. Eds. NJ Holbrook, GR Martin, and RA Lockshin, Wiley-Liss, New York 1996.
18. Chin JH, Okazaki M, Hu ZW et al. Activation of heat shock protein (Hsp)70 and proto-oncogene expression by alpha1 adrenergic agonist in rat aorta with age. J Clin Invest 1996; 97:2316-2323.
19. Udelsman R, Blake MJ, Stagg CA et al. Vascular heat shock protein expression in response to stress. Endocrine and autonomic regulation of this age-dependent response. J Clin Invest 1993; 91:465-473.
20. Udelsman R, Li D, Stagg CA et al. Aortic crosstransplantation between young and old rats: Effect upon the heat shock protein 70 stress response. J Geront 1995; 50A:B187-B192.
21. Heydari AR, Wu B, Takahashi R et al. Expression of heat shock protein 70 is altered by age and diet at the level of transcription. Mol Cell Biol 1993; 13:2909-2918.
22. Shpund S, Gershon D. Alterations in the chaperone activity of HSP70 in aging organisms. Arch Geront Geriatr 1997; 24:125-131.
23. Blake MJ, Fagnoli J, Gershon D et al. Concomitant decline in heat-induced hyperthermia and Hsp70 mRNA expression in aged rats. Am J Physiol 1991; 260:R663-R667.
24. Pahlavani MA, Harris MD, Moore SA et al. The expression of heat shock protein 70 decreases with age in lymphocytes from rats and rhesus monkeys. Exp Cell Res 1995; 218:310-318.
25. Fargnoli J, Kunisada T, Fornace AJ et al. Decreased expression of heat shock protein 70 mRNA and protein after heat shock treatment in cells of aged rats. Proc Natl Acad Sci USA 1990; 87:846-850.
26. Wu B, Gu MJ, Heydari AR et al. The effect of age on the synthesis of two heat shock proteins in the Hsp70 family. J Geront 1993; 48:B50-B56.
27. Luce M, Cristofalo V. Reduction in heat shock gene expression correlates with increased thermosensitivity in senescent human fibroblasts. Exp Cell Res 1992; 202:9-16.
28. Fawcett TW, Sylvester SL, Sarge KD et al. Effects of neurohormonal stress and aging on the activation of the mammalian heat shock factor 1. J Biol Chem 1994; 269:32272-32278.
29. Kregel KC, Moseley PL. Differential effects of exercise and heat stress on liver Hsp70 accumulation with aging. J Appl Physiol 1996; 80:547-551.
30. Nitta Y, Abe K, Aoki M et al. Diminished heat shock protein 70 mRNA induction in aged rats after ischemia. Am J Physiol 1994; 267:H1795-H1803.
31. Snoeckx LHEH, van der Vusse GJ, Coumans WA et al. Differences in ischemia tolerance between hypertrophied hearts of adult and aged spontaneously hypertensive rats. Cardiovasc Res 1993; 27:874-881.
32. Buckberg GD. Left ventricular subendocardial necrosis. Ann Thorac Surg 1977; 24:379-393.
33. Bongrazio M, Comini L, Gaia G et al. Hypertension, aging, and myocardial synthesis of heat shock protein 72. Hypertension 1994; 24:620-624.
34. Gaia G, Comini L, Pasini E et al. Heat shock protein 72 in cardiac and skeletal muscles during hypertension. Mol Cell Biochem 1995; 146:1-6.

35. Locke M, Tanguay RM. Diminished heat shock response in the aged myocardium. Cell stress chaperones 1996; 1:251-260.
36. Kregel KC, Moseley PL, Skidmore R et al. Hsp70 accumulation in tissues of heat-stressed rats is blunted with advancing age. J Appl Physiol 1995; 79:1673-1678.
37. Snoeckx LHEH, van der Vusse GJ, Coumans WA et al. The effects of global ischemia and reperfusion on compensated hypertrophied hearts of aortabanded rats. J Mol Cell Cardiol 1990; 22:1439-1451.
38. Snoeckx LHEH, van der Vusse GJ, Coumans WA et al. Myocardial function in normal and spontaneously hypertensive rats during reperfusion after a period of global ischemia. Cardiovasc Res 1986; 20:67-75.
39. Cooley DA, Reul GJ, Wukash DC. Ischemic contracture of the heart: "stone heart". Am J Cardiol 1972; 29:575-577.
40. Hamet P, Malo D, Tremblay J. Increased transcription of a major stress gene in spontaneously hypertensive mice. Hypertension 1990; 15:904-908.
41. Malo D, Schlager G, Tremblay J et al. Thermosensitivity, a possible new locus involved in genetic hypertension. Hypertension 1989; 14:121-128.
42. Isoyama S. Age-related changes before and after imposition of hemodynamic stress in the mammalian heart. Life Sci 1996; 58:1601-1614.
43. Hutter MM, Sievers RE, Barbosa V et al. Heat-shock protein induction in rat hearts. A direct correlation between the amount of heat-shock protein induced and the degree of myocardial protection. Circulation 1994; 89(1):355-60.
44. Jornot L, Mirault ME, Junod AF. Differential expression of Hsp70 stress proteins in human endothelium cells exposed to heat-shock and hydrogen peroxide. Am J Respir Cell Mol Biol 1991; 5:265-275.
45. Campanini C, Petronini P, Alfieri R, Borghetti A. Decreased expression of heat shock protein 70 mRNA and protein in WI-38 human fibroblasts aging in vitro. Ann N Y Acad Sci 1994:665.
46. Amici C, Palamara AT, Santoro MG. Induction of thermotolerance by prostaglandine A in human cells. Exp Cell Res 1993; 207:230-234.
47. Snoeckx LHEH, Contard F, Samuel JL et al. Expression and cellular distribution of heat-shock and nuclear oncogene proteins in rat hearts. Am J Physiol 1991; 259:H1443-H1451.
48. Delcayre C, Samuel J-L, Marotte F et al. Synthesis of stress proteins in rat cardiac myocytes 2-4 days after imposition of hemodynamic overload. J Clin Invest 1988; 82:460-468.
49. Knowlton AA, Eberli FR, Brecher P et al. A single myocardial stretch or decreased systolic fiber shortening stimulates the expression of heat-shock protein 70 in the isolated, erythrocyte perfused rabbit heart. J Clin Invest 1991; 88:2018-2025.
50. Xu Q, Li D, Holbrook NJ et al. Acute hypertension induces heat shock protein 70 gene expression in rat aorta. Circulation 1995; 92:1223-1229.
51. Bauters C, Moalic JM, Bercovici J et al. Coronary flow as a determinant of c-myc and c-fos proto-oncogene expression in an isolated adult heart. J Mol Cell Cardiol 1988; 20:97-101.
52. Moalic JM, Bauters C, Himbert D et al. Phenylephrine, vasopressin and angiotensin II as determinants of proto-oncogene and heat-shock protein gene expression in adult rat heart and aorta. J Hypertens 1989; 7(3):195-201.
53. Kohane D, Sarzani R, Schwartz J et al. Stress-induced proteins in aortic smooth muscle cells and aorta of hypertensive rats. Am J Physiol 1990; 258:H1699-H1705.
54. Jegadeesh-Babu G, Prabhakar R, Kartha C et al. Expression of proto-oncogenes, genes for muscle specific isoforms and heat shock protein (Hsp)-70 gene in hypertrophied cardiac muscles from patients with atrial septal defects or tetralogy of Fallot. Biochem Mol Biol Int 1994; 34:627-637.
55. McGrath LB, Locke M. Myocardial self-preservation: Absence of heat shock factor activation and heat shock proteins 70 mRNA accumulation in the human heart during cardiac surgery. J Card Surg 1995; 10:400-406.
56. McGrath LD, Locke M, Cane M et al. Heat shock protein (HSP72) expression in patients undergoing cardiac operations. J Thorac Cardiovasc Surg 1995; 109:370-376.
57. Knowlton AA, Kapadia S, Torre-Amione G et al. Differential expression of heat shock proteins in normal and failing human hearts. In press 1998.

58. Maulik N, Engelman RM, Wei Z et al. Drug-induced heat shock preconditioning improves postischemic recovery after cardiopulmonary bypass. Circ 1995; 92 (supll II):II-381-II-388.
59. Liu X, Engelman RM, Moraru II et al. Heat shock. A new approach for myocardial preservation in cardiac surgery. Circulation 1992; 86:II-358-II-363.
60. Yellon DM, Alkhulaifi AM, Pugsley WB. Preconditioning the human myocardium. Lancet 1993; 342(8866):276-7.
61. Marber MS, Latchman DS, Walker JM, Yellon DM. Cardiac stress protein elevation 24 hours after brief ischemia or heat stress is associated with resistance to myocardial infarction. Circulation 1993; 88(3):1264-1272.
62. Kuzuya T, Hoshida A, Yamashita N et al. Delayed effects of sublethal ischemia on the acquisition of tolerance to ischemia. Circ Res 1993; 72:1293-1299.
63. Tanaka M, Fujiwara H, Yamasaki K et al. Ischemic preconditioning elevates cardiac stress protein but does mot limit infarct size 24 or 48 hours later in rabbits. Am J Physiol 1994; 267:H1476-H1482.
64. Donnelly TJ, Sievers RE, Vissern FL, Welch WJ, Wolfe CL. Heat-shock protein induction in rat hearts. A role for improved myocardial salvage after ischemia and reperfusion. Circulation 1991; 85:769-778.
65. Karmazyn M, Mailer K, Currie RW. Acquisition and decay of heat-shock-enhanced post-ischemic ventricular recovery. Am J Physiol 1990; 259:H424-H431.
66. Cornelussen RN, de Bruin LGA, Vork MM et al. Biphasic effect of heat stress pretreatment on ischemic tolerance of isolated rat hearts. J Mol Cell Cardiol 1998; 30:In press.
67. Welch WJ, Suhan JP. Morphological study of the mammalian stress response: Characterization of changes in cytoplasmic organelle, cytoskeleton, and nucleoli, and the appearence of intranuclear actin filaments in rat fibroblasts after heat shock treatment. J Biol Chem 1985; 101:1198-1211.
68. Welch WJ. Mammalian stress response: Cell physiology, structure/function of stress proteins, and implications for medicine and disease. Physiol Rev 1992; 72:1063-1081.
69. Cornelussen RN, van der Vusse GJ, Reneman RS et al. Inability of the heat-shocked heart to adjust its preischemic and postischemic performance to variable loading conditions. J Mol Cell Cardiol 1996; 28:291-298.
70. Mestril R, Giordano FJ, Conde AG et al. Adenovirus-mediated gene transfer of a heat shock protein 70 (Hsp70) protects against simulated ischemia. J Mol Cell Cardiol 1996; 28:2351-2358.
71. Aoki M, Morishita R, Muraishi A et al. Efficient in vivo gene transfer into the heart in the rat myocardial infarction model using the HVJ (Hemaglutinating virus of Japan)—liposome method. J Mol Cell Cardiol 1997; 29:949-959.
72. Levy D, Garrison RJ, Savage DD et al. Prognostic implications of echocardiographic determined left ventricular mass in the Framingham Heart Study. N Engl J Med 1990; 322:1561-1566.

CHAPTER 6

Hsp72 in the Regulation of TNF-α Production:

Mechanistic Implication of Protection Against Postischemic Myocardial Dysfunction

Xianzhong Meng

Abstract

Myocardial ischemia/reperfusion induces the production of the cardiac depressant cytokine tumor necrosis factor-α (TNF-α). Macrophages (Mϕ) are the main sources of tissue TNF-α, and nuclear factor-κB (NF-κB) is a key transcription factor regulating TNF-α production. Thus, NF-κB may represent a therapeutic target for myocardial dysfunction associated with dysregulated TNF-α production. Accumulating evidence shows that some known cardioprotective agents, such as adenosine, inhibit myocardial TNF-α production and that inhibition of NF-κB improves myocardial recovery after ischemia/reperfusion. Heat shock protein (Hsp) 72, an inducible isoform of 70 kD Hsp family, is expressed in the myocardium in response to various forms of stress and has been linked to myocardial functional resistance to ischemia/reperfusion. The mechanism by which cardiac Hsp72 preserves myocardial function during stress remains obscure. In vitro heat stress inhibits TNF-α production by monocytes or Mϕ following endotoxin stimulation. We have noted that cardiac interstitial cells including Mϕ preferentially express Hsp72 after whole body hyperthermia in rats and that this pattern of Hsp72 expression is associated with enhanced cardiac resistance to both subsequent endotoxemic and ischemic dysfunction. It is likely that Hsp72 plays an important role in the regulation of local inflammatory response and thereby preserves tissue function. Indeed, induction of Hsp72 downregulates stress-induced TNF-α production in tissues including the myocardium and lungs, and the downregulation of TNF-α production in the lungs has been attributed to inhibition of NF-κB. Further delineation of the role of cardiac Hsp72 in the regulation of myocardial NF-κB activity and TNF-α production, and the exploration of molecular interaction of Hsp72 with NF-κB will provide insights into the mechanism by which Hsp72 preserves myocardial function.

Introduction

Tumor necrosis factor-α (TNF-α) is a proinflammatory cytokine produced and released dominantly by circulating monocytes and tissue macrophages (Mϕ). Dysregulated TNF-α production provokes organ dysfunction.[1] A well described disorder is myocardial contractile dysfunction induced by bacterial lipopolysaccharide (LPS), where TNF-α has been found to

Heat Shock Proteins in Myocardial Protection, edited by Rakesh C. Kukreja and Michael L. Hess.

be a cardiodepressive factor.[2] It is now known that TNF-α induces contractile depression in isolated cardiac myocytes,[3] myocardial preparations,[4,5] and intact heats.[6] Myocardial ischemia also initiates an inflammatory response leading to the production of TNF-α in the heart,[7] and suppression of TNF-α production or neutralization of TNF-α cytotoxicity preserves myocardial contractile function after ischemia/reperfusion.[8]

All living organisms have evolved mechanisms to maintain homeostasis in the face of diverse and complex environmental stresses. The heat shock response, represented as the expression of a group of heat shock protein (Hsp), is one of the conserved protective mechanisms.[9] First observed as a morphologic change (puffing) of *Drosophila* chromosomes in response to heat, the heat shock response has been observed in all mammalian species, and multiple inducers of this ubiquitous response are now recognized. The major Hsp in mammals belongs to the 70 kD Hsp family which consists of Hsp72 and Hsp73. Hsp73 is constitutively expressed whereas Hsp72 is an inducible isoform. Both Hsp73 and Hsp72 function as "molecular chaperones", guiding the folding and refolding of proteins as they are synthesized and conveyed between subcellular organelles.[10] Hsp72 has been proposed to play an important role in adaptive responses since it is induced by different forms of stress.[9] Molecular analysis of the Hsp70 genes and their protein products indicates extraordinary evolutionary conservation from bacteria to man. The importance of these genes and their protein products are demonstrated through "knock-out" and transgenic studies. Microinjection of anti-Hsp70 antibodies into individual cells renders them exquisitely sensitive to minor perturbations of temperature and nutrients.[11]

Heat-stress-induced myocardial protection against ischemia/reperfusion (I/R) injury is a well described phenomenon.[12,13] Hsp72 has been linked to myocardial functional resistance to I/R,[14-16] and the mechanism by which Hsp72 preserves myocardial function during stress remains obscure. In vitro heat stress has been known to inhibit TNF-α production by monocytes or Mϕ following LPS stimulation.[17,18] A recent study by our laboratory has shown that cardiac interstitial cells including Mϕ preferentially express Hsp72 after whole body hyperthermia in rats, and this pattern of Hsp72 expression is associated with attenuated myocardial TNF-α production and improved contractile function following myocardial I/R.[19] Regulation of myocardial TNF-α production may be a novel mechanism by which Hsp72 protects the myocardium against stress-induced dysfunction. This review will summarize recent investigations defining the role of TNF-α in post-ischemic myocardial dysfunction and the effects of Hsp72 expression on TNF-α production. Particularly, this review will focus primarily on the advances in our understanding of the effects of Hsp72 on TNF-α gene transcription and the molecular events that may mediate these effects.

Hsp70 in Myocardial Protection

The role of Hsp70 in myocardial protection against infarction has been discussed in recent reviews.[12,13] A particularly intriguing finding is that induction of Hsp70 improves cardiac functional recovery after I/R.[14-16,19-21] To examine the role of endogenous cardiac Hsp70 in the preservation of postischemic myocardial function, we have used three different stress models, i.e., endotoxemic stress by injection of LPS,[22-25] hemodynamic stress by injection of norepinephrine[21,26] and heat stress by whole body hyperthermia.[19] All of the three forms of stress induced cardiac Hsp72[19,21,22] and enhanced postischemic functional recovery (Fig. 6.1). These observations suggest that Hsp72 somehow preserves myocardial contractility during I/R or promotes the recovery of myocardial contractility during reperfusion. Indeed, constitutive overexpression of Hsp70 in transgenic mice has also been shown to enhance cardiac functional recovery after I/R.[27-30] Similarly, in vivo transfection of myocardium with Hsp70 gene enhances myocardial resistance to I/R injury in rats.[31] Thus, Hsp70 protects myocardial function although the protective mechanism remains unknown.

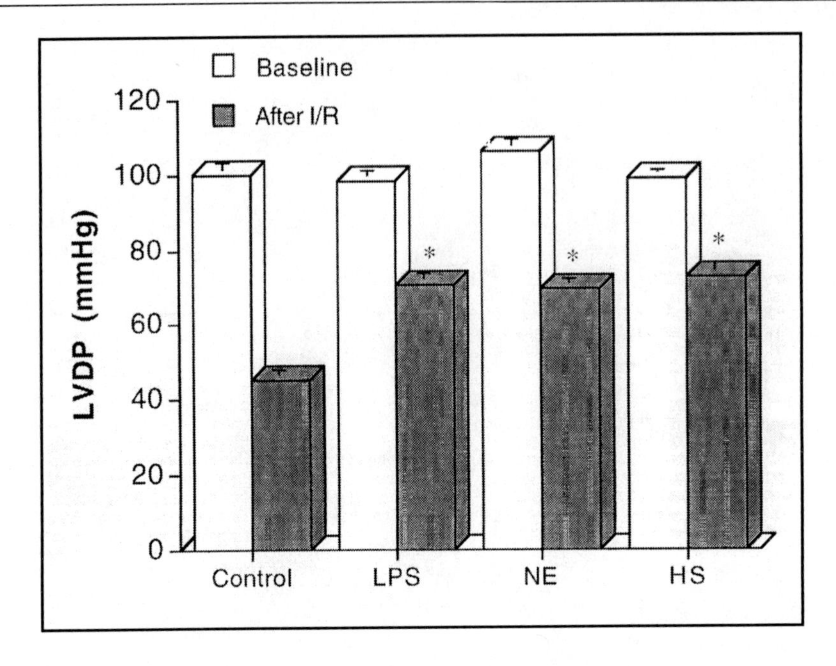

Fig. 6.1. The influence of a prior stress on myocardial function after ischemia/reperfusion (I/R). Rats were pretreated with lipopolysaccharide (LPS, 0.5 mg/kg ip), norepinephrine (NE, 0.53 mg/kg ip) or whole body heat stress (HS, 42°C for 15 min). Hearts were isolated from control rats and pretreated animals 24 h after treatment, perfused with the Krebs-Henseleit buffer by the Langendorff technique and subjected to global I/R (25/40 min). Left ventricular developed pressure (LVDP) was recorded before ischemia (baseline) and at the end of reperfusion after I/R. Data are mean ± SE. * P<0.01 vs. controls.

Myocardial Ischemia and TNF-α Production

The proinflammatory cytokine TNF-α is a well-known myocardial depressant factor and is responsible for myocardial dysfunction associated with systemic inflammation.[32] TNF-α induces contractile depression in myocardial preparations,[4,5] isolated cardiac myocytes[3] and intact hearts.[6] The mechanisms by which TNF-α causes myocardial dysfunction are complex. Multiple hypotheses have been proposed, including calcium dyshomeostasis, direct cytotoxicity, oxidant stress, disruption of excitation-contraction coupling, myocyte apoptosis and induction of other myocardial depressant substances.[33] TNF-α appears to exert immediate and delayed effects on the myocardium.[32] The immediate effect of TNF-α may involve disruption of calcium homeostasis,[34] induction of oxidant stress,[35] and attenuation of cardiac myocyte responsiveness to adrenergic stimulation.[36] Oral and colleagues have recently demonstrated that sphingosine mediates the immediate negative inotropic effect of TNF-α in cultured cardiac myocytes.[37] The delayed effect of TNF-α may involve induction of other cardiac depressant factors such as inducible nitric oxide synthase[38] and interleukin-1[39] as well as promotion of cardiac myocyte apoptosis.[40] Indeed, nitric oxide independently depresses myocardial contractility,[41] and interleukin-1 synergistically enhances TNF-α-induced myocardial depression.[5,42]

Monocytes and Mϕ are the main sources of TNF-α. It is now clear that NF-κB is a primary initiator for TNF-α gene transcription in monocytic cells.[43] NF-κB is located in the cytoplasm, and it translocates into the nucleus where it binds to gene promoters following activation. NF-κB activity is regulated by the inhibitory protein IκB which binds to NF-κB, forming an inactive cytoplasmic complex. Phosphorylation of IκB by IκB kinase allows for the release of NF-κB and its intranuclear translocation.[44]

I/R activates myocardial NF-κB[45] and thereby transduces extracellular signals into the nucleus. A number of studies suggest a link between cardiac TNF-α and myocardial dysfunction after I/R. Increased cardiac expression of TNF-α occurs in animal models of myocardial I/R[46-51] and in humans after coronary bypass surgery.[7,52,53] Recent studies by our laboratory have demonstrated that both ischemic preconditioning and adenosine, a proposed mediator of ischemic preconditioning, inhibit myocardial TNF-α production after I/R and that a decreased level of myocardial TNF-α is associated with improved postischemic myocardial function.[50,54,55] It has been previously reported that adenosine inhibits TNF-α production and enhances systemic resistance to LPS in mice.[56] Other studies have also shown that adenosine decreases LPS-stimulated myocardial TNF-α production (neonatal rat myocytes, adult rat ventricular myocytes and rat papillary muscle).[57] It appears that A3 receptors are required in the regulation of TNF-α production by adenosine.[58] Manipulation of TNF-α bioactivity has been shown to improve postischemic myocardial function.[8] Suppression of myocardial TNF-α production may be another permissive strategy for preservation of myocardial function during I/R and other forms of stress.

Hsp70 in the Regulation of TNF-α Production

The potential role of heat shock response in anti-inflammation defense has recently been explored. Studies from a number of laboratories have demonstrated that animals that have recovered from heat stress or those that have been treated with sodium arsenite (a potent inducer of Hsp70) are resistant to the lethality of LPS or sepsis.[59-62] Using a rat endotoxemia model, we have demonstrated that treatment with LPS results in increased cardiac resistance to the cardiodepressive effect of subsequent LPS.[22] LPS-induced enhancement of cardiac resistance is associated with the expression of Hsp72 in the myocardial interstitial cells including resident Mϕ. Interestingly, heat stress appears to induce Hsp72 selectively in myocardial interstitial cells and similarly enhances cardiac resistance against endotoxemic myocardial depression. Chi and colleagues have demonstrated that transfection of cultured cardiac myocytes with the Hsp70 gene increases their resistance to LPS toxicity.[63] However, the role of Hsp70 in the enhanced cardiac resistance to sepsis-induced depression remains to be determined. Whereas Hsp70 has been reported to protect cells against stress-induced apoptosis,[64] the enhancement of cardiac resistance to endotoxemic depression by prior heat stress may not involve an increase in myocytic resistance to apoptosis because no detectable Hsp72 expression was observed in cardiac myocytes following whole body heat stress. Perhaps, Hsp70 down-regulates cardiac TNF-α production since Mϕ and other interstitial cells are the main cell types expressing Hsp72 following whole body heat stress.[22]

Dinarello and colleagues initially reported that heat stress suppressed interleukin-1 production in LPS-stimulated human peripheral monocytes.[65] This group demonstrated that the production of interleukin-1 by LPS-stimulated monocytes was decreased after incubation at 39°C for 24 h. Schmidt and Abdulla found that incubation of the human myelomonocytic cells at 39°C or 41°C for 4 h induced Hsp70.[66] The synthesis of pro-interleukin-1β (p35) in response to LPS stimulation was decreased by incubation of cells at 39°C and abolished by incubation of cells at 41°C.[66] These studies suggest that induction of the heat shock response down-regulates monocytic response to LPS. In 1989, Klostergaard and colleagues[67] reported that LPS-simulated in vitro TNF-α production by murine peritoneal Mϕ was strongly inhibited by an antecedent heat stress. The down-regulation of TNF-α production was observed in cells incubated at 42° or 43°C but not in those incubated at 40.5°C. Furthermore, the down-regulation of TNF-α production was not induced in cells subjected to heat stress 2 or 4 h after the addition of LPS. It was assumed that the induction of inhibitory factors by prior heat stress was required for down-regulation of LPS-stimulated TNF-α production and that the expression of these factors took place only when incubation temperature was above a critical point. Snyder and colleagues[68] then demonstrated that incubation of murine peritoneal Mϕ at 45°C for 12 min resulted in an increase in cellular Hsp70, with maximal increase at 2 to 5 h after heat stress. TNF-α was not detectable in the culture supernatant when Mϕ were stimulated with LPS at 2 to 6 h following heat stress. Utilizing slot blot analysis, these investigators found that heat-stressed Mϕ expressed high levels of Hsp70 mRNA whereas TNF-α transcripts were significantly reduced. These results are consistent with transcriptional regulation of TNF-α, similar to what was demonstrated for interleukin-1 in human peripheral monocytes.[66] Although the heat stress used in the study by Snyder and colleagues was severe (12 min at 45°C), they noted that heat stress did not affect cellular phagocytic function. It appears that the effect of heat stress on LPS-stimulated cytokine transcription is specific in Mϕ effector functions.

Inhibition of LPS-stimulated in vitro TNF-α synthesis by the heat stress response has been confirmed by recent studies.[17,18] In rat peritoneal Mϕ[18] and in human peripheral monocytes,[17] heat stress pretreatment resulted in decreased TNF-α mRNA level and total TNF-α produced (both cell-associated and released) following LPS stimulation. The inhibition of TNF-α synthesis appeared to be related to the expression of Hsp70 since the induction of Hsp70 by chemical inducers also effectively inhibited TNF-α production.[18] However, the expression of Hsp70 in monocytic cells, especially the subcellular distribution of this stress protein, remains to be characterized. Furthermore, it is unclear whether Hsp70 is the most important factor, among many induced by heat stress, in mediating the effects of the heat shock response on monocytic cells.

A regulatory role of Hsp70 in TNF-α production has been suggested by recent in vivo studies.[69,70] Ribeiro and colleagues[69] demonstrated that rats exposed to heat stress or sodium arsenite 18 h prior to LPS administration had significantly lower levels of plasma TNF-α.[69] Interestingly, this study demonstrated that Hsp70 and TNF-α were coprecipitated, using immunoprecipitation techniques, from in vitro heat-stressed alveolar Mϕ following LPS stimulation,[69] suggesting that Hsp70 may regulate TNF-α release/bioactivity at posttranslational level. Klosterhalfen and co-workers reported that treatment of rats with zinc salt (an inducer of the heat shock response) induced the expression of Hsp70 in all tissues examined (lung, liver and kidney) and that induction of the heat shock response decreased plasma TNF-α level following a challenge with a lethal dose of LPS, along with attenuated tissue injury and decreased mortality rate.[70]

The influence of Hsp70 on myocardial TNF-α production during I/R has recently been examined by our laboratory.[19] Adult rats were subjected to whole body heat stress (42°C for 15 min) and 24 h recovery. Immunoblotting confirmed the expression of cardiac Hsp72. Immunofluorescent staining detected Hsp72 in cardiac interstitial cells including Mϕ-like cells (Fig. 6.2). Hearts were isolated and subjected to global I/R after heat stress. I/R caused a significant increase in myocardial TNF-α. The increase in myocardial TNF-α was blunted by prior whole body heat stress (Fig. 6.3) and the reduced myocardial TNF-α level was correlated with improved postischemic functional recovery. This study demonstrated that induction of cardiac Hsp72 inhibits myocardial TNF-α production during I/R and suggests that suppression of myocardial TNF-α production may be one of the mechanisms by which Hsp70 protects myocardium against postischemic dysfunction. With the development of local heating techniques,[71] prior induction of Hsp70 in selective tissue may be applied to suppress inflammatory response and prevent tissue injury, especially in surgical settings.

Many attempts have been made to prevent myocardial depression by suppression of TNF-α production or neutralization of TNF-α cytotoxicity. We have demonstrated that pretreatment of rats with dexamethasone increases cardiac resistance to LPS-caused contractile depression.[32,72,73] Specific neutralization of TNF-α with TNF-binding proteins or TNF-neutralizing antibody

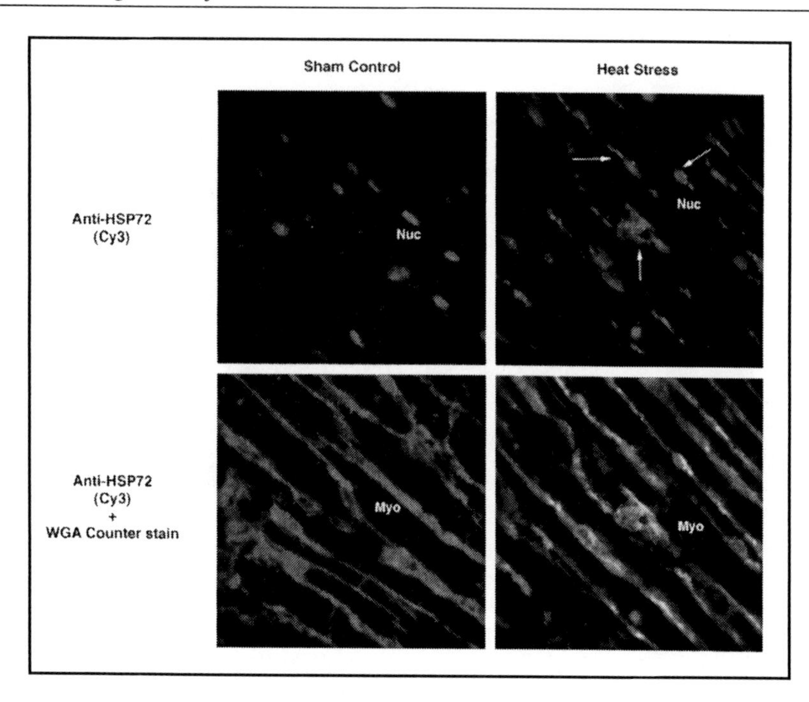

Fig. 6.2. Localization of heat shock protein 72 (Hsp72) in ventricular myocardium. Rats were subjected to whole body heat stress (42°C for 15 min), and hearts were isolated 24 h after the treatment. After flushing coronary blood vessels, ventricular myocardium was embedded in OCT compound and frozen on dry ice. Cryosection was stained with mouse monoclonal anti-Hsp72 followed by Cy3-labeled rabbit anti-mouse IgG. The nucleus was counterstained with bis-benzimide and cell surface with fluorescein-labeled wheat germ agglutinin (WGA). In ventricular myocardium of sham-treated heart, Hsp72 was undetectable. Whole body heat stress induced Hsp72 in cardiac interstitial cells but not in myocytes.

has been shown to prevent endotoxemic myocardial depression or septic shock in a variety of animal models.[3,32,74] Interleukin-10[75] and adenosine[58] inhibit in vitro TNF-α expression in peripheral monocytes or tissue Mϕ. Thus, suppression of TNF-α production is pharmacologically achievable, and represents one category of potential therapy for the myocardial dysfunction associated with systemic inflammation.

NF-κB is a central factor in regulating TNF-α production, and it also regulates the expression of many other proinflammatory cytokines and adhesion molecules.[76] Glucocorticoids inhibit NF-κB,[77] which may be a mechanism for their suppressive effect on TNF-α production. Selective and transient inhibition of myocardial NF-κB is critical in suppression of myocardial TNF-α production and prevention of subsequent myocardial dysfunction. Cardiac resistance to LPS is associated with an increased level of myocardial IκB-α, attenuated NF-κB activation and decreased TNF-α production.[73] Cardiac resistance to LPS may involve Hsp70.[22] Few studies have examined the influence of the heat shock response on NF-κB activation.[78,79] Using a human lung adenocarcinoma cell line (representative of distal respiratory epithelium), Wong and coworkers[79] demonstrated that induction of the heat shock response in vitro by heat stress (43°C for 1 h) or sodium arsenite treatment inhibited TNF-α-stimulated NF-κB intranuclear translocation.[79] The inhibition was attributed to both increased IκB-α expression and attenuated IκB-α degradation.[79] Feinstein and colleagues[78] demonstrated in brain astrocytes that prior heat stress (43°C for 20 min to 1 h) decreased intranuclear accumulation of NF-κB and the

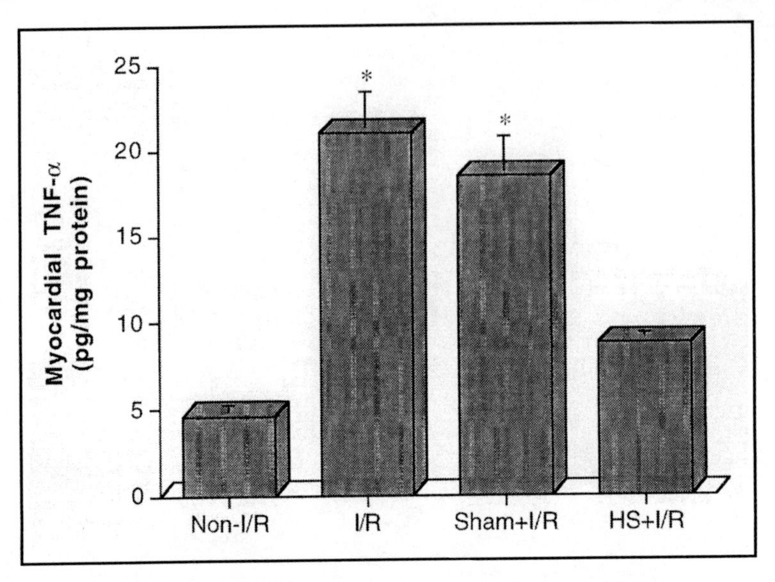

Fig. 6.3. The influence of induction of cardiac heat shock protein 72 on myocardial tumor necrosis factor-α (TNF-α) level after ischemia/reperfusion (I/R). Hearts were isolated from rats without pretreatment (I/R), pretreated with whole body heat stress (HS + I/R) or sham (sham + I/R), perfused with the Krebs-Henseleit buffer by the Langendorff technique, and subjected to I/R (25/40 min). Ventricular myocardium was homogenized after I/R. Myocardial TNF-α was determined by enzyme-linked immunosorbent assay and compared with myocardium without I/R (Non-I/R). Data are mean ± SE. * $P<0.01$ vs. Non-I/R.

expression of inducible nitric oxide synthase following LPS-stimulation. The effect of heat shock response on inducible nitric oxide synthase expression was partially replicated in fibroblasts by transfection of the Hsp70 gene to the cells. It remains unclear whether Hsp70 per se regulates NF-κB activity and what the regulatory mechanisms are if it does. If Hsp70 regulates NF-κB intranuclear translocation, it may exert an influence on the kinase cascade leading to the activation of IκB kinase or may directly inhibit IκB kinase (Fig. 6.4). In this regard, Gabai and colleagues have shown that Hsp70 inhibits MAPK activation in vitro.[80] Alternatively, Hsp70 may stabilize NF-κB-IκB complex (Fig. 6.4) by binding to one or more of the molecules in the complex as it does in the case of stabilization of newly synthesized proteins. Nevertheless, further delineation of the regulatory role of Hsp70 in TNF-α production and the regulatory mechanisms is necessary for the elucidation of immunological functions of this family of stress proteins.

Perspectives

Dysregulated myocardial TNF-α production contributes to postischemic cardiac contractile dysfunction. Whereas neutralization of TNF-α bioactivity constitutes one strategy for preservation of myocardial function, agents which prevent TNF-α synthesis may provide additional benefits when used alone or in combination with post-release neutralizing agents. Inhibition of transcription factor NF-κB may provide relatively selective inhibition of TNF-α production and has theoretic appeal for therapy. Antecedent heat stress increases cardiac functional resistance to I/R and decreases postischemic myocardial TNF-α production, suggesting that myocardial functional protection associated with heat shock response involves inhibition of cardiac TNF-α production. Indeed, heat stress inhibits TNF-α production by monocytic cells, and cardiac Hsp70 induced by heat stress has been localized to interstitial cells

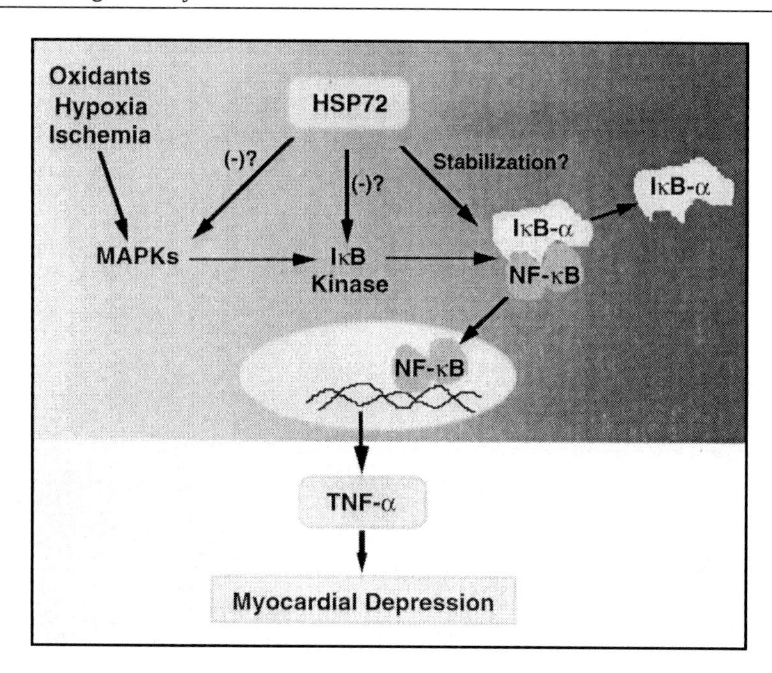

Fig. 6.4. Signal transduction in stress-induced tumor necrosis factor-α (TNF-α) production and potential regulation by heat shock protein 72 (Hsp72). NF-κB activity is regulated by the inhibitory protein IκB which binds to NF-κB, forming an inactive cytoplasmic complex. Noxious signals, such as oxidants, hypoxia and ischemia, activate a protein kinase cascade, leading to IκB phosphorylation and degradation. The released NF-κB translocates into the nucleus and initiates TNF-α gene transcription. Hsp72 may regulate NF-κB intranuclear translocation through its influence on the kinase cascade or by stabilization of the NF-κB-IκB complex.

including resident Mϕ. However, it needs to be determined whether the mechanism of myocardial functional protection associated with heat shock response involves inhibition of cardiac TNF-α production. It remains unclear whether Hsp70 is the factor which inhibits monocytic TNF-α production following heat stress since heat stress may induce the expression of many other genes. Furthermore, it needs to be determined how Hsp70 regulates NF-κB activity if it has any regulatory function on this transcription factor. Further research is required to determine the role of Hsp70 in the regulation of TNF-α production and delineate the molecular interaction of Hsp70 with transcription factor NF-κB. This research may create therapies for preservation of myocardial function by relatively selective inhibition of TNF-α production with an endogenous protein.

References

1. Casey LC. Role of cytokines in the pathogenesis of cardiopulmonary-induced multisystem organ failure. Ann Thorac Surg 1993; 56:S92-S96.
2. Natanson C, Eichenholz PW, Danner RL, et al. Endotoxin and tumor necrosis factor challenges in dogs simulate the cardiovascular profile of human septic shock. J Exp Med 1989; 169:823-832.
3. Kapadia S, Torre-Amione G, Yokahama T, et al. Soluble TNF binding proteins modulate the negative inotropic properties of TNF alpha in vitro. Am J Physiol 1995; 268:H517-H525.
4. Finkel MS, Oddis CV, Jacob TD, et al. Negative inotropic effects of cytokines on the heart mediated by nitric oxide. Science 1992; 257:387-389.

5. Cain BS, Meldrum DR, Dinarello CA et al. TNF-α and IL-1β synergistically depress human myocardial function. Crit Care Med 1999; 27:1309-1318.
6. Pagani FD, Baker LS, Hsi C et al. Left ventricular systolic and diastolic dysfunction after infusion of tumor necrosis factor-α in conscious dogs. J Clin Invest 1992; 90:389-398.
7. Meldrum DR, Meng X, Dinarello CA et al. Human myocardial tissue TNF-α expression following acute global ischemia in vivo. J Mol Cell Cardiol 1998; 30:1683-1689.
8. Gurevitch J, Frolkis I, Yuhas Y et al. Anti-tumor necrosis factor-alpha improves myocardial recovery after ischemia and reperfusion. J Am Coll Cardiol 1997; 30:1554-1561.
9. Minowada G, Welch WJ. Clinical implications of the stress response. J Clin Invest 1995; 95:3-12.
10. Brown CR, Martin RL, Hansen WJ et al. The constitutive and stress inducible forms of Hsp 70 exhibit functional similarities and interact with one another in an ATP-dependent fashion. J Cell Biol 1993; 120:1101-1112.
11. Gunther E, Walter L. Genetic aspects of the Hsp70 multigene family in vertebrates. Experientia 1994; 50:987-1001.
12. Knowlton AA. The role of heat shock proteins in the heart. J Mol Cell Cardiol 1995; 27:121-131.
13. Plumier JC, Currie RW. Heat shock-induced myocardial protection against ischemic injury: A role for Hsp70? Cell Stress Chaperones 1996; 1:13-17.
14. Karmazyn M, Mailer K, Currie RW. Acquisition and decay of heat-shock-enhanced post-ischemic ventricular recovery. Am J Physiol 1990; 259:H424-H431.
15. Yellon DM, Pasini E, Cargnoni A et al. The protective role of heat stress in the ischemic and reperfused rabbit myocardium. J Mol Cell Cardiol 1992; 24:859-907.
16. Kontos MC, Shipley JB, Kukreja RC. Heat stress improve functional recovery and induces synthesis of 27- and 72-kDa heat shock proteins without preserving sarcoplasmic reticulum function in the ischemic rat heart. J Mol Cell Cardiol 1996; 28:1885-1894.
17. Ensor JE, Wiener SM, McCrea KA et al. Differential effects of hyperthermia on macrophage interleukin-6 and tumor necrosis factor-α expression. Am J Physiol 1994; 266:C967-C974.
18. Fouqueray B, Philippe C, Amrani A et al. Heat shock prevents lipopolysaccharide-induced tumor necrosis factor-α synthesis by rat mononuclear phagocytes. Eur J Immunol 1992; 22:2983-2987.
19. Meng X, Banerjee A, Ao L et al. Inhibition of myocardial TNF-α production by heat shock: a potential mechanism of stress-induced cardioprotection against postischemic dysfunction. Ann NY Acad Sci 1999; 847:69-82.
20. Currie RW, Karmazyn M, Kloc M et al. Heat-shock response is associated with enhanced post-ischemic ventricular recovery. Circ Res 1988; 63:543-549.
21. Meng X, Brown JM, Ao L et al. Norepinephrine induces cardiac heat shock protein and delayed cardioprotection in the rat through α1-adrenoceptors. Cardiovasc Res 1996; 32:374-383.
22. Meng X, Brown JM, Ao L et al. Endotoxin induces cardiac heat shock protein 70 and resistance to endotoxemic myocardial dysfunction. Am J Physiol 1996; 271:C1316-C1324.
23. Meldrum DR, Cleveland JC, Rowland RT et al. Early and delayed preconditioning: Differential mechanisms and additive protection. Am J Physiol 1997; 273:H725-H733.
24. Rowland RT, Meng X, Cleveland JC et al. Delayed myocardial adaptation enhances acute preconditioning to optimize post-ischemic myocardial function. Am J Physiol 1997; 272:H2708-H2715.
25. Rowland RT, Cleveland JC, Meng X et al. A single endotoxin challenge induces delayed myocardial protection against infarction. J Surg Res 1996; 63:193-198.
26. Meng X, Cleveland JC, Rowland R et al. Norepinephrine-induced sustained myocardial adaptation to ischemia is dependent on α1 adrenoceptors and protein synthesis. J Mol Cell Cardiol 1996; 28:2017-2025.
27. Marber MS, Mestril R, Chi S-H et al. Overexpression of the rat inducible 70-kD heat stress protein in a transgenic mouse increases the resistance of the heart to ischemic injury. J Clin Invest 1995; 95:1446-1456.
28. Plumier JL, Ross BM, Currie RW et al. Transgenic mice expressing the human heat shock protein 70 have improved post-ischemic myocardial recovery. J Clin Invest 1995; 95:1854-1860.
29. Radford NB, Fina M, Benjamin IJ et al. Cardioprotective effects of 70-KDa heat shock protein in transgenic mice. Proc Natl Acad Sci USA 1996; 93:2339-2342.
30. Trost SU, Omens JH, Karlon WJ et al. Protection against myocardial dysfunction after a brief ischemic period in transgenic mice expressing inducible heat shock protein 70. J Clin Invest 1998; 101:855-862.

31. Suzuki K, Sawa Y, Kaneda Y et al. In vivo gene transfection with heat shock protein 70 enhances myocardial tolerance to ischemia-reperfusion injury in the rat. J Clin Invest 1997; 99:1645-1650.
32. Meng X, Ao L, Meldrum DR et al. TNF-α and myocardial depression in endotoxemic rats: Temporal discordance of an obligatory relationship. Am J Physiol 1998; 275:R502-R508.
33. Meldrum DR. Tumor necrosis factor in the heart. Am J Physiol 1998; 274:R577-R595.
34. Yokoyama T, Vaca L, Rossen RD et al. Cellular basis for the negative inotropic effects of tumor necrosis factor-α in the adult mammalian cardiac myocyte. J Clin Invest 1993; 92:2303-2312.
35. Mayer AMS, Pittner RA, Lipscomb GE et al. Effect of in vivo TNF administration on superoxide production. Am J Physiol 1993; 264:L43-L52.
36. Gulick T, Chung MK, Pieper SJ et al. Interleukin-1 and tumor necrosis factor inhibit cardiac myocyte adrenergic responsiveness. Proc Natl Acad Sci USA 1989; 86:6753-6757.
37. Oral H, Dorn GW, Mann DL. Sphingosine mediates the immediate negative inotropic effects of tumor necrosis factor-α in the adult mammalian cardiac myocyte. J Biol Chem 1997; 272:4836-4842.
38. Schultz R, Panas DL, Catena R et al. The role of nitric oxide in cardiac depression induced by interleukin-1β and tumor necrosis factor-α. Brit J Pharmacol 1995; 114:27-34.
39. Dinarello CA. Biologic basis for Interleukin-1 in disease. Blood 1996; 87:2095-2147.
40. Krown KA, Page MT, Nguyen C et al. Tumor necrosis factor alpha-induced apoptosis in cardiac myocytes: Involvement of the sphingolipid signaling cascade in cardiac cell death. J Clin Invest 1996; 98:2854-2865.
41. Brady AJB, Warren JB, Poole-Wilson PA et al. Nitric oxide attenuates cardiac myocyte contraction. Am J Physiol 1993; 265:H176-H182.
42. Kumar A, Thota V, Dee L et al. Tumor necrosis factor-alpha and interleukin 1-beta are responsible for the in vitro myocardial cell depression induced by human septic shock serum. J Exp Med 1996; 183:949-958.
43. Baeuerle PA, Henkel T. Function and activation of NF-κB in the immune system. Ann Rev Immunol 1994; 12:141-179.
44. DiDonato JA, Hayakawa M, Rothwarf DM et al. A cytokine-responsive IkappaB kinase that activates the transcription factor NF-kappaB. Nature 1997; 388:548-554.
45. Chandrasekar B, Freeman GL. Induction of nuclear factor kappaB and activation protein 1 in postischemic myocardium. FEBS Lett 1997; 401:30-34.
46. Squadrito F, Altavilla D, Zingarelli B et al. Tumor necrosis factor involvement in myocardial ischemia-reperfusion injury. Eur J Pharmacol 1993; 237:223-230.
47. Herskowitz A, Choi S, Ansari AA et al. Cytokine mRNA expression in the postischemic/reperfused myocardium. Am J Pathol 1995; 146:419-428.
48. Gurevitch J, Frolkis I, Yuhas Y et al. Tumor necrosis factor-alpha is released from the isolated heart undergoing ischemia and reperfusion. J Am Coll Cardiol 1996; 28:247-252.
49. Chandrasekar B, Colston JT, Freeman GL. Induction of proinflammatory cytokine and antioxidant enzyme gene expression following brief myocardial ischemia. Clin Exp Immunol 1997; 108:346-351.
50. Meldrum DR, Cain BS, Cleveland JC et al. Adenosine decreases post-ischemic myocardial TNF-α: Anti-inflammatory implications for preconditioning and transplantation. Immunology 1997; 92:472-477.
51. Meldrum DR, Cleveland JC, Cain BS et al. Increased myocardial tumor necrosis factor-α in a crystalloid-perfused model of cardiac ischemia-reperfusion injury. Ann Thorac Surg 1998; 65:439-443.
52. Hattler BG, Zeevi A, Oddis CV et al. Cytokine induction during cardiac surgery: analysis of TNF-alpha expression pre- and postcardiopulmonary bypass. J Card Surg 1995; 10:418-422.
53. Wan S, DeSmet JM, Barvais L et al. Myocardium is a major source of proinflammatory cytokines in patients undergoing cardiopulmonary bypass. J Thorac Cardiovasc Surg 1996; 112:806-811.
54. Meldrum DR, Dinarello CA, Shames BD et al. Ischemic preconditioning decreases postischemic myocardial tumor necrosis factor-α production: Potential ultimate effector mechanism of preconditioning. Circulation 1998; 98:II214-II219.
55. Cain BS, Meldrum DR, Dinarello CA et al. Adenosine reduces cardiac TNF-α production and human myocardial injury following ischemia-reperfusion. J Surg Res 1998; 76:117-123.

56. Parmely MJ, Zhou WW, Edwards CK et al. Adenosine and a related carbocyclic nucleoside analogue selectively inhibit tumor necrosis factor-α production and protect mice against endotoxin challenge. J Immunol 1993; 151:389-396.
57. Wagner DR, Combes A, McTiernan C et al. Adenosine inhibits lipopolysaccharide-induced cardiac expression of tumor necrosis factor-α. Circ Res 1998; 82:47-56.
58. Sajjadi FG, Takabayashi K, Foster AC et al. Inhibition of TNF-α expression by adenosine: Role of A3 adenosine receptors. J Immunol 1996; 156:3435-3442.
59. Hotchkiss R, Nunnally I, Lindquist S et al. Hyperthermia protects mice against the lethal effects of endotoxin. Am J Physiol 1993; 265:R1447-R1457.
60. Ryan AJ, Flanagan SW, Moseley PL et al. Acute heat stress protects rats against endotoxin shock. J Appl Physiol 1992; 73:1517-1522.
61. Villar J, Ribeiro SP, Mullen JBM et al. Induction of the heat shock response reduces mortality rate and organ damage in a sepsis-induced acute lung injury model. Crit Care Med 1994; 22:914-921.
62. Ribeiro SP, Villar J, Downey GP et al. Sodium arsenite induces heat shock protein-72 kilodalton expression in the lungs and protects rats against sepsis. Crit Care Med 1994; 22:922-929.
63. Chi SH, Mestril R. Stable expression of a human Hsp70 gene in a rat myogenic cell line confers protection against endotoxin. Am J Physiol 1996; 270:C1017-C1021.
64. Mosser DD, Caron AW, Bourget L et al. Role of the human heat shock protein Hsp70 in protection against stress-induced apoptosis. Mol Cell Biol 1997; 17:5317-5327.
65. Dinarello CA, Dempsey RA, Allegretta M et al. Inhibitory effects of elevated temperature on human monokine production and natural killer cell activity. Cancer Res 1986; 46:6236-6241.
66. Schmidt JA, Abdulla E. Downregulation of IL-1β biosynthesis by inducers of the heat-shock response. J Immunol 1988; 141:2027-2034.
67. Klostergaard J, Barta M, Tomasovic SP. Hyperthermic modulation of tumor necrosis factor-dependent monocyte/macrophage tumor cytotoxicity in vitro. J Biol Resp Modif 1989; 8:262-277.
68. Snyder YM, Guthrie L, Evans GF et al. Transcriptional inhibition of endotoxin-induced monokine synthesis following heat shock in murine peritoneal macrophages. J Leukoc Biol 1992; 51:181-187.
69. Ribeiro SP, Villar J, Downey GP et al. Effects of the stress response in septic rats and LPS-stimulated alveolar macrophages: Evidence for TNF-α posttranslational regulation. Am J Respir Crit Care Med 1996; 154:1843-1850.
70. Klosterhalfen B, Hauptmann S, Offner F-A et al. Induction of heat shock protein 70 by zinc-bis-(DL-hydrogenaspartate) reduces cytokine liberation, apoptosis, and mortality rate in a rat model of LD100 endotoxemia. Shock 1997; 7:254-262.
71. Gowda A, Yang C, Asimakis GK et al. Cardioprotection by local heating: improved myocardial salvage after ischemia and reperfusion. Ann Thorac Surg 1998; 65:1241-1247.
72. Meng X, Ao L, Brown JM et al. Nitric oxide synthase is not involved in cardiac contractile dysfunction in a rat model of endotoxemia without shock. Shock 1997; 7:111-118.
73. Shames BD, Meldrum DR, Selzman CH et al. Increased levels of myocardial IκB-α protein promotes tolerance to endotoxin. Am J Physiol 1998; 275:H1084-H1091.
74. Ashkenazi A, Marsters SA, Capon DJ et al. Protection against endotoxic shock by a tumor necrosis factor receptor immunoadhesin. Proc Natl Acad Sci USA 1991; 88:10535-10539.
75. Wang P, Wu P, Siegel MI et al. IL-10 inhibits transcription of cytokine genes in human peripheral blood mononuclear cells. J Immunol 1994; 153:811-816.
76. Baldwin AS. The NF-κB and IκB proteins: New discoveries and insights. Ann Rev Immunol 1996; 14:649-681.
77. Adcock IM, Brown CR, Gelder CM et al. Effects of glucocorticoids on transcription factor activation in human peripheral blood mononuclear cells. Am J Physiol 1995; 268:C331-C338.
78. Feinstein DL, Galea E, Aquino DA et al. Heat shock protein 70 suppresses astroglial-inducible nitric oxide synthase expression by decreasing NFκB activation. J Biol Chem 1996; 271:17724-17732.
79. Wong HR, Ryan M, Wispe JR. Stress response decrease NFκB nuclear translocation and increases I-κB-α expression in A549 cells. J Clin Invest 1997; 99:2423-2428.
80. Gabai VL, Meriin AB, Mosser DD et al. Hsp70 prevents activation of stress kinases. A Novel pathway of cellular thermotolerance. J Biol Chem 1997; 272:18033-18037.

CHAPTER 7

Preconditioning of Cardiac Myocytes:
Studies Using Cultured Neonatal Rat Heart Myocytes and Simulated Ischemia

Jan A. Post, Chris T.W.M. Schneijdenberg and Arie J. Verkleij

The acquisition of tolerance towards myocardial ischemia and reperfusion can be acquired by several preconditioning procedures. The original preconditioning protocol described for myocardial tissue was reported by Murry et al[1] and comprised a few short periods of ischemia of 5 to 10 minutes. Since induction of cross-tolerance between various stresses has been known for quite some time, attempts were made to induce tolerance towards ischemia by preconditioning the hearts or animals by elevated temperatures. These studies showed both a protective effect and the absence of a protective effect.[2-5] In order to be able to study specific responses of the myocardial myocytes during preconditioning and/or ischemia/reperfusion and to discriminate between responses of muscle and non-muscle cells in the intact heart, a very valuable tool is a system in which isolated myocardial cells can be subjected to conditions which mimic ischemia and/or reperfusion. The last ten years we have been working on and with a system of simulated ischemia and reperfusion. This model of simulated ischemia elicits responses of the myocytes, which closely resemble the in vivo and in vitro responses of the myocytes in situ in the heart. In this Chapter we would like to discuss the model we developed, the insight it gave in possible mechanisms resulting in myocyte injury during ischemia/reperfusion and the of use this system to study preconditioning in cultured neonatal rat heart cells at a functional level and at gene-expression level.

With regard to preconditioning it is concluded that Hsp70 cannot be the exclusive factor responsible for providing tolerance towards ischemia. Furthermore, it is shown that a preceding heat shock can even result in increased cellular damage during a subsequent ischemic insult, depending on the height of the heat shock temperature and the length of the recovery phase.

A Model System for Simulated Ischemia/Reperfusion

In order to study the cellular response of myocardial cells towards ischemic conditions one needs a model in which molecular events during the development of ischemia can be studied. Focussing specifically on the myocardial cells also implies that one either can separate material originating from muscle cells and non-muscle cells, such as fibroblasts, endothelial and nerve cells, or that one uses a model which only involves one cell type, the cardiac myocyte. Obviously, the system used should bear as much as possible resemblance to the in vivo situation of ischemia/reperfusion.

We decided to use the cultured neonatal rat heart cells and isolated these cells from 0-2 days old Wistar rats, as described by Harrary and Farley.[6] These cells can be kept in culture for several weeks and exhibit spontaneous contractile activity. After a few days in culture the cells

Heat Shock Proteins in Myocardial Protection, edited by Rakesh C. Kukreja and Michael L. Hess.

from a synchronously beating functional syncytium, due to the formation of gap junctions between the cells. During ischemia the oxygen and nutrients supply to the heart is strongly reduced or even prevented, as is the washout of metabolic products. This results in a decreased high energy phosphate production and content, an accumulation of metabolic waste products and a lowering of the intracellular pH. To simulate ischemia-like conditions a system to incubate the cells, originally described by Vemuri et al,[7] was modified and used.[8-10] Dishes with cultured neonatal cells were washed to remove culture medium and the cells were subsequently incubated in buffer W, which is devoid of metabolic substrate and which contains (in mM) NaCl, 133; KCl, 5; $MgCl_2$, 1; $CaCl_2$, 1; Tris-HCl, 10 (pH 7.35 at 37°C). The incubation volume is kept as low as possible, in order to simulate the interstitium and to mimic and allow an accumulation of waste products during the ischemic period. Subsequently the cells are placed in an incubation device, consisting of a special Plexiglas-constructed chamber, covered by a plexiglas lid (Fig. 7.1A). A rubber O-ring and two screw-hooks result in an airtight attachment of the cover to the chamber. The cover is perforated by seven holes, closed by rubber stoppers, enabling the injecting of solutions or the withdrawal of samples during the ischemic period, without opening the ischemia-device. Temperature in the compartment containing the dishes with cells is monitored continuously, using a thermocouple. The temperature was kept at 37°C by means of a continuous stream of heated water circulating in the lower compartment. Ischemia is simulated by creating an atmosphere of argon (99.992%), rather than nitrogen, which contained sufficient traces of oxygen to allow the cells to produce high energy phosphates. The argon atmosphere is created by a continuous argon gas flow which was water saturated in order to reduce evaporation of the incubation medium. As can be seen in Figure 7.1B, the oxygen present in the incubation medium dropped rapidly and was undetectable (using a calibrated oxygen electrode) within 20 minutes after the onset of ischemia. Subjection of the cells to simulated ischemia conditions results in a loss of spontaneous contractile activity and after 60 minutes of simulated ischemia a decrease of cellular ATP levels to 40% of control is observed (Fig. 7.2). At this time point no irreversible damage, as monitored by cytosolic enzyme release, could be detected (see Fig. 7.2). Reoxygenation and resupply of nutrients to these cells result in restoration of cellular ATP content and resumption of spontaneous contractile activity.[11] Prolongation of the ischemic period results in cell death and lysis (see Fig. 7.2), which is aggravated by reoxygenation and resupply of nutrients ("reperfusion injury"). So in this respect the response of the cultured neonatal rat heart myocytes closely resembles the response of cardiomyocytes subjected to ischemia/reperfusion in situ. Ultrastructural changes observed during ischemia of cardiomyocytes in situ include swelling and blebbing of mitochondria, an aggregation of the sarcolemmal transmembrane proteins and the extrusion of pure lipid structures from the sarcolemma.[12-14] These same ultrastructural phenomena are also observed in the present simulated ischemia model.[8] Another phenomenon occurring during ischemia is the increased transcription of heat shock protein 70 (Hsp70) mRNA and the subsequent increased expression of this protein. The induction of Hsp70 mRNA synthesis is also observed in the above discussed model of simulated ischemia.[9,15] Also expression of the protein takes place, which will be discussed in detail in the section on preconditioning using the present model of ischemia/reperfusion.

So in many aspects this simulated ischemia model closely resembles the in vivo and in situ situation of ischemia/reperfusion. Having to deal with isolated cells has several advantages over the intact heart and allows studies impossible in the intact heart. The system creates the possibility to tightly control the extracellular environment of the cells (for instance with respect to [Ca^{2+}] and [H^+]), to alter cell components of interest by varying the culturing conditions (e.g., lipid composition), to alter specific proteins by the introduction of modified proteins by transvection, and to apply drugs and probes specifically to the cardiomyoctyes. This is done to gain insight in the cellular and molecular events occurring during ischemia/reperfusion and to determine the

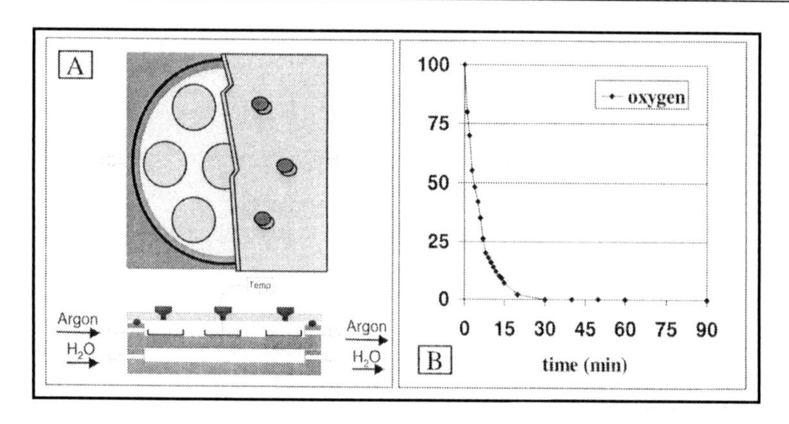

Fig. 7.1. Panel A gives a schematic drawing of the device developed to subject cultured neonatal rat heart cells to simulated ischemia. The upper compartment, in which the dishes with cells are placed, is constantly flushed with water-saturated argon. The lower compartment is kept at a constant temperature, to ensure a 37°C incubation temperature of the cells. Samples from the incubation medium can be taken through the rubber stoppers in the lid of the chamber. Panel B shows the oxygen concentration, measured in the medium covering the cells. At 30 minutes no oxygen could be detected, using an oxygen electrode.

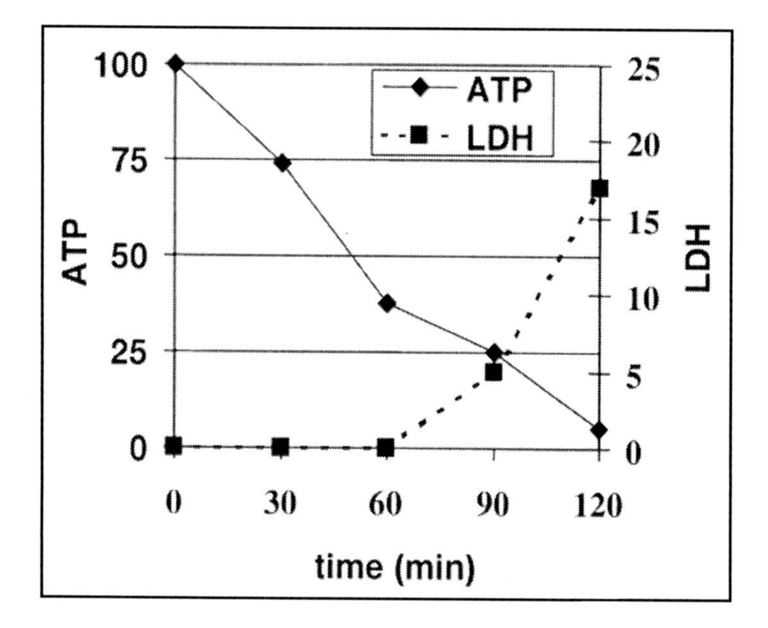

Fig. 7.2. ATP content of the cells and LDH release upon various periods of simulated ischemia. ATP content is normalized to control values and LDH release is expressed as percentage of total cellular LDH.

process(es) involved. As will be discussed below, the simulated ischemia model allowed us to study events in the sarcolemma during ischemia/reperfusion and was used to study the role of Hsp70 in preconditioning of the cardiomyocytes.

Using the Model to Study Sarcolemmal Processes During Ischemia/Reperfusion

The large similarity between the altered parameters during ischemia in situ (in the heart) and in the simulated ischemia model, as discussed in the preceding part, justified detailed studies on the sarcolemma of the myocardial cells during simulated ischemia. This is of importance, since a loss of sarcolemmal integrity clearly hallmarks a point of no return in the development of irreversible damage of the myocyte during ischemia. The sarcolemmal phospholipids are asymmetrically distributed over the two monolayers of the lipid bilayer:[16]

a) The negatively charged phospholipids, phosphatidylserine (PS) and phosphatidylinositol (PI) are located exclusively in the inner or cytoplasmic leaflet;
b) 75% of phosphatidylethanolamine (PE) is in the inner leaflet;
c) 93% of sphingomyelin (Sph) is in the outer leaflet;
d) 43% of phosphatidylcholine (PC) is in the outer leaflet.

Maintenance of the asymmetrical distribution of PE and PS is thought to be maintained by an ATPase, which actively transports these phospholipids from the outer to the inner leaflet, and by an interaction of the headgroups of PE and PS with the underlying membrane-cytoskeleton, as discussed in reference 17. During ischemia ATP content is reduced and the interaction between the sarcolemma and the underlying membrane-cytoskeleton is altered and indeed especially the asymmetrical distribution of PE is lost upon 60 minutes of simulated ischemia.[10] Reoxygenation of the cells and a resupply of nutrient, before cell lysis starts, results, as mentioned above, in a recovery of cellular ATP content and a concomitant restoration of the asymmetrical distribution of PE.[11] This clearly shows that, despite the distinct morphological, biochemical and functional changes induced, 60 minutes of simulated ischemia does not result in irreversible damage of the cardiomyocytes.

Based on the morphological data and the fact that some of the sarcolemmal phospholipids have a preference for non-bilayer configurations (which is expressed during ischemia and reperfusion) a hypothesis is put forward which explains the irreversible sarcolemmal disruption during ischemia/reperfusion by altered physicochemical behavior of the sarcolemmal phospholipids (for a review see reference 17). This hypothesis is strengthened by the finding that a reduction of the non-bilayer preferring phospholipids results in an attenuation of irreversible cell damage during simulated ischemia.[18]

Using the Model of Simulated Ischemia in Preconditioning Studies

We attempted to induce tolerance to simulated ischemia in beating cultured neonatal rat cardiomyocytes by subjecting them either to elevated temperatures or to a short period of simulated ischemia. This was done to investigate whether development of tolerance can be observed at the isolated, contracting myocyte level, as has been already described for intact organs; and whether the effect of preconditioning already becomes apparent during ischemia alone. This, as opposed to ischemia/reperfusion protocols, was used in isolated heart studies. We used the cells and culture conditions described above, because these cells respond to the simulated ischemia in a manner much alike to cells in the intact organ. We investigated whether these cells could be made tolerant to heat by a prior heat shock and if this thermotolerance coincides with a state of tolerance to ischemia. We also studied the preconditioning effect of a prior non-lethal period of simulated ischemia.[15] Since members of the 70 kDa heat shock protein family have been implicated in the increased resistance to ischemia of preconditioned hearts and evidence of their protective role is accumulating, we compared the levels of Hsp70 induction and the observed degree of preconditioning.

At first the thermotolerance of the cultured neonatal rat heart cells was studied and it was found that the cells are extremely resistant to elevated temperatures, compared to other cells. As is shown in Figure 3A no cell lysis occurred during 4 hours incubation at temperatures of up to 43°C and cell lysis was only observed at incubation temperatures of 44°C and 45°C. Subsequently it was checked whether development of thermotolerance could be detected, using enzyme release as a parameter of irreversible cell damage. Cells were heat-shocked for 60 minutes at 42°C, allowed to recover for 16 minutes in full medium at 37°C and subjected to a severe heat-shock (5 hrs, 45°C). Figure 3B clearly shows that the heat-shocked cells show a decreased percentage of LDH release ($p<0.01$) and that thermotolerance can be induced in cultured neonatal rat heart cells. Subsequently it was tested whether the observed thermotolerance coincides with a tolerance towards ischemic damage. Myocytes were again subjected to 60 minutes of heat shock at 42°C and allowed to recover for 16 hours and subjected to simulated ischemia. As can be seen in Figure 7.3B, no tolerance towards ischemic damage was induced by the preceding heat shock and even a tendency toward increased cell lysis was observed after long periods of ischemia.

Since studies using intact animals or isolated hearts did show a preconditioning effect of heat shock towards ischemic damage we investigated whether varying the heat shock temperature and the length of the recovery period would alter the effectiveness of the preceding heat shock towards preconditioning the cardiomyocytes. Therefore the cardiomyocytes were subjected to a larger range of temperatures and three different recovery periods prior to ischemic insult. One hour incubation at 37°C (control), 42°C, 43°C, 44°C or 45°C was followed by no recovery period; or 3 hours of recovery at 37°C; or 16 hours of recovery. At the end of this protocol cells were subjected to 3 hours of simulated ischemia and cell damage was assessed by determining LDH release (Fig. 7.4A). This figure clearly shows that subjecting the cells to ischemic conditions directly upon heat shock significantly increases cell lysis. At higher preconditioning temperatures this increase in cellular sensitivity to ischemia was still present after 3 hours of recovery. This increased sensitivity faded away after 16 hours of recovery for all but the pretreatment at 45°C. Next to the observed increased sensitivity towards ischemia, a second conclusion can be drawn from these experiments: no protective effect of any heat treatment was apparent under the conditions used.

Thus the question arose whether the cultured neonatal rat heart cells could be preconditioned at all. As discussed in the section on the ischemia model used in these studies, the cells can fully recover from a 60 minute ischemic insult. Therefore, we subjected the cells to 60 minutes of simulated ischemia and allowed them to recover for 0, 3 and 16 hours before they were subjected to 3 hours of simulated ischemia. In the absence of recovery cells subjected to the second ischemic insult showed increased irreversible damage (results not shown). However, when the cells were allowed to recover for 3 hours a clear reduction of cell lysis was observed. This protective effect was even more pronounced after 16 hours of recovery, when cell lysis of the treated cells fell to 10% of the non-treated cells (Fig. 7.4B). This then clearly shows that cultured neonatal rat heart cells can be preconditioned in a simulated ischemia model, which has very strong resemblance with the in vivo situation.

Hsp70 Expression During Preconditioning of Cultured Neonatal Rat Heart Cells

These experiments show that prior heat treatment does not provide protection during prolonged simulated ischemia in cultured neonatal cardiomyocytes, whereas prior ischemic treatment does. As the stress protein Hsp70 has been implicated in providing protection against

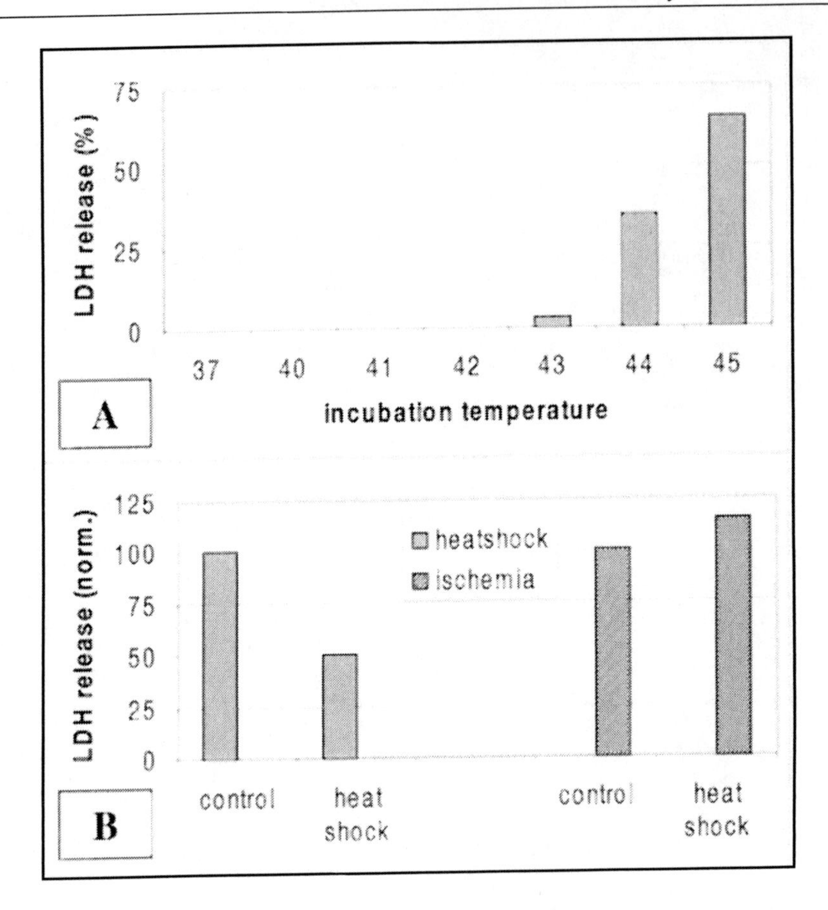

Fig. 7.3. Panel A shows LDH release during 4 hrs incubation at various temperatures (and LDH release is expressed as percentage of total cellular LDH). It can be seen that the cultured neonatal rat heart cells are rather resistant towards heat. In panel B the response of pre-heat-shocked cells (42°C, 16 hrs recovery) on a subsequent heat-shock (left part) and a subsequent ischemic insults (right part) is shown. Pre-heat-shock clearly reduces cell lysis during the second heat shock (5 hrs, 45°C). However, it does not reduce cell lysis during 3 hrs of simulated ischemia.

ischemic insult, we investigated whether and to what extent this protein is expressed by the treatments described, by using Western blot with an antibody raised against the inducible Hsp70, obtained from Stressgen. Figure 7.5A shows a typical Western blot using this antibody, comparing control cells and cells subjected to heat shock at 42°C and 43°C and 16 hours of recovery. Densitometric analysis of the blots allowed the determination of the relative quantities of Hsp70 present after the various protocols. Figure 7.5B shows the presence of Hsp70 upon the various heat shock protocols, showing the Hsp70 content of the cells at the onset of the 3 hours ischemic period to which the cells where subjected to test the presence of the preconditioning phenomenon, as shown in Figure 7.4. It can be seen that at the onset of the ischemic insult, after 3 or 16 hrs of recovery, Hsp70 is clearly present. However, none of these preconditioning conditions resulted in tolerance to simulated ischemia.

Figure 7.6 shows the time course of the induction of Hsp70 after both preconditioning treatments. Using immunofluorescence it can be clearly seen that both heat shock (42°C and

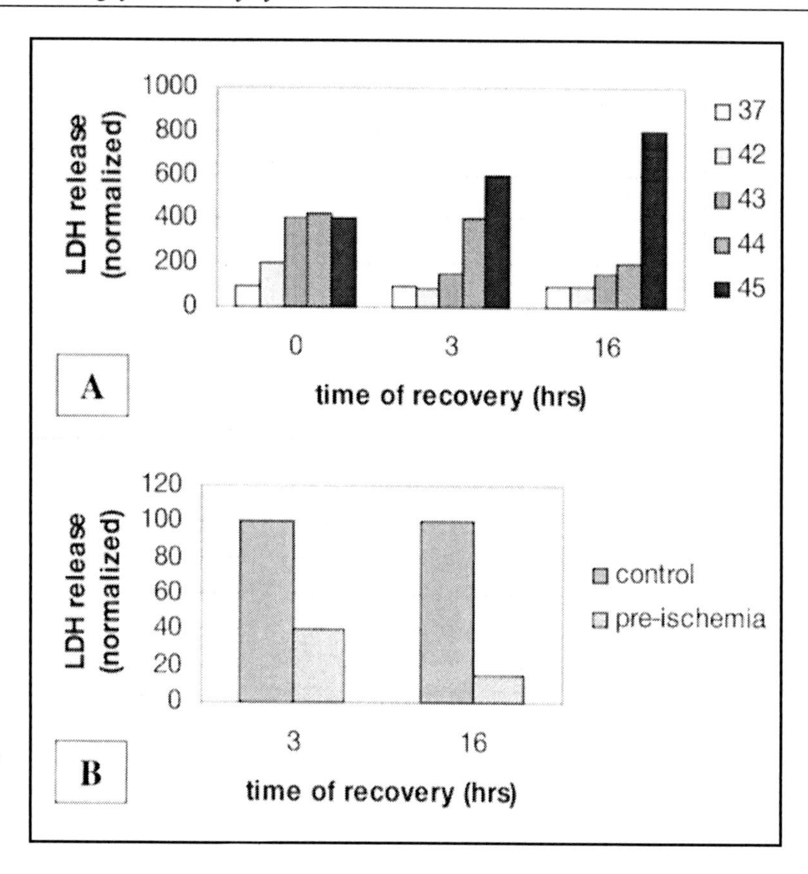

Fig. 7.4. Effect of pre-heat-shock or pre-ischemia on LDH release during a subsequent 3 hr period of simulated ischemia. LDH release is normalized toward LDH release by not pretreated cells. Panel A shows the effect of 1 hr heat-shock at various temperatures and with 0, 3 or 16 hrs of recovery. Non of the pretreatments reduces LDH significantly and several conditions results in an increased cell lysis during the ischemic insult. Panel B shows that 60 minutes of pre-ischemia, followed by 3 or 16 hrs of recovery, significantly reduces LDH release during 3 hrs of simulated ischemia.

5 hrs of recovery) and simulated ischemia (and 5 hrs of recovery) result in the appearance of Hsp70 in the cytoplasm of the cells. Panel G shows quantification of Hsp70 content of the cells (using Western blot analysis) during the recovery phase after both preconditioning protocols. It can be seen that Hsp70 is absent in control cells and that ischemia induces this protein to a level which can still be detected after 72 hours. Heat shock induces Hsp70 to a higher level, which however almost completely decays after a period of 24-48 hours. We conclude that heat shock is a stronger inducer of Hsp70 than is ischemia, but, curiously when induced by ischemia the level of the protein stays elevated for a longer period of time.

The Role of Hsp70 in Preconditioning Cultured Neonatal Rat Heart Cells

What then can be said about the role of Hsp70 in being the determinant factor in preconditioning of cardiomyocytes? Figures 7.5 and 7.6 show that almost all the heat shock

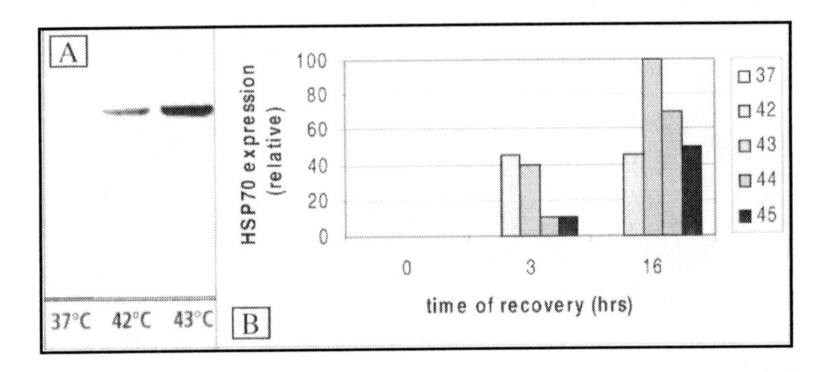

Fig. 7.5. Induction of Hsp70 by heat-shock protocols as described by Figure 7.4. Panel A shows a typical Western blot, probed with the anti-Hsp70 antibody. Panel B shows the densitometric analysis of the blots, the highest expression is set at 100%. Control cells did not contain any Hsp70 and it can be clearly seen that a recovery phase is needed to express the protein.

conditions which have been investigated for their potential to induce tolerance to ischemia, induce the expression of Hsp70. The rapidity of induction of Hsp70 is clearly dependent on the temperature as Hsp70 is found 3 hours after a heat shock in cells exposed to 42°C or 43°C, but induction is delayed in cells exposed to higher temperatures. In cells subjected to 44°C or 45°C the Hsp70 protein is hardly found after 3 hours, but is clearly present after a recovery period of 16 hours. After 16 hours of recovery, Hsp70 is always present in sufficient amounts, as compared to the amounts induced by ischemia, to confer tolerance to ischemia, if Hsp70 were to have this function. However, as can be clearly seen in Figure 7.3, none of the heat shock protocols rendered tolerance towards ischemia. Because of the absence of a relation between the presence of Hsp70 and tolerance towards ischemia, it must be concluded that Hsp70 cannot be the exclusive factor responsible for providing tolerance towards ischemia. Furthermore, the data show that a preceding heat shock can even result in increased cellular damage during an ischemic insult, depending on the height of the heat shock temperature and the length of the recovery phase.

Acknowledgments

Part of the results shown in this chapter were part of the theses of Dr. R.J.Ph. Musters and Dr. H. Ovelgönne. Dr. C. Bronke is thanked for the immunofluorescence experiments.

References

1. Murry CE, Jennings RB, Reimer KA. Preconditioning with ischemia: A delay of lethal cell injury in ischemic myocardium. Circulation 1986; 74:1124-1136.
2. Marber MS, Latchman DS, Walker JM, et al. Cardiac stress protein elevation 24 hours after brief ischemia or heat stress is associated with resistance to myocardial infarction. Circulation 1993; 88:1264-1272.
3. Donnelly TJ, Sievers RE, Vissern FLJ, et al. Heat shock protein induction in rat hearts. A role for improved myocardial salvage after ischemia and reperfusion? Circulation 1992; 85:769-778.
4. Walker DM, Pasini E, Kucukoglu S, et al. Heat stress limits infarct size in the isolated perfused rabbit heart. Cardiovasc Res 1993; 27:962-967.
5. Yellon, DM, Marber MS. Hsp70 in myocardial ischemia. Experienta 1994; 50: 1075-1084.
6. Harary I, Farley B. In vitro studies of single rat heart cells. I. Growth and organization. Exp Cell Res 1963; 29:451-465.

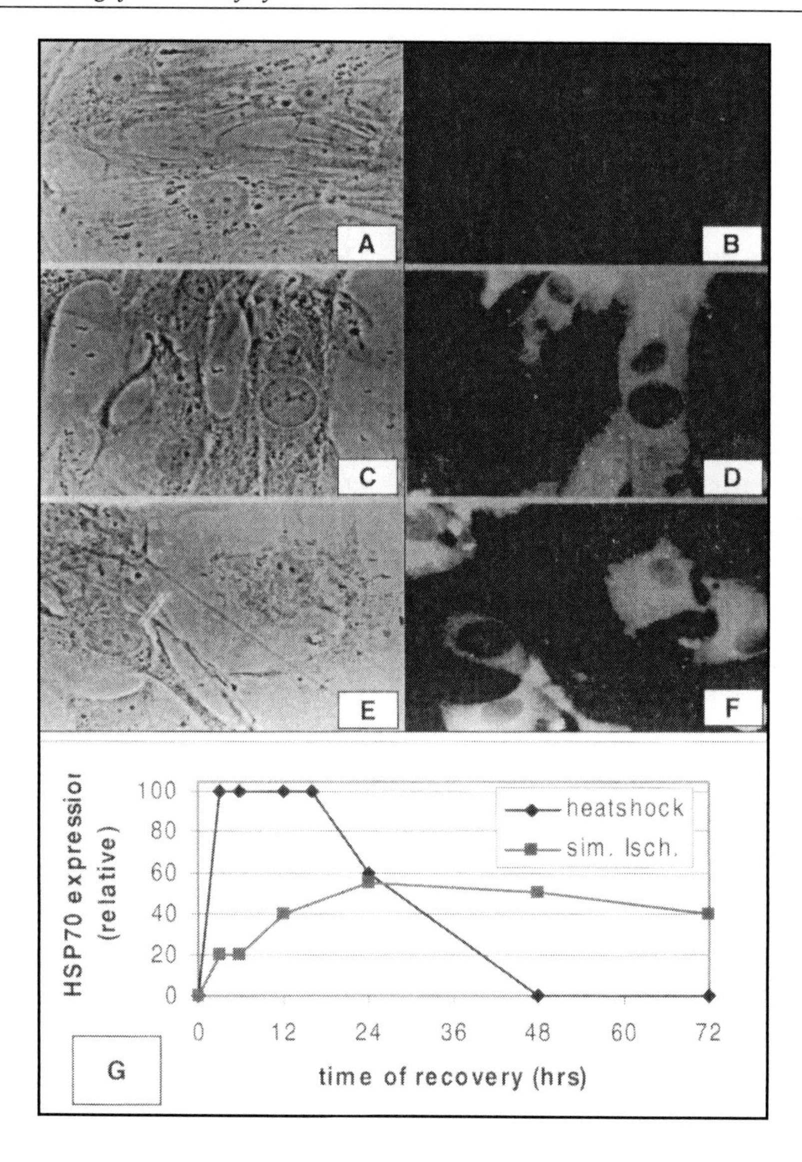

Fig. 7.6. Induction of Hsp70 by heat shock (42°C) and ischemia. Panels A-F show micrographs of cells analyzed after 5 hours of recovery. A/B: control cells; no Hsp70 could be detected. C/D: ischemia; a clear induction of Hsp70 can be observed. E/F: heat shock; Hsp70 is clearly present in the cells. (A,C,E: phase-contrast, B,D,F: immunofluorescence, using anti-Hsp70). Panel G shows the results of quantitative analysis of Hsp70 content by Western blot during the recovery phase upon the two pretreatments. Heat shock is a stronger inducer of Hsp 70, compared to simulated ischemia. However, the expression is prolonged upon ischemia and the protein is still present after 72 hrs of recovery, whereas it is non-detectable after 48 hrs of recovery upon heat shock.

7. Vemuri R, Yagev S, Heller M, et al. Studies on oxygen and volume restrictions in cultured cardiac cells, I: A model for ischemia and anoxia with a new approach. In Vitro 1985; 21:521-525.
8. Musters, RJPh, Post JA, Verkleij AJ. The isolated neonatal rat-cardiomyocyte used in an in vitro model for "ischemia",I: A morphological study. Biochim Biophys Acta 1991; 1091:270-277.
9. Tuijl MJM, van Bergen en Henegouwen PMP, Van Wijk R, et al. The isolated neonatal rat-cardiomyocyte used in an in vitro model for 'ischemia': Induction of the 68 kD heat shock protein. Biochim Biophys Acta 1991; 1091:278-284.
10. Musters RJPh, Otten E, Biegelmann E, et al. Loss of phosphatidylethanolamine transbilayer asymmetry in the sarcolemma of the isolated neonatal rat cardiomyocyte during simulated ischemia. Circ Res 1993; 73:514-523.
11. Musters RJPh, Pröbstl-Biegelmann E, van Veen TAB, et al. Sarcolemmal phospholipid reorganization during simulated ischemia: Reversability and ATP dependency. Mol. Membr. Biol. 1996; 13:159-164.
12. Post JA, Leunissen-Bijvelt J, Ruigrok TJC, et al. Ultrastructural changes of sarcolemma and mitochondria in the isolated rabbit heart during ischemia and reperfusion. Biochim Biophys Acta 1985; 845:119-123.
13. Ahsraf M, Halverson C. Structural changes in freeze-fractured sarcolemma ot the ischemic myocardium. Am J Pathol 1977; 88:853-594.
14. Frank JS, Beydler S, Wheeler N, et al. Myocardial sarcolemma in ischemia: A quantitative freeze-fracture study. Am J Physiol (Heart Circ Physiol) 1988; 255:H467-H475.
15. Ovelgönne H, van Wijk R, Verkleij AJ, et al. Cultured neonatal rat heart cells can be preconditioned by ischemia, but not by heat shock. The role of stress proteins. J Mol Cell Cardiol 1996; 28:1617-1629.
16. Post JA, Langer GA, Op den Kamp JAF, et al. Phospholipid asymmetry in cardiac sarcolemma. Analysis of intact cells and "gas-dissected" membranes. Biochim Biophys Acta 1988; 943:256-266.
17. Post JA, Verkleij AJ, Langer GA. Organization and function of sarcolemmal phospholipids in control and ischemic/reperfused cardiomyocytes. J Mol Cell Cardiol 1995; 27: 749-760.
18. Post JA, Bijvelt, JJM, Verkleij AJ. The role of phosphatidylethanolamine in sarcolemmal damage of cultured heart myocytes during simulated ischemia and metabolic inhibition. Am J Physiol (Heart Circ Physiol) 1995; 268:H773-H780.

CHAPTER 8

Antisense, Heat Shock Proteins and the Heart

A. A. Knowlton

Antisense technology provides a tool with which to dissect the components of the stress response. There are two known endogenous sets of protective proteins, the heat shock proteins (Hsps) and the antioxidants, such as superoxide dismutase;[1-4] components of both sets of proteins have been found to be induced in different stress settings, such as heat shock and ischemia. At the current time our ability to manipulate expression of these important genes is limited. The known stimuli induce multiple different stress response genes, which curtails our ability to understand the function of each of these genes. One approach to this question has been overexpression of individual Hsp, such as Hsp72 and Hsp27, each of which has now been shown to protect against injury such as ischemia, hypoxia, or heat.[5-10] However, overexpression prior to injury does not clarify the role of a given protein in the endogenous stress response. Understanding this role increases our comprehension of protein function and also provides insight into the mechanisms of injury. Antisense technology permits selective inhibition of single genes. Such an approach allows the analysis of the contribution of individual heat shock proteins and antioxidant genes to cardiac protection.

Overview of Antisense Technology

Antisense treatment involves the use of agents that specifically recognize a sequence and bind to it, inhibiting expression of that sequence. The commonly used approaches to antisense therapy have been either oligonucleotides, short, single-stranded sequences of 30 bases or less, which bind to the complementary sequence on RNA, or antisense RNA, which involves expression of part or all of a cDNA in an antisense direction. There have been a number of excellent reviews of phosphorothioate oligonucleotide compounds and antisense technology.[11-17]

Antisense Compounds

The application of short oligonucleotides less than 30 bases in length has been the most frequent approach to antisense treatment. Phosphodiesters (standard DNA) are problematic as antisense compounds because they are readily degraded both in the cell culture dish and in vivo by naturally occurring nucleases. A number of variations of phosphodiesters have been developed to try to increase the half-life of the molecules while obtaining high intracellular concentrations. The most successful compound to date has been phosphorothioate oligonucleotides. This is a modified form of phosphodiester, where a sulfur has been substituted for one of the oxygen atoms in the phosphodiester backbone of the molecule. The resulting compound is resistant to nucleases, crosses the cell membrane, and hybridizes well with RNA. The phosphorothioate-RNA dimer activates RnaseH, resulting in the destruction of the associated mRNA. These properties make these compounds suitable for both in vitro and in vivo application. Phosphorothioate oligos have been used in the vast majority of antisense experiments that utilized oligos.

Heat Shock Proteins in Myocardial Protection, edited by Rakesh C. Kukreja and Michael L. Hess.

Antisense RNA through the expression of the antisense cDNA sequence of a gene is another approach to inhibiting gene expression. This can be used in conjunction with an inducible promoter allowing selective inhibition. This approach works well, but necessitates either transfecting the target cell with very high efficiency, such as with a viral vector, or selecting clones.

Alternative Antisense Compounds: Aptamers, Triplex and Ribozymes

There are at least three other approaches to inhibiting gene expression: aptamers, triplex formation, and ribozymes.[18] Aptamers involve the clever use of a DNA decoy to mimic a normal DNA-protein interaction. Most commonly this approach is used to inhibit transcription factors.[19,20] Thus, cells are treated with double-stranded phosphorothioate oligonucleotides, which encode the consensus binding sequence for a transcription factor. The activated transcription factor binds to the oligonucleotide dimer rather than to the gene promoter, and gene activation does not occur.

Triplex formation and ribozymes involve a greater degree of complexity in design than simple antisense oligonucleotides. Ribozymes are catalytic RNA molecules that can cleave a specific RNA sequence.[21,22] The catalytic domain is flanked by the targeting antisense sequences. Triplex formation occurs when an antisense oligo binds in the major groove of DNA in a sequence dependent fashion.[23,24] This can occur because certain base combinations can bond as threesomes; for example, thymine can form hydrogen bonds with an adenine that is already bonding to another thymine. The same can occur with the bonding of cytosine to guanine. This is termed Hoogsteen base pairing. The advantage to triplex formation, which involves more difficult design of the antisense molecule, is that it blocks gene expression by preventing transcription, so fewer molecules of antisense can inhibit expression of a given gene.

Complications and Controls

There have been a number of reports of nonspecific effects (i.e., not sequence dependent) of antisense compounds. Burgess et al have reported that phosphorothioate oligonucleotides containing 3 or 4 sequential guanosine residues nonselectively inhibit smooth muscle cell growth, raising questions about some of the reported effects of antisense constructs to c-myb and c-myc.[25] Phosphorothioate oligos have been reported to interfere with binding of bFGF (basic fibroblast growth factor) at concentrations in the range of 0.1 to 50 μM.[26] Certain sequences are more frequent in bacteria and viruses than vertebrates and can trigger B-cell activation.[27] Phosphorothioate oligonucleotides are efficiently taken up by the kidney, which makes the kidney a good site for antisense therapy, but also a site of potential antisense toxicity.[28] Although these other effects are of concern, they do not exclude the use of this powerful tool; rather, careful oligonucleotide design and careful selection of controls are important. With proper attention to experimental design, use of appropriate controls, such as scrambled sequences, sequences with increasing substitution to decrease matching with the target sequence, and even additional antisense to another gene, as we have used previously,[29] antisense treatment can provide a powerful tool to elucidate gene function.

Antisense and the Cardiovascular System

Cardiovascular application of antisense technology has focused on smooth muscle cells and the vessel cell wall.[11-13] Antisense treatment has been used to prevent restenosis after angioplasty.[11,30] We have successfully applied phosphorothioate oligonucleotides to alter the expression of two different heat shock proteins in adult cardiac myocytes, as discussed below. Antisense RNA has been used to decrease Hsp25 expression in neonatal cardiac myocytes.[31]

Different approaches have been tried to increase uptake of oligonucleotides including reversible permeabilization, liposomes, and polyethylenimine.[32-34] Recently several studies have described systemic effects of antisense phosphorothioate compounds administered by intraperitoneal or tail vein injection in mice.[35,36] Although intriguing, these studies demonstrated only moderate uptake by the heart, and no distinction was made between uptake by endothelial cells and myocytes.

Heat Shock Proteins and Antisense

Studies on inhibition of heat shock protein expression by antisense have been limited. Most work has focused on Hsp27, but there have been reports on Hsp60, HSC70, Hsp72, GRP78, and Hsp90. These studies are reviewed in detail below.

Hsp72 (Inducible Hsp70)

In our own laboratory we have found that antisense phosphorothioate oligonucleotides are readily taken up by adult cardiac myocytes.[29] 5′-CAGGTCGATGCCGA-3′, corresponds to bases 508 to 521 in the human gene and is very close to the start site for translation. The sense sequence and a second antisense to MHCI (major histocompatibility complex 1) were used as controls. The latter oligonucleotide was to control for activation of RnaseH by dimer formation between the oligonucleotide and mRNA as activation of RnaseH by itself might have a deleterious effect. Preliminary experiments were done to determine uptake of the oligonucleotides by the myocytes. As shown in Figure 8.1, labeled oligonucleotides accumulated in the myocytes reaching a plateau after 12 hours of treatment. Therefore, myocytes were pretreated with oligos for 12 hours prior to starting hypoxia, and 2.27 μM concentration of the oligonucleotide was found to be sufficient to block the increase in Hsp72 following hypoxia and reoxygenation. With this selective inhibition of Hsp72 synthesis, mild hypoxic injury was converted to severe injury, supporting the importance of this protein in myocardial protection as shown in Figure 8.2.

To demonstrate the specificity of the antisense to Hsp72, examination of levels of Hsp60 and HSC70 was done by western blot and no changes in these proteins were found. Both reduction in mRNA by Northern blotting and reduction in new Hsp72 synthesis, by exhaustive immunoprecipitation of S^{35}-labeled protein (Fig. 8.3), were found consistent with destruction of the Hsp72 mRNA by RnaseH.

Dose response studies demonstrated no increase in antisense effect with doses higher than 2.27 μM. Reducing the dose to 1.13 μM still inhibited the increase in Hsp72 with hypoxia and reoxygenation, and even with 0.22 uM Hsp72 levels tended to be lower, but this reduction was not statistically significant. Thus, very low concentrations of antisense were sufficient to inhibit the induction of Hsp72 without effecting the expression of other heat shock proteins.

In another study in collaboration with our colleague, Douglas Mann, we have used the same antisense oligonucleotide to block the increase in Hsp72 found in feline cardiac myocytes in response to TNF-α.[37] In contrast to hypoxia/reoxygenation-induced Hsp72, we were not able to completely block the increase in Hsp72 in response to TNF-α. Ongoing work in our laboratory suggests that the TNF-α mediated increase in Hsp72 may be more complex than a simple increase in Hsp72 mRNA transcription. Furthermore, TNF-α appeared to be a stronger inducer of Hsp72 than hypoxia/reoxygenation, and hence, may be more difficult to inhibit.

Several other laboratories have inhibited Hsp72 with antisense treatment in non-cardiac systems. Wei et al used a phosphorothioate oligonucleotide complementary to the initiation codon and the first four codons of human Hsp72, 5′-CGCGGCTTTGGCCAT-3′, to inhibit Hsp72 expression in tumor cells.[38] Mivechi et al used antisense to selectively inhibit expression of Hsp72 (referred to as Hsp 70A in their paper) in K562 cells, an erythroleukemia cell line where hemin induces cell-differentiation and Hsp expression is increased through

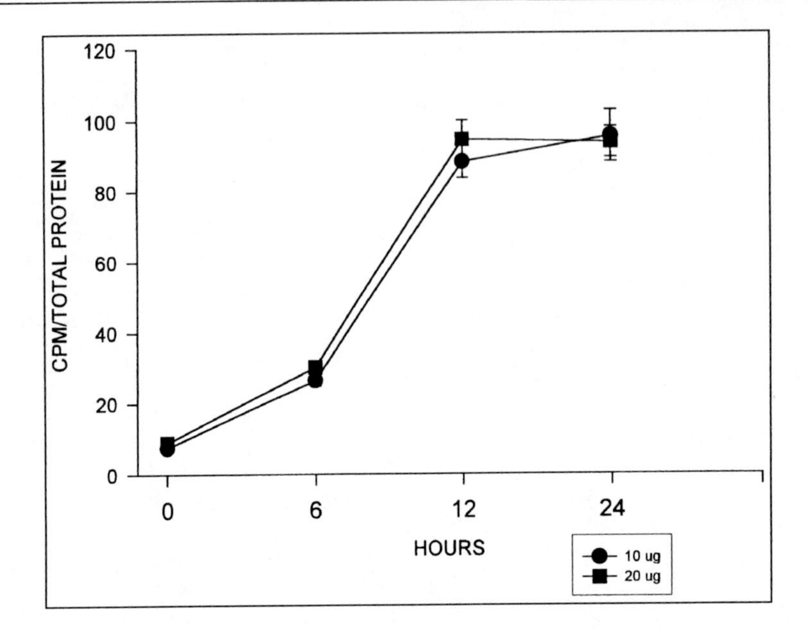

Fig. 8.1. Uptake of P^{32}-oligonucleotide by cardiac myocytes as a function of time. Two doses were used, 2.27 μM (Λ) and 4.54 μM (N) μg/plate (P-35). Each point is a mean of three different plates. Reprinted with permission from Circulation 1997; 95:1523-1531.

activation of HSF-2.[39] Two antisense oligonucleotides were used simultaneously, one against the 5′-untranslated region and one against the 3′-untranslated region of Hsp72. The corresponding sense sequences were used as controls. In other studies of monocytes an antisense construct was used to reduce Hsp72 expression.[40]

Antisense treatment has also been used to inhibit HSC70 expression. As HSC70 is present at significant levels in the normal cell, almost 1% of the soluble protein in human myocardium,[41] it is more difficult to block with antisense than an inducible response, such as Hsp72. Aquino et al used a 30-mer antisense phosphorothioate oligonucleotide to the first 10 codons of rat HSC70, 5′-ATCAATGCCAACTGCAGGTCCCTTAGACAT-3′, to reduce HSC70 expression by 31% at 24 hours and 66% at 48 hours.[42] In contrast to many other studies, transfection with lipofectin was used to deliver the oligos to the cultured oligodendrocytes. An antisense cDNA construct with the first 33% of the coding sequence of rat HSC70 under the control of a dexamethasone inducible promoter was used in NIH 3T3 cells to try to reduce HSC70 levels.[43] The homology between the rat HSC70 and the mouse (NIH 3T3 cells) is 95%, and this was sufficient to reduce mRNA levels. Although the expression of the antisense construct could be detected by Northern blot and HSC70 mRNA levels were reduced, HSC70 protein synthesis was unaffected. The difference in observed effects between these two studies likely reflects differences between the cell types studied.

Heat Shock Protein 60

Studies of Hsp60 have been limited in comparison with Hsp27. Steinhoff et al used antisense phosphoramidite oligonucleotides to decrease Hsp60 levels in primary mouse Schwann cell cultures. The oligonucleotide they used, 5′-AGCATTTCTGCGGGG-3′, contains four

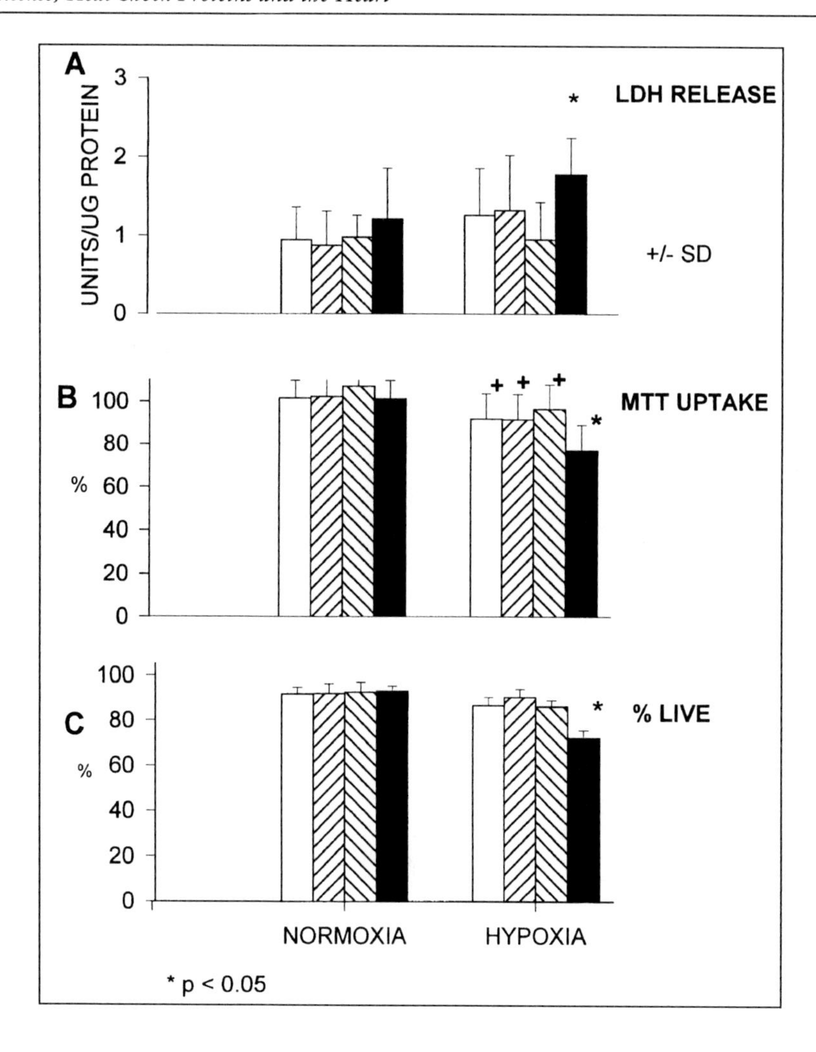

Fig. 8.2. Assessment of cardiac myocyte injury after 8 hours of hypoxia followed by reoxygenation. A—LDH release immediately after 8 hours of hypoxia. Open bars were treated with diluent only (n = 32, 27), striped bars with S (sense) to Hsp72 (n = 26, 26) and AS (antisense) to MHCI (n = 10, 21), respectively, and solid bars with AS (n = 26, 26). Results are expressed as LDH/μg of protein. Only the AS treated hypoxic cells show a significant increase in LDH with hypoxia, as compared to all other groups (* $p < 0.05$). B—MTT uptake after 8 hours of hypoxia. Results are expressed as percent uptake, compared to standard curve, as described under Methods, ± the SD. Open bars were treated with diluent only (n = 83, 84), striped bars with S to Hsp72 (n = 86, 79) and AS to MHCI (n =36, 48), respectively, and solid bars with AS to Hsp72 (n = 83, 82) * $p < 0.05$ vs. all other groups. + $p < 0.05$ vs. normoxic groups. C—Viability (Live/dead)—ratio of live to total cells (live + dead). N = 4 to 7 plates for all groups with at least 30 cells counted per plate. Open bars were treated with diluent only, striped bars with S or AS to MHCI, respectively, and solid bars with AS to Hsp72. * $p < 0.05$ vs. all other groups. All data ± the SD. Reprinted with permission from Circulation (1997) 95:1523-1531.

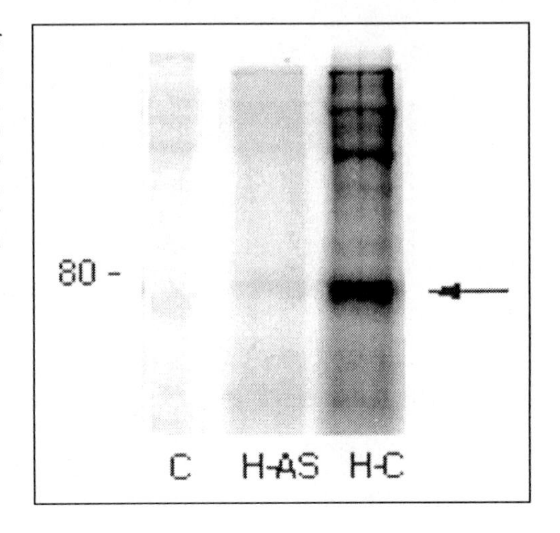

Fig. 8.3. Exhaustive immunoprecipitation of S^{35}-methionine labeled Hsp72. 80 indicates kDa, and arrow indicates Hsp72. C = control, normoxic cells, H-AS = cells treated with 8 hours of hypoxia and AS, and H-C = cells treated with 8 hours of hypoxia and diluent. All cells were labelled with S^{35}-methionine for 4 hours. Reprinted with permission from Circulation 1997; 95:1523-1531.

G=s, which as discussed above has been associated with a number of nonspecific effects. The sense oligonucleotide was used as a control.

In ongoing studies in our own laboratory we have been able to reduce Hsp60 levels by two thirds in adult rat cardiac myocytes using a phosphorothioate 15-mer antisense sequence, which was selected to avoid known nonspecific sequence effects. Preliminary findings suggest this treatment increases myocardial cell injury with hypoxia and reoxygenation.

Small Heat Shock Proteins

A number of investigators have used antisense technology to alter Hsp27 expression. All of the studies on antisense treatment and the small heat shock proteins have used expression of an antisense cDNA construct to generate antisense RNA. McGarry and Lindquist originally observed that *Drosophila* Hsp26 could be reduced by transfection of an antisense cDNA without effecting the expression of other Hsp's.[44] Full length antisense cDNA=s have been used to decrease or abolish Hsp27 expression in MCF-7 cells, a breast cancer cell line.[45,46] Reduction in Hsp27 was associated with a change in microfilament distribution from diffuse to punctate, and inhibition of cell growth. A similar approach was used to reduce Hsp27 in HT-29 cells,[47] and in another study blocking Hsp27 expression with an antisense cDNA inhibited release of basic fibroblast growth factor from cultured endothelial cells.[8]

Martin et al[31] used an adenoviral vector with an antisense cDNA to Hsp25 (rodent equivalent of Hsp27) to decrease the levels of the protein in cardiocytes. This decrease in Hsp25 resulted in increased injury during simulated ischemia as determined by LDH release. The same approach was used to reduce αβ-crystallin.[31] Reduction in αβ-crystallin was seen by western blot, but this had no effect on cardiac myocyte injury during simulated ischemia. In contrast, expression of an antisense cDNA for αβ-crystallin in glial cells reduced αβ-crystallin levels and was accompanied by reduction in cell size, microfilament disorganization, and reduced cell adhesion.[48]

Other Hsp's

Both Hsp90 and GRP78 have been inhibited through the application of antisense cDNA expression constructs (antisense RNA). Induction of GRP78 expression was inhibited in a mouse cell line (B/C10ME) using an antisense cDNA construct to hamster GRP78.[49] Hsp90 expression in a monoblastoid line (U937) was reduced by half by transfection with an antisense cDNA construct and selection of clones.[50] It was further observed that this reduction in Hsp90 was accompanied by a reduction in HSC70. The changes in Hsp90 persisted over five months of maintenance of the cell lines in culture.

Conclusions

Antisense provides a powerful tool to alter gene expression, and will help dissect the contribution of the various heat shock proteins and the antioxidant genes to cardiac protection. Unlike other stimuli such as heat shock, antisense can selectively inhibit the expression of single genes. Such studies will provide complementary data to experiments utilizing overexpression, or to currently ongoing studies where HSF1 has been knocked-out to create a mouse without a heat shock response.[51]

Acknowledgments

This work supported in part by HL92510.

References

1. Knowlton AA. The role of heat shock proteins in the heart. J Mol Cell Cardiol 1995; 27:121-131.
2. Das DK, Engelman RM, Kimura Y. Molecular adaption of cellular defences following preconditioning of the heart by repeated ischemia. Cardiovascular Research 1993; 27:578-584.
3. Yamashita N, Hoshida S, Nishida M, et al. Heat shock-induced manganese superoxide dismutase enhances the tolerance of cardiac myocytes to hypoxia-reoxygenation injury. J Mol Cell Cardiol 1997; 29:1805-1813.
4. Kloner RA, Przyklenk K, Whittaker P. Deleterious effects of oxygen radicals in ischemia/reperfusion: Resolved and unresolved issues. Circulation 1989; 80:1115-1127.
5. Radford NB, Fina M, Benjamin IJ, et al. Cardioprotective effects of 70-kDa heat shock protein in transgenic mice. Proc Natl Acad Sci USA 1996; 93:2339-2342.
6. Marber MS, Mestril R, Chi S-H, et al. Overexpression of the rat inducible 70-kD heat stress protein in a transgenic mouse increases the resistance of the heart to ischemic injury. J Clin Invest 1995; 95:1854-1860.
7. Heads RJ, Latchman DS, Yellon DM. Stable high level expression of a transfected human Hsp 70 gene protects a heart-derived muscle cell line against thermal stress. J Mol Cell Cardiol 1994; 26:695-699.
8. Piotrowicz RS, Martin JL, Dillman WH, et al. The 27-kDa heat shock protein facilitates basic fibroblast growth factor release from endothelial cells. J Biol Chem 1997; 272:7042-7047.
9. Giordano F, Mestril R, Dillmann W. Adenovirus mediated inducible heat shock protein 70 gene transfer protects against simulated ischemia in a muscle derived cell line. J Am Coll Cardiol 1995; 25:324A(abst.).
10. Plumier J-CL, Robertson HA, Currie RW. Differential accumulation of mRNA for immediate early genes and heat shock genes after ischemic injury. J Mol Cell Cardiol 1996; 28:1251-1260.
11. Simons M, Edelman ER, DeKeyser J, et al. Antisense c-myb oligonucleotides inhibit intimal arterial smooth muscle cell accumulation in vivo. Nature 1992; 359:67-70.
12. Shi Y, Hutchinson HG, Hall DJ, et al Downregulation of c-myc expression by antisense oligonucleotides inhibits proliferation of human smooth muscle cells. Circulation 1993; 88:1190-1195.
13. Bennett MR, Anglin S, McEwan JR, et al. Inhibition of vascular smooth muscle cell proliferation in vitro and in vivo by c-myc antisense oligonucleotides. J Clin Invest 1994; 93:820-828.
14. Leonetti JP, Degols G, Clarenc JP, et al. Cell delivery and mechanisms of action of antisense oligonucleotides. Progress in Nucleic Acid Research 1993; 44:143-166.
15. Whitesell L, Neckers L. Antisense technology: Biological utility and practical considerations. Am J Physiol 1993; 265:L1-L12.
16. Cazenave C, Hélène C. Antisense Oligonucleotides. In: Mol JNM, van der Krol AR, eds. Antisense nucleic acids and proteins: Fundamentals and applications. New York: Marcel Dekker, Inc., 1991:47-93.

17. Marcus-Sekura CJ. Techniques for using antisense oligodeoxyribonucleotides to study gene expression. Anal Biochem 1988; 172:289-295.
18. Stull RA, Szoka J FC. Antigene, ribozyme and aptamer nucleic acid drugs: Progress and prospects. Pharm Res 1995; 12:465-483.
19. Bielinska A, Shivdasani RA, Zhang L, et al. Regulation of gene expression with double-stranded phosphorothioate oligonucleotides. Science 1990; 250:997-1000.
20. Morishita R, Gibbons GH, Horiuchi M, Ellison KE, Nakajima M, Zhang L, Kaneda Y, Ogihara T, Dzau VJ. A gene therapy strategy using a transcription factor decoy of the E2F binding site inhibits smooth muscle proliferation in vivo. Proc Natl Acad Sci USA 1995; 92:5855-5859.
21. Tanner NK, Vasseur M. Control of gene expression by synthetic ribozymes. In: Crooke ST, Lebleu B, eds. Antisense Research and Applications. Boca Raton: CRC Press, 1993:415-26.
22. Marschall P, Thomson JB, Eckstein F. Inhibition of gene expression with ribozymes. Cell Mol Neurobiol 1994; 14:523-538.
23. Hélène C. Control of gene expression by triple-helix-forming oligonucleotides: The antigene strategy. In: Crooke ST, Lebleu B, eds. Antisense Research and Applications. Boca Raton: CRC Press, 1993:375-85.
24. Kandimalla ER, Agrawal S. Single-strand-targeted triplex formation: stability, specificity and RNaseH activation properties. Gene 1994; 149:115-121.
25. Burgess TL, Fisher EF, Ross SL, Bready JV, Qian Y-X, Bayewitch LA, Cohen AM, Herrera CJ, Hu SS-F, Kramer TB, Lott FD, Martin FH, Pierce GF, Simonet L, Farrell C. 1995. The antiproliferative activity of c-myb and c-myc antisense oligonucleotides in smooth muscle cells is caused by a nonantisense method. ProcNatlAcadSci USA 92:4051-4055.
26. Fennewald SM, Rando RF. Inhibition of high affinity base fibroblast growth factor binding by oligonucleotides. J Biol Chem 1995; 270:21718-21721.
27. Rajamanickam C, Merten S, Kwiatkowska-Patzer B, et al. Changes in mitochondrial DNA in cardiac hypertrophy in the rat. Circ Res 1979; 45:505-515.
28. Rappaport J, Hanss B, Kopp JB, et al. Transport of phophorothioate oligonucleotides in kidney: Implications for molecular therapy. Kidney International 1995; 47:1462-1469.
29. Nakano M, Mann DL, Knowlton AA. Blocking the endogenous increase in Hsp72 increases susceptibility to hypoxia and reoxygenation in isolated adult feline cardiocytes. Circulation 1997; 95:1523-1531.
30. Bennett MR, Schwartz SM. Antisense therapy for angioplasty restenosis: Some critical considerations. Circulation 1995; 92:1981-1993.
31. Martin JL, Mestril R, Hilal-Dandan R, et al. Small heat shock proteins and protection against ischemic injury in cardiac myocytes. Circulation 1997; 96:4343-4348.
32. Samali A, Cotter TG. Heat shock proteins increase resistance to apoptosis. Exp Cell Res 1996; 223:163-170.
33. Boussif O, Lezoualc'h F, Zanta MA, et al. A versatile vector for gene and oligonucleotide transfer into cells in culture and in vivo: Polyethylenimine. Proc Natl Acad Sci USA 1995; 92:7297-7301.
34. Litzinger DC, Brown JM, Wala I, et al. Fate of cationic liposomes and their complex with oligonucleotide in vivo. Biochimica et Biophysica Acta 1996; 1281:139-149.
35. Dean NM, McKay R. Inhibition of protein kinase C-α expression in mice after systemic administration of phosphorothioate antisense oligonucleotides. Proc Natl Acad Sci USA 1994; 91:11762-11766.
36. Cossum PA, Sasmor H, Dellinger D, et al. Disposition of the 14C-labeled phosphorothioate oligonucleotide ISIS 2105 after intravenous administration in rats. J Pharmacol Exp Ther 1993; 267:1181-1190.
37. Nakano M, Knowlton AA, Dibbs Z, et al. Tumor necrosis factor-α confers resistance to hypoxic injury in the adult mammalian cardiac myocyte. Circulation 1998; 97:1392-1400.
38. Wei Y-q, Zhao X, Kariya Y, et al. Induction of apoptosis by quercetin: Involvement of heat shock protein. Cancer Research 1994; 54:4952-4957.
39. Mivechi NF, Park Y-MK, Ouyang H, et al. Selective expression of heat shock genes during differentiation of human myeloid leukemic cells. Leukemia Research 1994; 18:597-608.
40. Jäättelä M, Wissing D. Heat shock proteins protect cells from monocyte cytotoxicity: Possible mechanism of self-protection. J Exp Med 1993; 177:231-236.

41. Knowlton AA, Kapadia S, Torre-Amione G, et al. Differential expression of heat shock proteins in normal and failing human hearts. J Mol Cell Cardiol 1998; 30:811-818.
42. Aquino DA, Lopez C, Farooq M. Antisense oligonucleotide to the 70-kDA heat shock cognate protein inhibits synthesis of myelin basic protein. Neurochem Res 1996; 21:417-422.
43. Li T, Hightower LE. Effects of dexamethasone, heat shock, and serum responses on the inhibition of HSC70 synthesis by antisense RNA in NIH 3T3 cells. J Cell Physiol 1995; 164:344-355.
44. McGarry J, Lindquist S. Inhibition of heat shock protein synthesis by heat-inducible antisense RNA. Proc Natl Acad Sci USA 1986; 83:399-403.
45. Mairesse N, Horman S, Mosselmans R, et al. Antisense inhibition of the 27 kDa heat shock protein production affects growth rate and cytoskeletal organization in MCF-7 cells. Cell BiolInterntl Rep 1996; 20:205-212.
46. Oesterreich S, Weng C-N, Qiu M, et al. The small heat shock protein Hsp27 is correlated with growth and drug resistance in human breast cancer cell lines. Cancer Research 1993; 53:4443-4448.
47. Garrido C, Mehlen P, Fromentin A, et al. Inconstant association between 27-kDa heat-shock protein (Hsp27) content and doxorubicin resistance in human colon cancer cells. The doxorubicin-protecting effect of Hsp27. Eur J Biochem 1996; 237:653-659.
48. Iwaki T, Iwaki A, Tateishi J, et al. Sense and antisense modification of glial αβ-crystallin production results in alterations of stress fiber formation and thermoresistance. J Cell Biol 1994; 125:1385-1393.
49. Sugawara S, Takeda K, Lee A, et al. Suppression of stress protein GRP78 induction in tumor B/C10ME eliminates resistance to cell mediated cytotoxicity. Cancer Research 1993; 53:6001-6005.
50. Galea-Lauri J, Latchman DS, Katz DR. The role of the 90-kDA heat shock protein in cell cycle control and differentiation of the monoblastoid cell line U937. Exp Cell Res 1996; 226:243-254.
51. Benjamin IJ, Curry BB, Xiao X, et al. Mice lacking heat shock transcription factor 1 exhibit increased susceptibility to cardiovascular challenge. Circulation 1997; 96:I-312 abst.

CHAPTER 9

Stress Proteins in Myocardial Protection:
Culture Shock Protein, Heme Oxygenase-1 (Hsp32), Induced by Sublethal Stresses Protects the Heart Against Oxidative Stress

Shiro Hoshida

The formation of a stress protein comprises a mechanism of cell protection highly conserved in evolution. As the induction of stress proteins makes cells more tolerant towards a second, more toxic, and otherwise lethal stress, the stress protein response might be involved in cardioprotective mechanisms.[1,2] The term 'culture shock' is used under some circumstances triggered on exposure to serum-free conditions, during proliferation from subconfluent densities, or during isolation from whole tissue.[3,4] The preferential synthesis of stress proteins by means of procedures for establishing primary cell cultures (culture shock) has been proposed; stress proteins (90, 70, 30 kD) are synthesized in Xenopus hepatocytes during the stepping up of primary cultures.[3] In cultured myocardial cells, heavy metals such as cadmium chloride and cytokines such as interleukin-1 also induce the synthesis of stress proteins (70 and 30 kD).[5,6] Although several reports showed a significant role of the 70 kD stress protein (Hsp70) in protection against oxidative stress of cardiac tissue,[7,8] no reports have shown the role of the 30 kD stress protein in cardioprotection against oxidative stress.

Heme oxygenase (HO), which constitutes the rate-limiting enzyme in the degradation of heme, cleaves heme to form biliverdin, with the concomitant formation of carbon monoxide. The biliverdin is subsequently reduced to form the antioxidant, bilirubin.[9-11] On the other hand, carbon monoxide, like nitric oxide, has the ability to bind to the iron atom of hemoproteins, and has been shown to activate guanylyl cyclase, resulting in an elevated cGMP content. The inducible type of HO (HO-1) is known to be Hsp32.[12] HO-1 is inducible in various tissues with a large number of agents, including heme compounds, heavy metals, sulfhydryl reagents and hydrogen peroxide.[13,14] The heart is rich in cytochromes and a site of heme synthesis. Myocardial cells are sensitive to changes in environment and can be considerably modified from their native in vivo state to a different state in culture. Considering with the functional properties of HO-related products, HO-1 could be involved in a mechanism of cellular adaptation.

In this Chapter we describe the formation of HO-1 (Hsp32) in a primary culture of neonatal rat myocardial cells and its relation to the intracellular gluthathione redox state. The effect of HO on cellular injury under hypoxia-reoxygenation was also examined. The results of our study constitute the evidence that sublethal stress can induce the synthesis of HO-1 and that the increased HO expression may protect the heart against otherwise lethal oxidative stress.

Heat Shock Proteins in Myocardial Protection, edited by Rakesh C. Kukreja and Michael L. Hess.

Increased HO-1 Expression in Myocardial Cells

HO-1 Expression During Primary Culture of Myocardial Cells

Myocardial cells were isolated from rat neonatal hearts by the method previously reported.[15] Briefly, neonatal Wistar-Kyoto rats were anesthetized with ether, and then their hearts were quickly removed and immersed in phosphate-buffered saline (PBS). The fine-chopped ventricles were placed in PBS containing collagenase. To obtain myocytes selectively, the dissociated cells were preplated for 1 hour and then unattached myocytes were collected. These myocytes were suspended in Dulbecco's modified Eagles medium (DMEM) containing a high glucose concentration and fetal bovine serum (FBS). In experiments involving assessment of HO-1 expression by Western blotting, myocardial cell sampling was performed 0, 12, 24 and 48 hours after the isolated cells had been cultured in DMEM with FBS at 37°C perfused with a normoxic gas mixture (95% Air, 5% CO_2; pO_2, 143 mmHg). Actinomycin D, cycloheximide or hemin was added to some dishes. When HO-1 expression was assessed by means of immunohistochemistry, the isolated cells were cultured under the same conditions in Lab-Tek chamber slides (Nunc Inc., Naperville, IL).

Immediately after isolation, HO-1 was not expressed in myocardial cells, as assessed by Western blot analysis (Fig. 9.1). However, HO-1 was obviously expressed in these cells 12 hours after isolation, although the extent of HO-1 expression was greater 24 hours than 12 or 48 hours after isolation (Fig. 9.1).[16] The expression of HO-1 was completely suppressed by treatment with actinomycin D (0.1 μg/ml) or cycloheximide (0.1 mM), but significantly augmented by treatment with hemin (data not shown). These findings were in accord with the immunohistochemical data (Fig. 9.2). No significant staining of HO-1 was observed in a 2-hour culture of myocardial cells. In a 12-hour or 24-hour culture, however, HO-1 appeared as clusters of aggregates in an equatorial perinuclear ring. The HO-1 aggregates were in close proximity to the nucleus, but often a clear nuclear boundary was apparent. By using a laser scanning microscope to obtain tomographic photographs of HO-1 staining, intracellular microsomal network was clearly observed in myocardial cells (Fig. 9.3). Although not shown, using an anti-rat HO-1 antibody, no obvious immunostaining for HO-1 was observed in myocardial cells of rat neonatal cardiac tissue. To assess the transcript level for HO-1 in myocardial cells, we used semiquantitative cDNA amplification as a sensitive method for assessing the level of HO-1 transcripts to obtain information on the time-course of stimulation with procedures for establishing primary cell cultures. Total RNA was isolated by repeated phenol-chloroform extraction and isopropanol precipitation. cDNA was synthesized from total RNA using random hexanucleotides (Gibco BRL) with Moloney murine leukemia virus reverse transcriptase. Polymerase chain reactions for semiquantitative comparison of HO-1 transcripts were normalized for the presence of β-actin. As shown in Figure 9.4, HO-1 transcripts were markedly increased in 6-24 hour cultured cells, although sparse transcripts were already observed immediately after cell isolation.[16] There was no associated change in β-actin transcripts. To confirm the identity of the amplification products, we performed amplification of the rat HO-1 cDNA with the HO-1 primers, and obtained products of the same expected sizes (data not shown).

Changes in HO-1 Expression by Redox State

When we examined gluthathione redox state during the first 24 hours after isolation, the degree of oxidative stress in cultured myocardial cells is high.[16] To determine whether changes in the degree of oxidative stress can modify the expression of HO-1 during primary myocardial cell culture, we evaluated the effects of reduced gluthathione (GSH) or hydrogen peroxide (H_2O_2) on the time-course of HO-1 expression as assessed by Western blot analysis and semiquatitative cDNA amplification. GSH markedly reduced but H_2O_2 inversely augmented

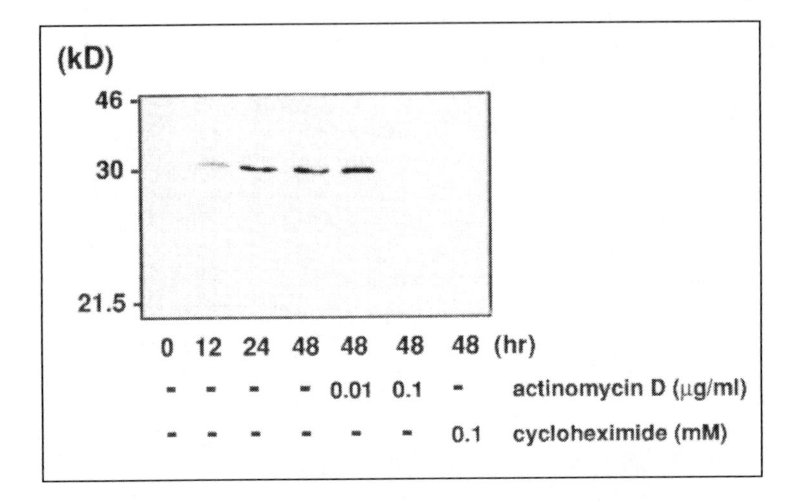

Fig. 9.1. Western blotting of protein obtained from cultured rat neonatal myocardial cells using anti-heme oxygenase-1 (HO-1) antibody. Equal amounts of total protein (20 μg/well) were loaded in each lane. Cells were cultured for 0, 12, 24 or 48 hours after isolation. Actinomycin D (0.01-0.1μg/ml), or cycloheximide (0.1 mM) was added immediately after cell isolation.

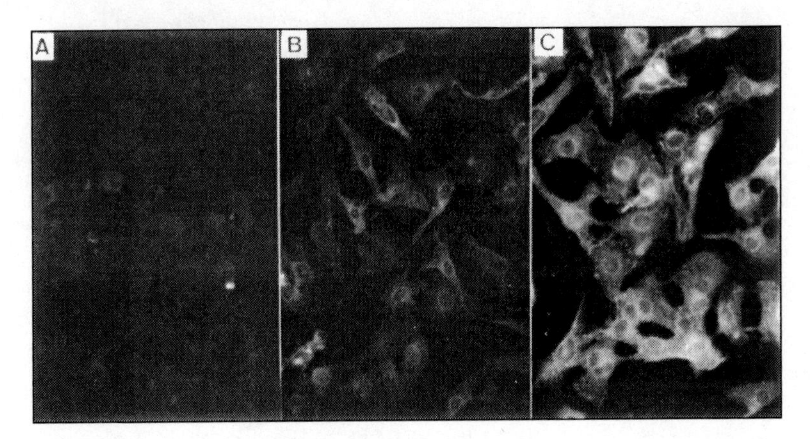

Fig. 9.2. Immunohistochemical staining for heme oxygenase-1 (HO-1) in rat neonatal myocardial cells. HO-1 was visualized using 3-amino-9-ethylcarbazole. Cells were cultured for 2 (A), 12 (B) or 24 (C) hours after isolation.

the protein levels of HO-1 in cultured myocardial cells 12 hours after cell isolation (Fig. 9.5). However, no significant difference in HO-1 expression was observed between control and GSH- or H_2O_2-treated myocardial cells in the 24-hour cultured cells. HO-1 transcripts were also reduced by treatment with GSH but were significantly augmented by treatment with H_2O_2 in the 2-hour cultured myocardial cells (Fig. 9.6). At 24 hours after cell isolation, however, there was no significant difference in the levels of HO-1 transcripts between control and GSH- or H_2O_2-treated cells. These results indicate that HO-1 expression is closely related to the oxidative stress levels in myocardial cells.

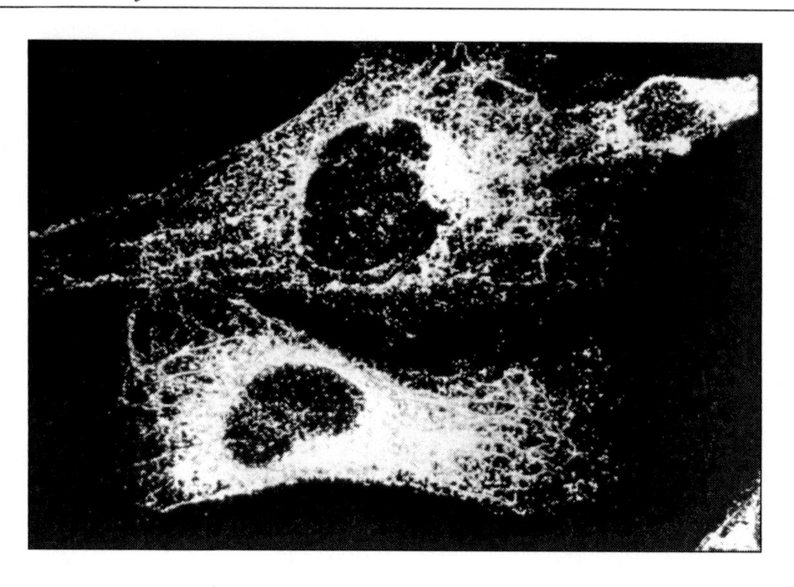

Fig. 9.3. Heme oxygenase-1 (HO-1) was visualized by immunohistochemical staining using a fluorescein isothiocyanate-conjugated secondary antibody in rat neonatal myocardial cells. Cells were cultured for 24 hours after isolation. Tomographic photographs were obtained using a laser scanning microscope (Olympus, LSM-GB200).

HO-1 as a "Culture Shock" Protein

We have shown that rat neonatal myocardial cells can be stimulated to rapidly induce HO-1 during the stepping up of primary cultures; immediately after isolation, myocardial cells did not express HO-1, but obviously expressed it after 12-48 hour culture, as assessed by Western blot analysis and immunohistochemistry. The facts that HO-1 was not synthesized in response to 'culture shock' in the presence of actinomycin D and that HO-1 transcripts were increased after cell isolation establish that HO-1 is transcriptionally regulated in primary cultures of rat neonatal myocardial cells. When cells are detached from their normal substratum, such as the basement membrane, and are required to restore their extracellular matrix, genes coding stress proteins may be specifically activated. Hemoproteins synthesized in myocardial cells may be catabolized, suggesting the essential need for a significant level of microsomal HO in these cells. As a result of HO induction, there would be resultant depletion of the content of cellular heme proteins and free heme.[17,18] Several lines of evidence have already suggested a link between immune mediators and stress response;[19] interleukin-1, -2, -3 and -6, and tumor necrosis factor stimulate the synthesis of a 30 kD stress protein (probably HO-1) in myocardial cells.[6] Cytokines induce generation of oxygen-derived free radicals, which are well known as strong stimuli for stress protein formation.[1,5] Complex mechanisms may be involved in the induction of HO-1 protein as a 'culture shock' protein. Although HO-1 expression markedly increased after cell isolation, other stress proteins would also express during the stepping up of primary cultures.

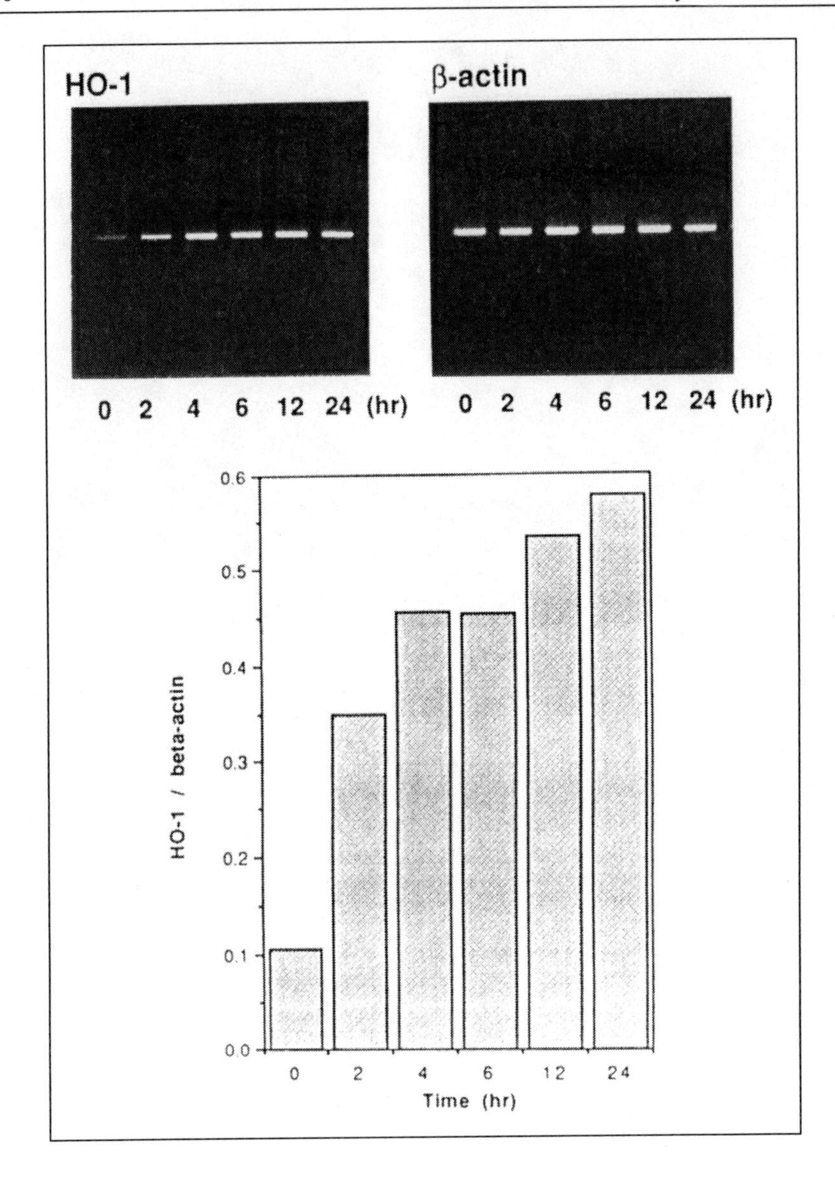

Fig. 9.4. Semiquantitative cDNA amplification of heme oxygenase-1 (HO-1) transcripts. Rat neonatal myocardial cells were cultured for various times after isolation. Total RNA was harvested and reverse transcribed, and then the cDNA was amplified. Cells were cultured for 0, 2, 4, 6, 12 and 24 hours after isolation. β-actin was not significantly influenced during the course of the experiment. Upper panels show the amplification product of one representative experiment, and lower panel presents the relative change in the amplification product (HO-1/β-actin).

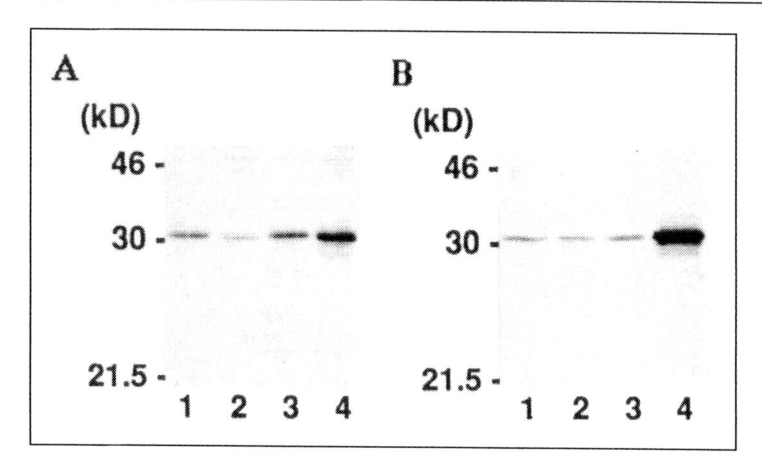

Fig. 9.5. HO-1 expression as seen by Western blotting of proteins obtained from rat neonatal myocardial cells after anti-heme oxygenase-1 antibody binding. Cells were treated with reduced gluthathione (1 mM, lane 2), hydrogen peroxide (100 μM, lane 3) or hemin (10 μM, lane 4) for 12 (A) and 24 (B) hours after isolation. Each lane 1 shows control, untreated cells.

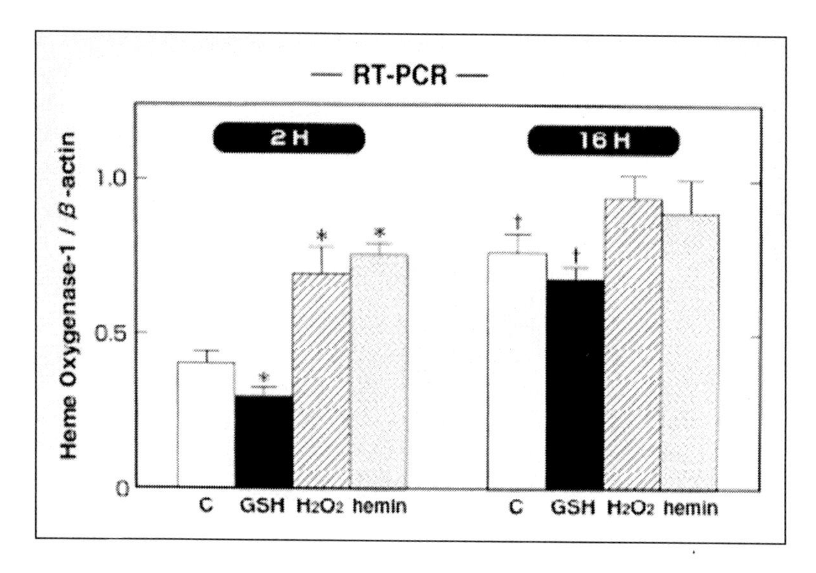

Fig. 9.6. Bar graphs showing relative changes in semiquantitative levels of transcripts (heme oxygenase-1/ β-actin) caused by treatment with reduced gluthathione (GSH, 1 mM), hydrogen peroxide (H_2O_2, 100 μM) or hemin (10 μM) in rat neonatal myocardial cells cultured for 2 and 16 hours. GSH, H_2O_2, or hemin was added at 0 hours of cell isolation. Data are expressed as mean±SEM. *$p<0.05$ vs control (C), †$p<0.05$ vs values at 2 hours after isolation.

HO-1-Induced Cardioprotection Against Hypoxia-Reoxygenation Injury

Augmentation of Myocardial Cell Injury by an HO Inhibitor

To evaluate the protective effect of HO against myocardial cell injury by oxidative stress, isolated cells were cultured in DMEM with FBS for 24 hours under normoxia, and then the medium was switched to serum-free DMEM. After 24 hours in serum-free medium, the cells were exposed to a hypoxic gas mixture (95% N_2, 5% CO_2) for 3 hours in DMEM without glucose, followed by switching to the normoxic gas mixture in DMEM for 1 hour.[15] To clarify the effect of HO on cellular injury, we examined the difference in cellular injury in the presence and absence of Zn-protoporphyrin (PP)-9, an inhibitor of HO activity.[20] Zn-PP-9 was added immediately before hypoxia and through to the end of the experiment.

The extent of myocardial cell injury was assessed by measuring creatine kinase (CK) activity in the culture medium using a standard spectrophotometric method. Under normoxia for 4 hours there was no significant difference in CK activity of the culture medium in the presence (0.1-1.0 μM) or absence of Zn-PP-9 (Fig. 9.7). Under hypoxia for 3 hours followed by reoxygenation for 1 hour, however, a significant increase in CK activity of the culture medium was observed, even in the absence of Zn-PP-9. Zn-PP-9 augmented the increase in CK activity in a dose-dependent manner, indicating the deleterious effect of Zn-PP-9 on cell injury under these conditions.

Alteration of Glutathione Redox State

The contents of reduced gluthathione (GSH) and oxidized gluthathione (GSSG) in cultured myocytes were determined as described previously.[21] The recycling assay involving 5,5¢-dithiobis (2-nitrobenzoic acid) and gluthathione reductase for determining total GSH is a sensitive and specific enzymatic procedure. For the determination of GSSG, the supernatant solutions of the cultured myocytes were pretreated with 2-vinylpyridine before 5,5¢-dithiobis (2-nitrobenzoic acid) was added. There was no significant difference in the cellular GSH/GSSG ratio under normoxia for four hours in the presence (0.1-1.0 mM) or absence of Zn-PP-9 (Fig. 9.8).However, a significant reduction in the cellular GSH/GSSG ratio was observed under hypoxia-reoxygenation, and the reduction was further augmented in the presence of Zn-PP-9 in a dose-dependent manner. Although not shown, a similar change in the cellular GSH level to that in the GSH/GSSG ratio was observed under normoxia or hypoxia-reoxygenation. To measure the activities of gluthathione-related enzymes, cultured myocardial cells were scraped into cold PBS, sonicated on ice, and then centrifuged. The activities of gluthathione peroxidase and gluthathione reductase were analyzed by the methods we previously described.[22] Gluthathione peroxidase activity did not differ among the groups under normoxia and hypoxia-reoxygenation (Fig. 9.8). However, gluthathione reductase activity was significantly increased in the presence of Zn-PP-9 even under normoxia, suggesting that the cellular GSH/GSSG ratio could be maintained through the increase in gluthathione reductase activity in the presence of Zn-PP-9.Under hypoxia-reoxygenation, a similar change in gluthathione reductase activity was observed, although the GSH/GSSG ratio was reduced in the presence of Zn-PP-9. These findings indicate that the increase in gluthathione reductase activity was not adequate to maintain the gluthathione redox state under these conditions.

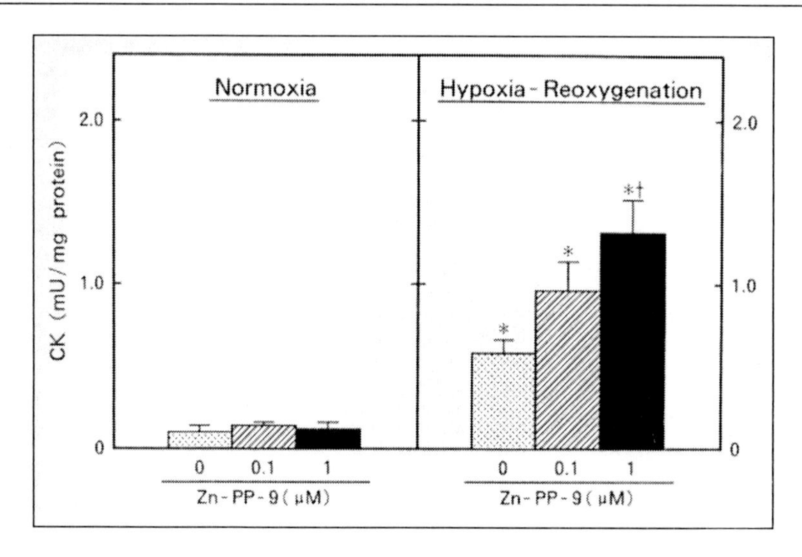

Fig. 9.7. Effect of Zn-protoporphyrin (PP)-9 on myocardial cell injury, as assessed by creatine kinase (CK) release, in culture medium under normoxia (4 hours) or hypoxia (3 hours)-reoxygenation (1 hour). *$p<0.01$ vs. normoxia, †$p<0.05$ vs without Zn-PP-9.

Mechanism for HO-Induced Cardioprotection

When we examined the protective effect of HO against oxidative stress using a hypoxia-reoxygenation model in cultured myocardial cells, CK activity in the culture medium significantly increased under hypoxia-reoxygenation, compared with the control, and was further increased in the presence of an HO inhibitor, Zn-PP-9, in a dose-dependent manner. Zn-PP-9 also augmented a decrease in the myocardial GSH/GSSG ratio. These results indicate that HO-1 expressed by means of procedures for establishing primary cell cultures is a 'culture shock' protein and may exert a significant protective effect against oxidative stress. It is agreed that HO-1 is a protein that exhibits increased activity under cellular stresses and in disease states.[23] It has been proposed that as one beneficial role of HO, bilirubin, a metabolite of the HO pathway, may act as a physiological antioxidant since, under a low oxygen concentration and when incorporated into liposomes, it scavenges peroxyl radicals as efficiently as α-tocopherol.[9] Bilirubin is also an efficient scavenger of singlet oxygen[10] and is able to react with the superoxide anion.[11] Another rationale of HO for cellular protection is the removal of the prooxidant heme substrate, which can participate in the Fenton reaction in which active hydroxyl radical is generated from peroxides.[24] Since there was no difference in the change in the cellular cGMP level on Zn-PP-9 treatment between normoxia and hypoxia-reoxygenation (data not shown), the cGMP level would not play a major role in cellular injury in our experimental model.

Sublethal Stress-Induced HO-1 Expression in Myocardial Cells

Sublethal Ischemia-Induced HO-1 Expression

HO-1 has been shown to be expressed in ischemic/reperfused myocardium,[25] and may be cytoprotective against oxidative stress. To determine the stimulus for induction of HO-1 in

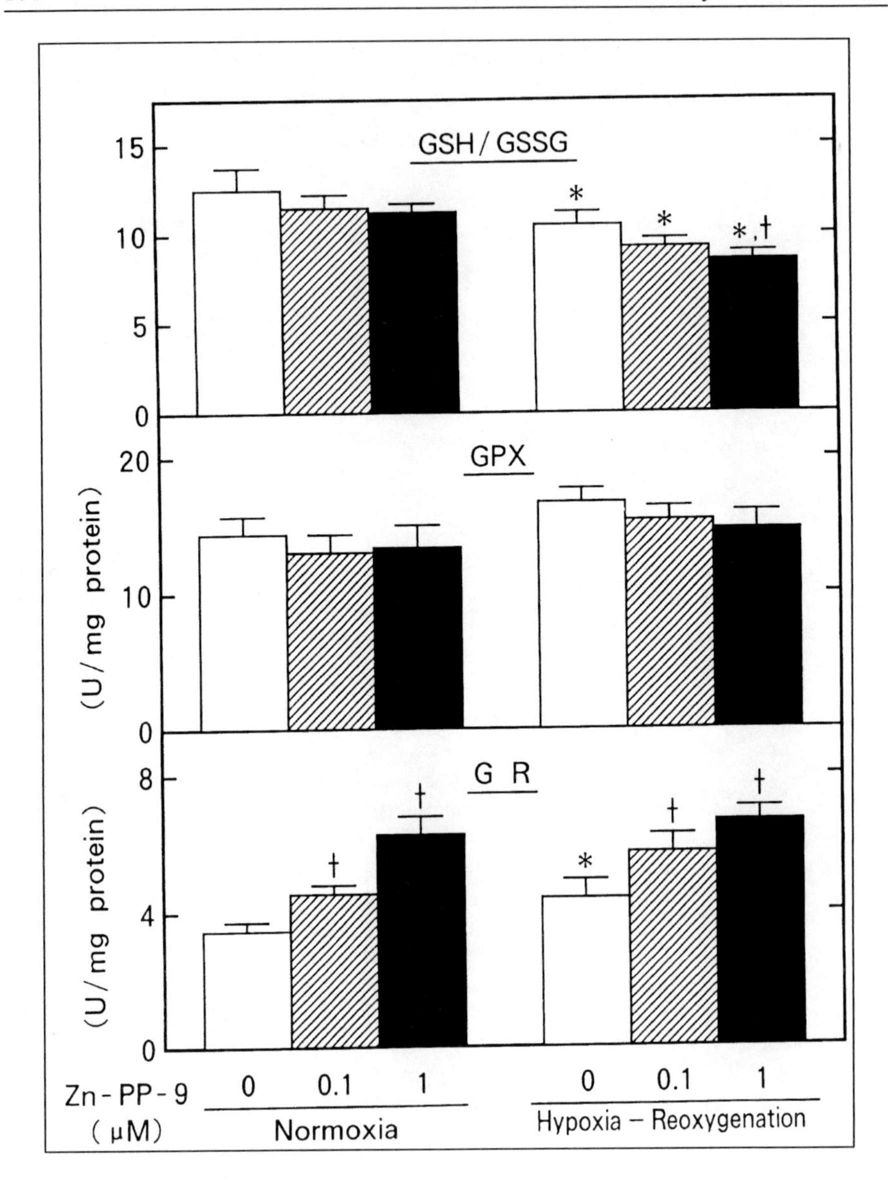

Fig. 9.8. Effect of Zn-protoporphyrin (PP)-9 on the myocardial gluthathione redox state under normoxia (4 hours) or hypoxia (3 hours)-reoxygenation (1 hour). GSH, reduced gluthathione; GSSG, oxidized gluthathione; GPX, gluthathione peroxidase; GR, gluthathione reductase. *$p<0.05$ vs normoxia, †$p<0.05$ vs without Zn-PP-9.

myocardial cells under ischemia/reperfusion, we examined the HO-1 expression in neonatal rat myocardial cells under

1. hypoxia (95% N_2, 5% CO_2)-reoxygenation (95% Air, 5% CO_2),
2. glucose-free medium, or
3. acidic medium (pH6.5, HEPES 25 mM).[26]

Under persistent hypoxia for 24-48 hours, HO-1 was induced in myocardial cells as assessed by Western blotting. Reoxygenation also induced HO-1 in these cells (24-hour hypoxia followed by 6-hour reoxygenation). Under glucose-free medium for 12 hours, HO-1 was induced similarly as assessed by Western and Northern blotting. HO-1 was also induced under acidic medium for 24 hours. These results indicate that HO-1 is induced via several stimuli under simulated ischemia/reperfusion in cultured myocardial cells. Other sublethal stress such as heat shock and low-dose cytokines also induced HO-1 expression in these cells.

HO-1 Induction by Protein Kinase C Activation

To clarify the involvement of protein kinase C (PKC) activation in stress protein expression, we added PKC inhibitors such as calphostin C and staurosporine, or PKC activators such as phorbol 12-myristate 13-acetate (PMA) to the cultured myocardial cells. PKC inhibitors effectively abrogated the HO-1 induction under glucose-free medium. However, they could partly reduce the expression induced by reoxygenation. PMA induced HO-1 protein after 3-hour stimulation in myocardial cells. These findings indicate that PKC activation is important to induce HO-1 protein in myocardial cells, but another pathway may also be involved in the HO-1 induction.[26]

HO-1 as a Rescue Protein in Pharmacological Preconditioning

Ebselen-Induced HO-1 Expression and Its Relation to Redox State

Selenium induces several proteins, including stress proteins and gluthathione. These proteins have been shown to be cardioprotective against oxidative injury. Ebselen is a seleno-organic compound. This agent exhibits a potent antioxidant action and mimics gluthathione peroxidase activity.[27-29] We examined the effects of ebselen on the induction of these proteins in myocardial cells isolated from rat neonatal hearts. After 24 hours of culture in DMEM with FBS, the medium was replaced with serum-free DMEM with or without ebselen (0, 0.3, 3.0, 30 μM). Incubation conditions were 37°C, with perfusion by a normoxic gas mixture (95% Air, 5%CO_2; pO_2 143 mmHg). After 24 hours in serum-free medium, cell samples for the expression of stress proteins and the measurement of gluthathione content and gluthathione-related enzyme activity were collected. Ebselen induced HO-1 expression in a dose-dependent manner as assessed by Western blot analysis.[30] This finding is consistent with the report that HO-1 has a metal responsive element in its 5′-noncoding region and transcription can be induced by heavy metals.[13,14]

HO-1 expression has been shown to be closely related to gluthathione redox state.[31] Exogenous GSH effectively reduced the increased HO-1 expression induced by ebselen. Treatment with ebselen for 24 hours significantly increased the content of both GSH and GSSG in myocardial cells in a dose-dependent manner.[30] The content of GSH in myocardial cells treated with ebselen (30 μM) showed an approximate 3-fold increase compared with that in control cells. GSH/GSSG ratio did not differ significantly between the control and ebselen-treated cells. To further investigate the effect of 24-hour ebselen treatment on gluthathione metabolism, we examined gluthathione-related enzyme activity. Gluthathione peroxidase activity in cells treated with ebselen was slightly higher than that in control cells, but the difference did not reach a significant level. In contrast, gluthathione reductase activity in myocardial cells treated with ebselen for 24 hours significantly exceeded that in control cells in a dose-dependent fashion.[30]

Selenium has been shown to increase intracellular GSH[32,33] and to increase the activities of r-glutamylcysteine synthetase, the first and rate-limiting enzyme in GSH biosynthesis, and of gluthathione reductase.[34] Gluthathione peroxidase is a seleno-enzyme. Ebselen is reported to mimic gluthathione peroxidase activity under various conditions.[27,28] Ebselen increases in the intracellular content of GSH and GSSG and the gluthathione reductase activity in cultured myocardial cells 24 hours after treatment. An increase in gluthathione reductase activity may occur in response to ebselen-mediated increase in GSSG content.

Preconditioning with Ebselen in Myocardial Cells

Since myocardial cells expressed stress proteins and gluthathione after treatment with ebselen for 24 hours, we evaluated the extent of cellular injury evoked by oxidative stress during this phase. Cultured myocytes pretreated with ebselen for 24 hours were exposed to H_2O_2 (100, 300 μM) for 1 hour and lactate dehydrogenase (LDH) activity in the culture medium was measured by the standard method. The injury to myocardial cells induced by H_2O_2 was reduced by pretreatment with ebselen in a dose-dependent manner.[30] To further investigate the cardiotolerance to ischemic injury, myocytes pretreated with ebselen for 24 hours were transferred to a simulated ischemic medium adapted from Esumi et al.[35] After exposure to the simulated ischemic medium followed by control medium, cytoprotective effect of myocardial cells pretreated with ebselen was also observed in a dose-dependent manner. These results indicate that pretreatment with ebselen significantly protects myocardial cells against the oxidative injury induced by H_2O_2 or simulated ischemic medium ("pharmacological preconditioning"). Pretreatment with ebselen per se did not result in significant LDH release, indicating that it did not produce significant cell damage.

Significance of HO-1 Induction in Pharmacological Preconditioning

Brief episodes of repeated ischemia produces cardioprotection that is acquired soon after ("ischemic preconditioning") as well as in the later phase (24 hours) following sublethal ischemia ("delayed preconditioning").[7,36,37] Beside ischemia, treatment with heat stress or cytokines has been shown to be effective in reducing myocardial injury resulting from prolonged myocardial ischemia and reperfusion 24-48 hours after the treatment.[38-40] Sublethal stresses such as brief ischemia/reperfusion, heat stress and low-dose cytokines can induce HO-1 expression in myocardial cells. The delayed preconditioning may be more effective in suppressing the propagation of myocardial necrosis in patients with unstable angina or coronary artery bypass surgery as compared with ischemic preconditioning. Treatment with agents such as ebselen may hold promise for the pharmacological preconditioning by inducing stress proteins such as HO-1 to render myocardial cells more resistant to ischemia and reperfusion.

Conclusions

Our results represent the evidence that HO-1 is induced by environmental stresses occurring during primary cultures of rat neonatal myocardial cells. They also provide the demonstration of a protective effect of HO against oxidative stress in these cultured cells. HO-1 expression is a general response to oxidative stress in mammalian cells,[24] and may also be a very sensitive indicator of oxidative stress. HO-1 may be a rescue protein relating to delayed preconditioning induced by sublethal stresses in myocardial cells. Whether or not our observations are of general significance and applicable to other cultured cells remains to be seen. In any event, the demonstration that a 'culture shock' protein, HO-1, could prevent oxidative stress in myocardial cells offers a new means of clarifying the transcriptional regulation of HO-1 expression and the important role in the function of myocardial cells.

References

1. Spitz DR, Dewey WC, Li GC. Hydrogen peroxide or heat shock induces resistance to hydrogen peroxide in Chinese hamster fibroblasts. J Cell Physiol 1987; 131:364-373.

2. Editorial: Stress proteins and myocardial protection. Lancet 1991; 337:271-272.
3. Wolffe AP, Glover JF, Tata JR. Culture shock. Synthesis of heat-shock-like proteins in fresh primary cell cultures. Exp Cell Res 1984; 154:581-590.
4. Sage H. Culture shock. Selective uptake and rapid release of a novel serum protein by endothelial cells. J Biol Chem 1986; 261:7082-7092.
5. Low I, Friedrich T, Schoeppe W. Synthesis of shock proteins in cultured fetal mouse myocardial cells. Exp Cell Res 1989; 180:451-459.
6. Low-Friedrich I, Weisensee D, Mitrou P et al. Cytokines induce stress protein formation in cultured cardiac myocytes. Exp Cell Res 1992; 87:12-18.
7. Marber MS, Latchman DS, Walker JM et al. Cardiac stress protein elevation 24 hours after brief ischemia or heat stress is associated with resistance to myocardial infarction. Circulation 1993; 88:1264-1272.
8. Hutter MM, Sievers RE, Barbosa V et al. Heat-shock protein induction in rat hearts. A direct correlation between the amount of heat-shock protein induced and the degree of myocardial protection. Circulation 1994; 89:355-360.
9. Stocker R, Yamamoto Y, McDonagh AF, et al. Bilirubin is an antioxidant of possible physiological importance. Science 1987; 235:1043-1046.
10. Stevens B, Small RD Jr. The photoperoxidation of unsaturated organic molecules-XV. O_2 $^1\delta g$ quenching by bilirubin and biliverdin. Photochem Photobiol 1976; 23:33-36.
11. Stocker R, Glazer AN, Ames BN. Antioxidant activity of albumin-bound bilirubin. Proc Natl Acad Sci USA 1987; 84:5918-5922.
12. Ewing JF, Maines MD. Rapid induction of heme oxygenase 1 mRNA and protein by hyperthermia in rat brain: Heme oxygenase 2 is not a heat shock protein. Proc Natl Acad Sci USA 1991; 88:5364-5368.
13. Maines MD, Kappas A. Metals as regulators of heme metabolism. Science 1977; 198:1215-1221.
14. Keyse SM, Tyrrell RM. Heme oxygenase is the major 32-kDa stress protein induced in human skin fibroblasts by UVA radiation, hydrogen peroxide, and sodium arsenite. Proc Natl Acad Sci USA 1989; 86: 99-103.
15. Yamashita N, Nishida M, Hoshida S et al. Induction of manganese superoxide dismutase in rat cardiac myocytes increases tolerance to hypoxia 24 hours after preconditioning. J Clin Invest 1994; 94:2193-2199
16. Hoshida S, Nishida M, Yamashita N et al. Heme oxygenase-1 expression and its relation to oxidative stress during primary culture of cardiomyocytes. J Mol Cell Cardiol 1996; 28:1845-1855.
17. Maines MD, Kappas A. The induction of heme oxidation in various tissues by trace metals: evidence for the catabolism of endogenous heme by hepatic heme oxygenase. Ann Clin Res 1976; 8:39-46.
18. Kappas A, Maines MD. Tin, a potent inducer of heme oxygenase in kidney. Science 1976; 192:60-62.
19. Polla BS. 1988. A role for heat shock proteins in inflammation. Immunol Today 1988; 9:134-137.
20. Maines MD. Zinc • protoporphyrin is a selective inhibitor of heme oxygenase activity in the neonatal rat. Biochim Biophys Acta 1981; 673:339-350.
21. Hoshida S, Kuzuya T, Yamashita N et al. Gamma-glutamylcysteine ethyl ester for myocardial protection in dogs during ischemia and reperfusion. J Am Coll Cardiol 1994; 24:1391-1397.
22. Hoshida S, Kuzuya T, Fuji H et al. Sublethal ischemia alters myocardial antioxidant activity in canine heart. Am J Physiol 1993; 264:H33-H39.
23. Abraham NG, Lin J H-C, Schwartzman ML et al. The physiological significance of heme oxygenase. Int J Biochem 1988; 20:543-558.
24. Applegate LA, Luscher P, Tyrrell RM. Induction of heme oxygenase: A general response to oxidant stress in cultured mammalian cells. Cancer Res 1991; 51:974-97.
25. Maulik N, Sharma HS, Das D K. Induction of the haem oxygenase gene expression during the reperfusion of ischemic rat myocardium. J Mol Cell Cardiol 1996; 28:1261-1270.
26. Aoki K, Hoshida S, Nishida M et al. Stimulus for stress protein induction under simulated ischemia/reperfusion in rat cardiac myocytes. Circulation 1997; 96(Suppl I):I- 312. (Abstract)
27. Muller A E, Cadenas E, Graf P et al. A novel biologically active seleno-organic compound. I. Glutathione peroxidase-like activity in-vitro and antioxidant capacity of PZ 51 (ebselen). Biochem Pharmacol 1984; 33:3235-3239.

28. Maiorino M, Roveri A, Ursini F. Antioxidant effect of ebselen (PZ 51): Peroxidase mimetic activity on phospholipid and cholesterol hydroperoxides vs. free radical scavenger activity. Arch. Biochem. Biophys 1992; 295:404-409.
29. Sies H. Ebselen, a selenoorganic compound as glutathione peroxidase mimic. Free Redical Biol Med 1993; 14:313-323.
30. Hoshida S, Aoki K, Nishida M et al. Effects of preconditioning with ebselen on glutathione metabolism and stress protein expression. J Pharmacol Exp Ther 1997; 281:1471-1475.
31. Kwok TT, Sutherland RM. The relationship between radiation response of human squamous carcinoma cells and specific metabolic changes induced by chronic hypoxia. Int J Radiat Oncol Biol Phys 1989; 16:1301-1305.
32. Dalvi RR, Robbins TJ. Comparative studies on the effect of cadmium, cobalt, lead, and selenium on hepatic microsomal monooxygenase enzymes and glutathione levels in mice. J Envir Path Toxic 1978; 1:601-607.
33. Eaton DL, Stacey NH, Wong KL et al. Dose-response effects of various metal ions on rat liver metallothionein, glutathione, heme oxygenase, and cytochrome p-450. Tox Appl Pharmacol 1980; 55:393-402.
34. Chung A-S, Maines MD. Effect of selenium on glutathione metabolism. Induction of r-glutamylcysteine synthetase and glutathione reductase in the rat liver. Biochem Pharmacol 1981; 30:3217-3223.
35. Esumi K, Nishida M, Shaw D et al. NADH measurements in adult rat myocytes during simulated ischemia. Am J Physiol 1991; 29:H1743-H1752.
36. Kuzuya T, Hoshida S, Yamashita N et al. Delayed effects of sublethal ischemia on the acquisition of tolerance to ischemia. Circ Res 1993; 72:1293-1299.
37. Sun J-Z, Tang X-L, Knowlton AA et al. Late preconditioning against myocardial stunning. An endogenous protective mechanism that confers resistance to postischemic dysfunction 24 h after brief ischemia in conscious pigs. J Clin Invest 1995; 95:388-403.
38. Brown JM , White CW, Terada LS et al. Interleukin 1 pretreatment decreases ischemia/reperfusion injury. Proc Natl Acad Sci USA 1990; 87:5026-5030.
39. Maulik N, Engelman R M, Wei Z et al. Interleukin-1a preconditioning reduces myocardial ischemia reperfusion injury. Circulation 1993; 88(Suppl II):387-394.
40. Yamashita N, Hoshida S, Taniguchi N et al. Whole-body hyperthermia provides biphasic cardioprotection against ischemia/reperfusion injury in the rat. Circulation 1998; 98:1414-1421.

CHAPTER 10

Physiological Role of Heat Shock Protein 27

Dipak K. Das and Nilanjana Maulik

Heat shock protein 27 (Hsp27) is a stress-inducible cytosolic protein that is ubiquitously present in many normal cells. The synthesis of Hsp27 is induced by heat shock and other environmental and pathophysiologic stresses such as UV radiation, hypoxia and ischemia.[1-4] Hsp27 is a member of small heat-shock protein family.[5] Besides its putative role in thermoresistance,[6] these proteins may be involved in the survival and recovery of the cells when exposed to stressful conditions.[7] A recent study demonstrated that Hsp27 may play a role in drug resistance.[8] However, the biological role of Hsp27 remains unknown. It is speculated that under stressful conditions, Hsp27 may act as energy-independent traps preventing irreversible protein aggregation. Following adaptation to stress, these proteins are refolded in cooperation with other chaperones.[9]

Several recent reports indicate that Hsp27 may be involved in signal transduction processes. For example, Hsp27 has been shown to play a role in tumor necrosis factor α (TNFα)-triggered signal transduction during oncoprotein-mediated neoplasticity.[10-12] Expression of Hsp27 or αβ-crystallin increased the intracellular level of gluthathione thereby enhancing the survival of cells following TNFα-treatment. Stress-mediated phosphorylation of specific serine residues in Hsp27 is believed to be involved in the coupling mechanism that regulates its biological function.[13] For example, Hsp27 was shown to be a physiological target for MAP (mitogen activated protein) kinase-activated protein (MAPKAP) kinase-2.[14,15]

Hsp27 was also shown to be involved in the regulation of apoptotic cell death.[16] Both Hsp27 and αβ-crystallin were found to protect the cells against necrosis as well as apoptosis.[12] In another related study, U937 and Wehi-s cells subjected to heat stress became resistant to apoptosis. The kinetics of the development of this resistance correlated with the kinetics of the Hsp synthesis. This received further support from the observation that transfection of Wehi-s cells with Hsp27 increased the resistance to apoptosis induced by actinomycin D, camptothesis or etoposide.[17]

Thus, a growing body of evidence is rapidly accumulating indicating a physiological role of Hsp27 in mammalian cells. The intention of this Chapter is to provide up-to-date information on the biological, physiological and molecular functions of Hsp27.

Hsp27: A Member of Small Hsp Family

The major Hsp's are classified into four protein families based on their molecular weights: the large molecular weight family [Hsp83—110KD]; Hsp70 family [Hsp66—79 KD]; Hsp60 family [Hsp60KD]; and the small Hsp family [Hsp's of less than 32 KD] (Table 10.1). To date, a single form of small Hsp is found in yeast and human cells and over 30 different forms found in plants. While much is known regarding the functions of Hsp70 families, only little is known

Heat Shock Proteins in Myocardial Protection, edited by Rakesh C. Kukreja and Michael L. Hess.

Table 10.1 Heat shock protein family

Family	Members	Known functions
Hsp90 Hsp89, Hsp90 Hsp110	Hsp83, Hsp87, polypeptides followed by escort to their specific location	Interaction with specific
Hsp70 Hsp72	Hsp 68, Hsp 70, in unfolded state thereby facilitating their translocation; cellular protection?	Maintenance of polypeptides
Hsp60	Hsp 58, Hsp60 in unfold state thereby facilitating their translocation	Maintenance of polypeptides
Small Hsp's Hsp22, Hsp23, Hsp25, Hsp27, Hsp32	Hsp 17, Hsp 18, function, Prevention of necrosis and apoptosis, Preservation of cytoskeletal structures, Role in drug resistance and tumor growth	Signal transduction, chaperone
Ubiquitin UB4	UB 1, UB 2, UB 3, with unfolded polypeptides for degradation	Conjugation followed by tagging

regarding the biological functions of small Hsp's. In contrast to well known Hsp70 family, the multiplicity of small Hsp's is variable between organisms. However, despite of the heterogeneity, these can be grouped under the Hsp20 family. Multiple small Hsp's are found in *Drosophila*, *Dictyostelium*, *Xenopus* and most of the plants.[18-21] To the contrary, single small Hsp's are found in yeasts (Hsp26), avians (Hsp24) or mammalian cells (Hsp27).

Hsp27 is closely related to αβ-crystallin and like other Hsp's engaged in protein-protein interactions. This protein is ubiquitously present in mammalian cells and plant cells (Hsp25) and induced several-fold in response to heat stress. Besides heat stress, a number of environmental stresses including oxidative stress also induce the expression of Hsp27.[22] All members of Hsp20 family contain a single 35 to 37 amino acid residue conserved domain for all proteins.[23] In the C-terminal part of all the genes encoding small Hsp's, a 36 amino acid residue sequence element is remarkably conserved.

Heat Shock Response: Thermoresistance and Increased Tolerance to Stress

Like other Hsp's, the most common inducer of Hsp27 is heat shock. The synthesis of this Hsp is also induced by other environmental and pathophysiologic stresses such as UV radiation, metals, and growth hormones.[1] The increased expression of Hsp27 is associated with thermotolerance, and increased ability to survive and tolerate stressful conditions. Phosphorylation is the primary step for the biochemical action of Hsp27. Following heat shock, Hsp is rapidly phosphorylated which is also accompanied by its nuclear translocation. Phosphorylation also occurs in unstressed cells upon stimulation with mitogens, cytokines or inducers of differentiation.[24] Increased expression of Hsp27 has been correlated with an increased stability of stress fibers during hyperthermia.[25]

Physiological Functions of Hsp27

As mentioned earlier, the physiological role of Hsp27 remains largely unknown. The primary function of this Hsp is thought to be regulation of structure, intracellular transport and secretion of other proteins.[1,7] This protein is also involved in the regulation of cell proliferation thereby acting as a molecular chaperone.[26] Besides rendering the cells heat resistant, Hsp27 also plays a role in drug resistance[8] and growth of certain tumors.[27] Hsp27 may be involved in preserving cytoskeletal proteins and thus, renders the cells tolerant to stress-induced structural damage.[28] It can make the cells resistant to hypoxic and ischemic injury caused by necrosis as well as apoptosis. Finally, evidence is rapidly accumulating in support of its role in signal transduction.

Role in Preservation of Cytoskeletal Structures

The most important factor for the physiological response of Hsp27 is probably the phosphorylation of the protein in response to stress and growth stimulation. This protein becomes phosphorylated after cells are stimulated by environmental stress or tyrosine kinase receptor-mediated growth factors and cytokines.[29] Phosphorylation of Hsp27 is catalyzed by MAPKAP kinase-2 and dephosphorylation by a protein phosphatase of the 2B type.[28] Actin polymerization-inhibiting activity of Hsp27 was first demonstrated using turkey small heat shock protein. Using Chinese hamster cell lines that constitutively overexpress either human phosphorylatable wild type Hsp27 or a non-phosphorylatable mutant form, it was shown that the wild type protein enhances while the mutant protein inhibits, growth factor-induced F-actin accumulation.[27] A more recent study demonstrated that the actin polymerization-inhibiting activity of the murine Hsp25 is dependent on the degree of its phosphorylation and structural organization.[28]

Phosphorylation of Hsp27 induced by stress is accompanied by its translocation from the cytoplasm to within or around the nucleus.[25] It has been suggested that Hsp27 behaves in vitro as an actin-capping protein and can function as a regulator of actin polymerization.[32] The protective function exerted by Hsp27 in stressed cells is believed to be due to phosphorylation-activated function of Hsp27 at the level of actin filament.[31,32] Phosphorylation of Hsp27 is likely to be accompanied by a change in the conformation of this protein, resulting in the dissociation of Hsp27 from the barbed (+) end of actin filaments.[30,32] The authors proposed that local phosphorylation of Hsp27 could regulate the spatial organization of F-actin by freeing barbed ends of microfilaments for addition of monomers.

Role in Tumor Growth

Several lines of evidence exist in the literature to indicate that expression of Hsp27 may be of some prognostic value in breast carcinomas,[33-35] in uterine carcinomas[36] and in gastric neoplasms.[37] Several intracranial tumors also express Hsp27.[38-40] Immunohistochemical detection revealed high expression of Hsp27 in tumors originating from both meningiomas and neuroepithelium.[41-43] In another recent study, the expression of Hsp27 was detected in 95 supratentorial astrocytic tumors of which 76 were previously untreated and 19 were previously treated.[27]

Increased constitutive levels of Hsp27 were found to be associated with decreased growth rates in Ehrlich ascites tumor cells, human B lymphocytes, osteoblasts and promyelocytic leukemia cells.[44] To the contrary, testis tumor cells were more sensitive to heat shock and expressed low levels of Hsp27.[45] Overexpression of Hsp27 increased the resistance of testis tumor cells to heat and chemotherapeutic drugs[46] suggesting that the sensitivity of testis tumors to heat stress may be accounted for by their low levels of constitutive expression of Hsp27.

Development of Drug Resistance

Increased expression of Hsp27 in cancer cells causes the development of chemotherapeutic drug resistance. Transfection of Chinese hamster ovary cells with Hsp27 gene developed resistance to drugs such as doxorubicin, colchicine and vincristine.[8] Increased expression Hsp27 induced by heat stress also renders the cells resistant to doxorubicin and actinomycin D.[47-49] Conversely, downregulation of Hsp27 in breast cancer cell line MCF-7/MG with antisense-Hsp27 enhanced the sensitivity of the cells to doxorubicin.[49] Recently, the effect of Hsp27 overexpression on the drug sensitivity of a human testis tumor cell line was examined.[44] Cells were cotransfected with plasmids containing a neomycin resistance gene and the full-length human Hsp27 gene, and four clones that overexpressed Hsp27 by factors of 3.7- to 38.3-fold compared with the parental cells were selected. The overexpressing cells were more resistant to heat shock, cisplatin, and doxorubicin, and this was associated with modest increases in population doubling times and a small reduction in the number of S-phase cells.[44]

Role in Ischemia/Reperfusion

A number of studies have shown that heat shock pretreatment is associated with reduction of myocardial ischemia/reperfusion injury. For example, heat shock resulted in significant infarct size reduction after prolonged coronary artery occlusion and reperfusion in the in vivo rat model.[50] Heat shock also ameliorated ischemia/reperfusion injury in isolated rat heart.[51] Another recent study has demonstrated a direct correlation between the amount of heat-shock protein induced and the degree of myocardial protection.[52] A recent study from our own laboratory showed that heat shock using warm blood cardioplegia resulted in significant myocardial protection during the reperfusion of ischemic swine heart.[53] Interestingly, all of these studies also demonstrated the induction of the expression of Hsp70. Diverse stresses including ischemia, ischemic preconditioning, and oxidative stress can induce the expression of Hsp70 mRNA simultaneously providing significant cardioprotection. Based on these findings, it was assumed that the induction of Hsp70 plays a significant role in myocardial protection. The results of two recent studies showed that hearts of transgenic mice overexpressing Hsp70 were more resistant to myocardial ischemia/reperfusion injury.[54,55]

While a great deal is known about Hsp70 and Hsp90 families, relatively little is known regarding the smaller Hsp's such as Hsp27. A number of studies from different laboratories demonstrated the induction of the expression of Hsp27 mRNA in the mammalian hearts after ischemia and reperfusion. For example, in a preconditioned pig heart model where the left anterior descending coronary artery was occluded for two periods of 10 min, separated by 30 min of reperfusion, a significant increase in Hsp27 mRNA level was found after the first occlusion which became 2- to 3- fold during 30 min of the first and second reperfusion periods.[56] During the prolonged reperfusion following the second occlusion, the Hsp27 mRNA levels in stunned tissue remained significantly raised. The authors also observed increased levels of Hsp27 mRNA in the adjacent non-stunned myocardium. This was significant during 30 min of the second reperfusion period as compared to sham operated animals. In another study using preconditioned isolated rat heart model where hearts were preconditioned either by 5 min of ischemia followed by 10 min of reperfusion (1 x PC) or repeating this process for four times (4 x PC), our own laboratory found the enhanced induction for the expression of Hsp27 mRNA only in the 4 X PC hearts.[57]

Recently, we have shown that both oxidative and heat stresses rapidly activated p38 MAPK and MAPKAP kinase-2 leading to the phosphorylation of heat shock protein (Hsp) 27.[58] To further define the role of MAPKAP kinase-2 in ischemia/reperfusion-mediated stress signaling pathway, we used a specific blocker of tyrosine kinase, genistein as well as a blocker for p38MAPK, SKF prior to ischemia and reperfusion. The results of our study demonstrated that stress induced by repeated ischemia/reperfusion resulted in the induction of the expression of Hsp27 which

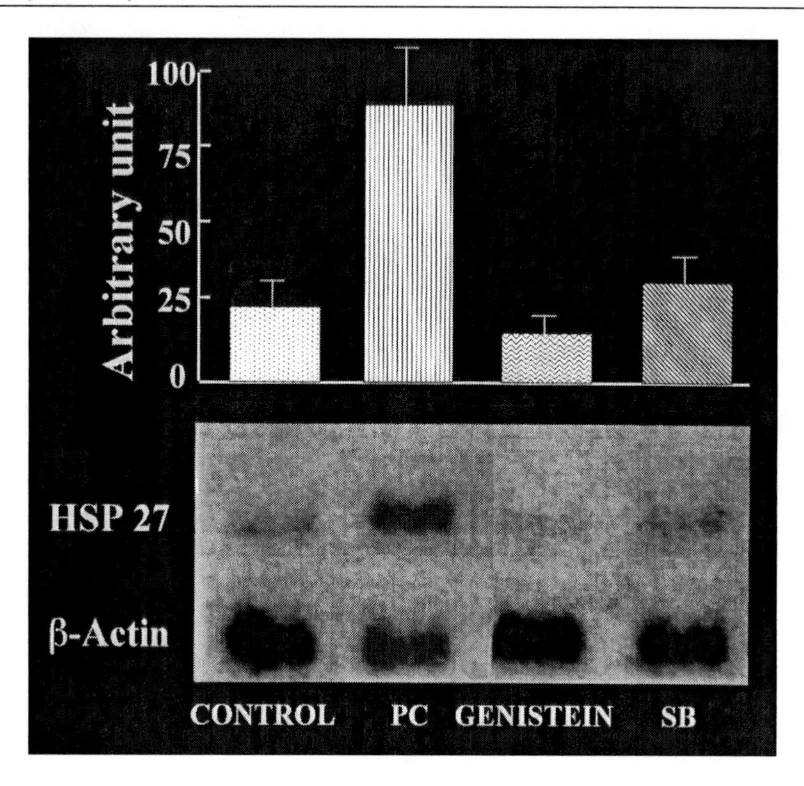

Fig. 10.1. Induction of the expression of Hsp27 by ischemic preconditioning and its inhibition by genistein and SKF. The blot was first probed with [^{32}P] Hsp27 cDNA, and then the same blot was stripped and re-probed with [^{32}P] β-actin cDNA. Lane 1: control; Lane 2: preconditioned; Lane 3: Genistein; Lane 4:SB The results of densitometric scanning (means ±SEM) for six different experiments for each time point are shown in bar graph above the Northern blot.

was blocked by both genistein and SKF suggesting a role of p38MAPK-MAPKAP kinase-2 signaling pathway in myocardial adaptation to stress (Fig. 10.1).

Hsp27 and Apoptosis

Recently, Hsp27 was found to be the negative regulator of apoptosis, programmed cell death. Apoptotic cell death is distinct from necrosis in the respect that apoptosis is associated with cell shrinkage, chromatin condensation and DNA fragmentation.[59,60] For example, an increased cellular level of Hsp27 was found to reduce apoptosis induced by actinomycin D, camptothecin and etoposide.[17,61] In this study, U937 and Wehi's cells were divided into two groups-control and heat shock. The cells were treated with the above-mentioned drugs to induce apoptosis. Wehi's cells were transfected with human Hsp27 genes. The cells exhibiting overexpression of Hsp27 were resistant to apoptosis. Another related study demonstrated that constitutive expression of human Hsp27 in murine L929 cells blocked Fas/APO-1-mediated apoptotic cell death.[16] Expression of Hsp27 prevented anti-APO-1-induced DNA fragmentation and morphological changes characteristic of apoptosis indicating that Hsp27 acts as a cellular inhibitor of Fas/APO-1-induced apoptosis. Constitutive expression of human Hsp27 and αβ-crystalline in L929 cells blocked staurosporine-induced apoptosis.

Hsp27 in Signal Transduction

In a recent study, our laboratory has found that Hsp25/27 is a major substrate for MAPKAP kinase-2 in rat cardiac myocytes.[62,63] In this study, MAPKAP kinase-2 proteins were fractionated from cultured H9c2 cells, and then phosphorylated in vitro with an active recombinant mutant MAPKAP kinase-2 (T334A). Phosphorylated proteins were then separated on SDS-PAGE and analyzed by autoradiography. Protein phosphorylation analysis indicated that MAPKAP kinase-2 significantly stimulated the phosphorylation of the 25 kDa cytosolic protein derived from rat cardiac myocytes. Furthermore, myocardial Hsp25 isolated from the cytosolic fraction of H9c2 cells using specific antibody, after immunoprecipitation, phosphorylation by the active recombinant MAPKAP kinase-2, separation by SDS-PAGE, and detection of the induced protein phosphorylation by autoradiography, revealed that myocardial Hsp25 was phosphorylated by MAPKAP kinase-2, and had a similar mobility on SDS-PAGE as the kinase-induced 25 kDa phosphoprotein derived from rat cardiac myocytes. This suggests that myocardial Hsp25/27 is a major substrate for MAPKAP kinase-2 in rat cardiac myocytes. Heat shock, oxidative stress and PMA—all stimulated the Hsp25 phosphorylation in the cardiac myocytes.

In a recent study, the enzymatic activity of tissue MAPKAP kinase-2 was examined with an in vitro protein phosphorylation assay using human recombinant Hsp27 as a specific substrate and the resultant autoradiograph is shown in Figure 10.2.[64] Preconditioning and/or ischemic stress of isolated rat hearts induced the tissue MAPKAP kinase-2 activation (lanes 2 and 3), which resulted from the p38 MAP kinase activation (lanes 2 and 3). The induced activation of MAPKAP kinase-2 was completely inhibited by genistein and SB 203580 (lanes 4 and 5). These results indicate that preconditioning and/or ischemic stress stimulate myocardial MAPKAP kinase-2 and the phosphorylation of Hsp27. The induced activation of MAPKAP kinase-2 and Hsp27 can be blocked by inhibition of tissue p38 MAP kinase with genistein and SB 203580.

Studies from other laboratories also support the role of Hsp27 in signal transduction. For example, an inhibitor of p38 MAP kinase was shown to suppress the activation of MAPKAP kinase-2 which in turn prevented the phosphorylation of Hsp27 in response to IL-1.[14] The results of this study indicated that Hsp27 is a physiological target for MAPKAP kinase-2 because the stimuli which activated MAPKAP kinase-2 also promoted the phosphorylation of Hsp27, and SB 203580, which prevented the activation of MAPKAP kinase-2 by each agonist, also blocked the phosphorylation of Hsp27 in vivo. The role of phosphorylation of Hsp27 is not clearly understood, but available evidence supports the notion that it promotes actin polymerization thereby counteracting the disruptive effects of stress on actin microfilament structure.[33]

It should be clear from the above discussion that both stress and mitogen stimulation result in the phosphorylation of the same serine residues and the phosphorylation is catalyzed by the same protein kinase.[65] This would tend to suggest that both growth and stress response may share the same signal transduction pathway via Hsp27. Following translocation and phosphorylation, cells readily rearrange their actin filaments leading the development of adaptive response. Indeed, disruption of the cytoskeleton and disaggregation of actin fibers comprise the immediate stress response and stability of actin filaments is the primary factor for the cellular adaptation to stress.

Cross-Talk with Oxidative Stress-Inducible Proteins

As mentioned earlier, after a heat shock, Hsp is rapidly phosphorylated and then its synthesis is enhanced. Such enhancement not only rendered the cells resistant to subsequent heat stress, but also made them more resistant to oxidative stress.[66] TGF-β1 was found to inhibit DNA synthesis in mouse osteoblastic cells in parallel with the phosphorylation of Hsp27[67] and that the effects of both events were abolished by catalase.[68] A recent study demonstrated that

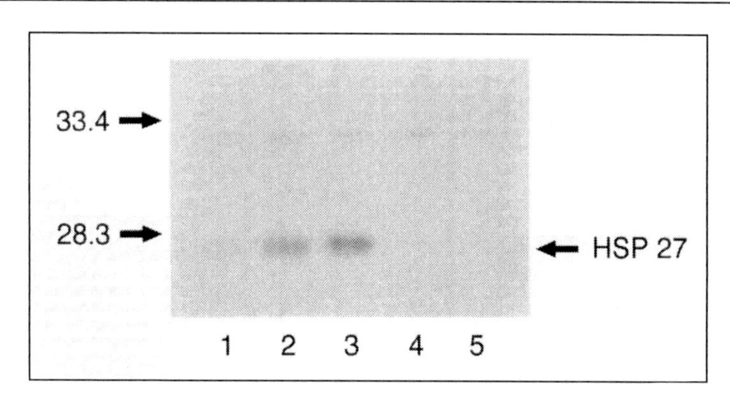

Fig. 10.2. Enzymatic activity assay of myocardial MAPKAP kinase-2. MAPKAP kinase-2 activity was evaluated using an in vitro protein phosphorylation assay with recombinant Hsp27 as the specific substrate. The phosphorylated proteins were separated on 11% SDS-PAGE and an autoradiograph is shown. Molecular weight standards are shown on the left. The position of phosphorylated Hsp27 is indicated on the right. A myocardial protein was phosphorylated in vitro and used as an internal marker to monitor equal protein amounts in each reactions. These results are representative of three similar experiments per group. Lane 1: control (Group I); Lane 2: preconditioned (Group II); Lane 3: preconditioned followed by 30 min ischemia and 2 hr reperfusion; Lane 4: 15 min reperfusion in presence of SB 203580 followed by preconditioning, 30 min ischemia and 2 hr reperfusion (Group IV); Lane 5: 15 min reperfusion in presence of genistein followed by preconditioning, 30 min ischemia and 2 hr reperfusion (Group V).

constitutively high expression of Hsp27 in the immortalized human fibroblast cell line, KMST-6, made them susceptible to oxidative stress resulting in growth arrest, and further suggested that this mechanism could involve the phosphorylation of Hsp27.[69]

Hsp27 gene expression was found when isolated rat hearts were subjected to oxidative stress induced by interleukin-1α (IL-1α).[22] In biological systems including heart, cytokines such as IL-1α and tissue necrosis factor (TNF) potentiate generation of oxygen free radicals. In this study, IL-1α induced the expression of Hsp27 mRNA within 2 hr and Hsp protein after 48 hours. The hearts pretreated with IL-1α for 48 hours and then subjected to 30 min of ischemia followed by 30 min of reperfusion showed increased tolerance to ischemia/reperfusion injury. In another related study, heat shock was induced by injecting the pigs with amphetamine and after 40 hr, the isolated in situ pig hearts were subjected to 1 hr of LAD occlusion followed by 1 hr of global hypothermic cardioplegic arrest and 1 hr of normothermic reperfusion.[4] Such heat shock was associated with the enhanced induction of the Hsp27 mRNA in the hearts in concert with the reduction of post-ischemic myocardial injury.[70] These hearts demonstrated reduction in oxidative stress in conjunction with increased tolerance to ischemia/reperfusion injury.

Clinical Significance

It should be clear from the above discussion that Hsp27 plays an important role in drug resistance as well as in the control of cell proliferation and growth. Thus, the detection of Hsp27 in tumor cells should be of prognostic value and may represent an useful clinical tool for establishing treatment for some specific tumors. Transition to the diuretic as well as to the antidiuretic state induced Hsp25 phosphorylation in the outer and inner medulla.[71] Further evidence for the involvement of Hsp25 in osmoregulatory processes can be found from the observation that a 2-fold increase of papillary Hsp25 mRNA occurred after 2 days of water restriction.[72] Finally, recent findings of the role of Hsp27 in the prevention of both necrotic and apoptotic cell death are of great clinical significance.

Summary and Conclusion

It should be clear from this review that the precise function of Hsp27 remains unclear, but the primary function of this protein is believed to be in embryogenesis, growth regulation and differentiation.[73] During progressive differentiation of rat osteoblasts and promyelocytic leukemia cells, the Hsp27 mRNA expression is increased with corresponding downregulation of proliferation.[47] In both normal and neoplastic human B lymphocytes, Hsp27 serves as a marker for growth arrest.[74] A recent study described a role of Hsp27 in controlling the growth rate of endothelial cells in an estrogen-responsive manner.[75]

There is some evidence that Hsp27 may function as a molecular chaperone.[5] For example, Hsp27 has been localized in different intracellular compartments. It is able to bind other proteins thereby affecting the protein assembly, and has been found to participate in protein degradation. More importantly, Hsp27 possesses a serine protease-like active site that is instrumental in regulating *Drosophila* development. Evidence also exists to show that Hsp27 may prevent aggregation and promote functional refolding of denatured proteins, because the expression of Hsp25/Hsp27 was found to be associated with an ATP-dependent increase in refolding of denatured substrate proteins, and prevent protein aggregation in in vitro systems.

The most striking feature of Hsp27 is probably the fact that it is phosphorylated in response to stress.[76,77] Hsp27 was showed to be involved in the modulation of actin microfilament dynamics and smooth muscle contraction.[78] Transfection of Chinese hamster cells with the human Hsp27 gene inhibited the disappearance of microfilaments commonly observed after heat shock. The signal transduction process is likely to involve tyrosine kinase and MAP kinases, especially MAPKAP kinase-2 (Fig. 10.3). It has been proposed that phosphorylation causes a change in the conformation of Hsp27 protein resulting in its dissociation from the barbed end of actin filaments. In this process, the actin filaments become free for the addition of monomers leading to polymerization. It is tempting to speculate that diverse stress signals including oxidative stress, heat shock and ischemia/reperfusion cause phosphorylation of Hsp27 leading to substantial reorganization of the cytoskeleton and modulation of actin-containing filaments. Induction of Hsp27 in response to these stresses simply reflect the adaptive response for survival in the stressful environment.

Acknowledgments

This work was supported by National Institute of Health Grants HL 22559, HL 33889, HL 34360, HL 56803, and a Grant-in-Aid from the American Heart Association.

References

1. Schlesinger MJ. Heat shock proteins. J. Biol Chem 1990; 265:12111-12114.
2. Jakob U, Gaestel M, Engel K et al. Small heat shock proteins are molecular chaperons. J. Biol Chem 1993; 268:1517-1520.
3. Morimoto RI, Tissieres C, Georgopoulos C. The Stress Response, Function of the Proteins, and Perspectives. In: Stress Proteins in Biology and Medicine (R. Morimoto, A. Tissieres, C. Georgopoulos eds), Cold Spring Harbor Laboratory Press, New York, 1990:1-36.
4. Maulik N, Wei Z, Liu X et al. Improved postischemic ventricular functional recovery by amphetamine is linked with its ability to induce heat shock. Mol Cell Biochem.1994; 137:17-24.
5. Ciocca DR, Oesterreich S, Chamness GC et al. Biological and clinical implications of heat shock protein 27000 (Hsp27): a review. J. Natl Cancer Inst. 1993; 85:1558-1570.
6. Landry J, Chretien P, Lambert H et al. Heat shock resistance conferred by expression of the human Hsp27 gene in rodent cells. J. Cell Biol 1989; 109:7-15.

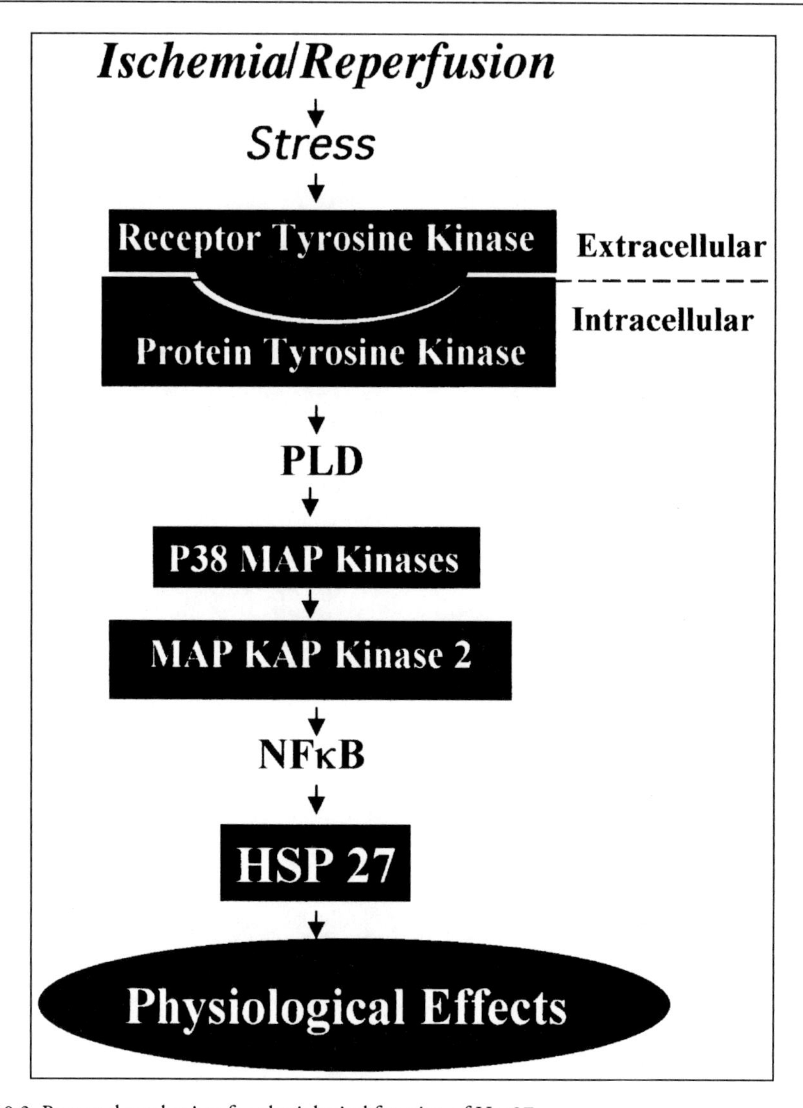

Fig. 10.3. Proposed mechanism for physiological function of Hsp27.

7. Hightower LE. Heat shock, stress proteins, chaperones, and proteotoxicity. Cell 1991; 66:191-197.
8. Huot J, Roy G, Lambert H et al. Increased survival after treatments with anticancer agents of Chinese hamster cells expressing the human Mr 27,000 heat shock protein. Cancer Res 1991; 51:5245-5252.
9. Lee GJ, Roseman AM, Saibil HR et al. A small heat shock protein stably binds heat-denatured model substrates and can maintain a substrate in a folding component state. EMBO J 1997; 16:659-671.
10. Aoyama A, Frohli E, Schäfer R, Klemenz R. αβ-crystallin expression in mouse NIH 3T3 fibroblasts: Glucocorticoid responsiveness and involvement in thermal protection. Mol Cell Biol 1993; 13:1824-1835.
11. Klemenz R, Frohli E, Steiger RH et al. Alpha β-crystallin is a small heat shock protein. Proc Natl Acad Sci, USA. 1991; 88:3652-3656.

12. Mehlen P, Preville X, Chareyron P et al. Constitutive expression of human Hsp27, *Drosophila* Hsp27, or human alpha B-crystallin confers resistance to TNF-α and oxidative stress induced cytotoxicity in stably transfected murine L929 fibroblasts. J. Immunol 1995; 154:363-369.
13. Mehlen P, Mehlen A, Guillet D et al. Tumor necrosis factor alpha induces changes in the phosphorylation, cellular localization, and oligomerization of human hsp27, a stress protein that confers cellular resistance to this cytokine. J. Cell Biochem 1995; 58:248-259.
14. Cuenda A, Rouse J, Doza YN et al. SB 203580 is a specific inhibitor of a MAP kinase homologue which is stimulated by cellular stresses and interleukin-1. FEBS Lett 1995; 364:229-233.
15. Maulik N, Watanabe M, Zu YL et al. Ischemic preconditioning triggers the activation of MAP kinases and MAPKAP kinase-2 in rat hearts. FEBS Lett 1996; 396:233-237.
16. Mehlen P, Schulze-Osthoff K, Arrigo AP. Small stress proteins as novel regulators of apoptosis. J. Biol Chem 1996; 271:16510-16514.
17. Samali A, Cotter TG. Heat shock proteins increase resistance to apoptosis. Exp Cell Res 1996; 223:163-170.
18. Ayme A, Tissieres A. Locus 67B of *Drosophila* melanogaster contains seven, not four, closely related heat shock genes. EMBO J 1985; 4:2949-2954.
19. Loomis WF, Wheeler S. Chromain-associated heat shock proteins in *Dictyostellium*. Dev. Biol. 1982; 90:412-418.
20. Darasch S, Mosser DD, Bols NC et al. Heat shock gene expression in *Xenopus laevis* A6 cells in response to heat shock and sodium arsenite. Biochem Cell Biol 1988; 66:862-870.
21. Mansfield MA, Key JL. Synthesis of low molecular weight heat shock proteins in plants. Plant Physiol 1987; 84:1007-1017.
22. Maulik N, Engelman RM, Wei Z et al. Interleukin-1α preconditioning reduces myocardial ischemia reperfusion injury. Circulation 1993; 88 (part II):387-394.
23. Neuman D, Nover L, Parthier B et al. Heat shock and other stress response systems of plants. Biol Zentralbl. 1989; 108:1-156.
24. Arrigo AP, Landry J. Expression and function of the low molecular-weight heat shock proteins, In R.I.Morimoto, A. Tissieres and C. Georgopoulos eds. The biology of heat shock proteins and molecular chaperones. Cold Spring Harbor, N.Y. 1993:335-373.
25. Lavoie JN, Gingras-Breton G, Tanguay RM et al. Induction of Chinese hamster Hsp27 gene expression in mouse cells confers resistance to heat shock Hsp27 stabilization of the microfilament organization. J. Biol Chem 1993; 268:3420-3429.
26. Pechan PM. Heat shock proteins and cell proliferation. FEBS Lett. 1991; 280:1-4.
27. Assimakopoulou M, Sotiropoulou-Bonikou G, Maraziotis T et al. Prognostic significance of Hsp27 in astrocyte brain tumors: An immunohistochemical study. Anticancer Res 1997; 17:2677-2682.
28. Gaestel M, Benndorf R, Haye K et al. Dephosphorylation of the small heat shock protein hsp25 by calcium/calmodulin-dependent (type 2B) protein phosphatase. J Biol Chem 1992; 267: 21607-21611.
29. Guesdon F, Freshney N, Waller RJ et al. Interleukin-1 and tumor necrosis factor stimulate two novel protein kinases that phosphorylate the heat shock protein Hsp27 and beta-casein. J Biol Chem 1993; 268:4236-4243.
30. Lavoie JN, Hickey E, Weber LA et al. Modulation of actin microfilament dynamics and fluid phase pinocytosis by phosphorylation of heat shock protein 27. J Biol Chem 1993; 268:24210-24214.
31. Benndorf R, Hayeb K, Ryazantsev S et al. Phosphorylation and supramolecular organization of murine small heat shock protein Hsp25 abolish its actin polymerization-inhibiting activity. J Biol Chem 1994; 269:20780-20784.
32. Lavoie JN, Lambert H, Hickey E et al. Modulation of cellular thermoresistance and actin filament stability accompanies phosphorylation-induced changes in the oligomeric structure of heat shock protein 27. Mol Cell Biol 1995; 15:505-516.
33. Love S, King RJB. A 27Kda heat shock protein has anomalous prognostic powers in early and advanced breast cancer. Br J Cancer 1994; 69:743-748.
34. Seymour L, Bezwoda WR, Meyer K. Tumor factors predicting for prognosis in metastatic breast cancer. The presence of p24 predicts for response to treatment and duration of survival. Cancer 1990; 66:2390-2394.

35. Thor A, Benz C, Moore II D et al. Stress responsive protein (srp27) determination in primary human breast carcinomas: clinical, histologic and prognostic correlations. J Natl Cancer Inst 1991; 83:170-178.
36. Puy LA, LoCastro G, Olcese JE et al. Analysis of a 24-kilodalton (KD) protein in the human uterine cervix during abnormal growth. Cancer 1989; 64:1067-1073.
37. Harrison JD, Jones JA, Ellis IO et al. Oestrogen receptor D5 antibody is an independent negative prognostic factor in gastric cancer. Br J Surgery 1991; 78:334-336.
38. Hitotsumatsu T, Iwaki T, Fukui M et al. Distinctive immunohistochemical profiles of small heat shock proteins (Heat Shock Protein 27 and αβ-Crystallin) in human Brain Tumors. Cancer 1996; 77:352-361.
39. Kato M, Herz F, Kato S et al. Expression of stress-responsive (heat shock) protein 27 in human brain tumors: An immunohistochemical study. Acta Neuropathol 1992; 83:420-422.
40. Khalid H, Yasunaga A, Kishikawa M et al. Immunohistochemical expression of the estrogen receptor-related antigen (ER-D5) in human intracranial tumors. Cancer 1995; 75:2571-2578.
41. Yokoyama N, Iwaki T, Goldman JE et al. Small heat shock protein is expressed in meningiomas and in granulofilamentous inclusion bodies. Acta Neuropathol Berl 1993; 85:248-255.
42. Richards EH, Hickey E, Weber L et al. Effect of overexpression of the small heat shock protein Hsp27 on the heat and drug sensitivities of human testis tumor cells. Cancer Res 1996; 56:2446-2451.
43. Knauf U, Bielka H, Gaestel M. Overexpression of the small heat shock protein, Hsp25, inhibits growth of Ehrlich ascites tumor cells. FEBS Lett. 1992; 309:297-302.
44. Spector NL, Samson W, Ryan C et al. Growth arrest of human B lymphocytes is accompanied by induction of the low molecular weight mammalian heat shock protein (Hsp28). J Immunol 1992; 148:1668-1673.
45. Shakoori AR, Oberdorf AM, Owen TA et al. Expression of heat shock genes during differentiation of mammalian osteoblasts and promyelocytic leukemia cells. J Cell Biochem 1992; 48:277-287.
46. Richards EH, Hickman JA, Masters JRW. Heat shock protein expression in testis and bladder cancer cell lines exhibiting differential sensitivity to heat. Br J Cancer 1995; 72:620-626.
47. Wallner K, Li GC. Adriamycin resistance, heat resistance and radiation response in Chinese hamster fibroblasts. Int J Radiat Oncol Biol Phys 1986; 12:829-833.
48. Ciocca DR, Fuqua SAW, Lock-Lim S et al. Response of human breast cancer cells to heat shock and chemotherapeutic drugs. Cancer Res 1992; 52:3648-3654.
49. Oesterreich S, Weng CN, Qui M et al. The small heat shock protein Hsp27 is correlated with growth and drug resistance in human breast cancer cell lines. Cancer Res 1993; 53:4443-4448.
50. Donnelly TJ, Sievers RE, Visseren FLJ et al. Heat shock protein induction in rat hearts: A role for improved myocardial salvage after ischemia and reperfusion? Circulation 1992; 85:769-778.
51. Currie RW, Karmazyn M, Kloc M et al. Heat shock response is associated with enhanced post-ischemic ventricular recovery. Circ Res 1988; 63:543-549.
52. Hutter MM, Sievers RE, Barbosa V et al. Heat shock protein induction in rat hearts. A direct correlation between the amount of heat-shock protein induced and the degree of myocardial protection. Circulation. 1994; 89:355-360.
53. Liu X, Engelman RM, Moraru II et al. Heat shock: A new approach for myocardial preservation in cardiac surgery. Circulation. 1992; 86 (suppl II):358-363.
54. Plumier JCL, Ross BM, Currie RW et al. Transgenic mice expressing the human heat shock protein-70 have improved post-ischemic myocardial recovery. J. Clin Invest. 1995; 95:1854-1860.
55. Marber MS, Mestril R, Chi S-H et al. Overexpression of the rat inducible 70-kD heat stress protein in a transgenic mouse increses the resistance of the heart to ischemic injury. J Clin Invest 1995; 95:1446-1456.
56. Andres J, Sharma HS, Knoll R et al. Expression of heat shock proteins in the normal and stunned porcine myocardium. Cardiovasc. Res 1993; 27:1421-1429.
57. Das DK, Engelman RM, Kimura Y. Molecular adaptation of cellular defences following preconditioning of the heart by repeated ischemia. Cardiovasc Res 1993; 27:578-584.
58. Das DK, Maulik N, Engelman RM et al. Signal transduction pathway leading to Hsp27 and Hsp70 gene expression during myocardial adaptation to stress. Annals NY Acad Sci 1998; 851:129-138.

59. Maulik N, Kagan V, Das DK. Redistribution of phosphatidylserine and phosphatidyl-ethanolamine precedes reperfusion-induced apoptosis. Am J. Physiol 1998; 274:H242-H248.
60. Maulik N, Yoshida T, Das DK. Oxidative stress developed during the reperfusion of ischemic myocardium induces apoptosis. Free Radical Biol Med 1998; 24:869-875.
61. Amici C, Rossi A, Santoro MG. Aspirin enhances thermotolerance in human erythroleukemic cells: An effect associated with the modulation of the heat shock response. Cancer Res 1995; 55:4452-4457.
62. Das D.K. Intracellular signaling mechanisms in delayed preconditioning. In: Baxter G, Yellon D eds), Delayed Preconditioning and Adaptive Cardioprotection, Kluwer Academic Publishers, The Netherlands. 1998.
63. Das D.K., Maulik N. Tyrosine and MAP kinase regulation of Hsp gene expression in ischemically adapted hearts. In: (Singal P ed) Adaptation Biology and Medicine, Volume 2, Narosa Publishing House. 1998.
64. Maulik N, Yoshida T, Zu Y-L et al. Ischemic preconditioning triggers tyrosine kinase signaling: A potential role for MAPKAP kinase-2. Am J Physiol 1998; 275:H1857-H1864.
65. Stokoe D, Engel K, Campbell DG et al. Identification of MAPKAP kinase-2 as a major enzyme responsible for the phosphorylation of the small mammalian heat shock proteins. FEBS Lett 1992; 313:307-313.
66. Mehlen P, Briolay J, Smith L et al. Analysis of the resistance to heat and hydrogen peroxide stress in Cos cells transiently expressing wild type or deletion mutants of the Drosophila 27-kDa heat shock protein. Eur J. Biochem. 1993; 215:277-284.
67. Shibanuma M, Kuroki T, Nose K. Cell cycle dependent phosphorylation of Hsp28 by TGF-β_1 and H_2O_2 in normal mouse osteoblastic cells (MC_3T_3-E_1), but not in their ras-transformants. Biochem Biophys Res Commun 1992; 187:1418-1425.
68. Nose K, Ohba M, Shibanuma M, Kuroki T. Involvement of hydrogen peroxide in the actions of TGF-β1. In: Oxidative stress, cell activation and viral infection. C. Pasquier, R.Y.Oliver, C. Auclair and L. Packer, eds. Birkhauser Verlag, Basel, Switzerland, 1994:21-34.
69. Arata S, Hamaguchi S, Nose K. Effects of the overexpression of the small heat shock protein, Hsp27, on the sensitivity of human fibroblast cells exposed to oxidative stress. J Cell Physiol 1995; 163:458-465.
70. Maulik N, Engelman RM, Wei Z et al. Drug-induced heat-shock preconditioning improves post-ischemic ventricular recovery after cardiopulmonary bypass. Circulation 1995; 92 (suppl II):381-388.
71. Muller E, Neuhofer W, Burger-Kentischer A et al. Effects of long-term changes in medullary osmolality on heat shock proteins Hsp25, Hsp60, Hsp72 and Hsp73 in the rat kidney. Pflugers Arch 1988;435:705-712.
72. Medina R, Cantley L, Spokes K, Epstein FH. Effect of water diuresis and water restriction on expression of Hsp27, -60 and -70 in rat kidney. Kidney Int. 1996; 50:1191-1194.
73. Zhou M, Lambert H, Landry J. Transient activation of a distinct serine protein kinase is responsible for 27 kDa heat shock protein phosphorylation in mitogen-stimulated and heat-shocked cells. J Biol Chem 1993; 268:35-43.
74. Spector NL, Samson W, Ryan C et al. Growth arrest of human B lymphocytes is accompanied by induction of the low molecular weight mammalian heat shock protein (Hsp28). J Immunol 1992; 148:1668-1673.
75. Piotrowicz R, Weber LA, Hickey E et al. Accelerated growth and senescence of arterial endothelial cells expressing the small molecular weight heat-shock protein Hsp27. FASEB J 1995; 9:1079-1084.
76. Santell L, Bartfel N, Levin E. Identification of a protein transiently phosphorylated by activators of endothelial cell function as the heat shock protein Hsp27. Biochem J 1992; 284:705-710.
77. Gaestel M, Schroder W, Benndorf R et al. Identification of the phosphorylation sites of the murine small heat shock protein Hsp25. J. Biol Chem 1991; 266:14721-14724.
78. Bitar K, Kaminski M, Hailat N et al. Hsp27 is a mediator of sustained smooth muscle contraction in response to bombesin. Biochem Biophys Res Commun 1991; 181:1192-1200.

CHAPTER 11

Ischemia/Reperfusion Injury and Heat Shock Proteins

Junichiro Nishizawa and Kazuhiro Nagata

Ischemic heart disease or myocardial infarction remains the most prevalent cause of death in developed countries despite advances in modern medicine. Recent advances in diagnosis and treatment have allowed at early stages, the rapid return of blood flow by surgical, interventional or pharmacological means, and the reduction of mortality or morbidity. However, prolonged ischemia results in such severe infarction or necrosis that reperfusion produces few beneficial effects and contributes to further tissue damage called reperfusion injury which includes severe arrhythmia or myocardial stunning.[1-3] Thus, myocardial protection against ischemia/reperfusion injury has been the subject of experimental and clinical research for a long time, but few pharmacological means have yet been established for effective clinical use. Therefore, it is of considerable importance to understand the mechanisms by which cells or tissues are damaged during ischemia/reperfusion, to identify compensatory responses that may augment cell survival, and to exploit methods of clinical application. In addition, there is room for improvement in strategies to protect the myocardium during high-risk cardiovascular surgery involving cardiopulmonary bypass or coronary intervention, and to preserve hearts prior to transplantation.

All living organisms, from bacteria to humans, share a common response to hyperthermia, ischemia/reperfusion, or other physiological stresses that are unfavorable to their survival through the induction of a group of protective proteins called heat shock or stress proteins (Hsp's). These proteins are highly conserved throughout evolution and play essential roles as molecular chaperones under normal conditions as well as under stressed conditions by facilitating the folding, intracellular transport, assembly, and disassembly of other cellular proteins.[4] The induction of Hsp's has been demonstrated to be directly involved in the acquisition of resistance to ischemia/reperfusion injury.[5-8]

In this chapter, we will summarize the mechanisms by which the myocardium is damaged during ischemia/reperfusion, review the induction of the heat shock response during ischemia/reperfusion in the heart, and discuss the mechanisms of this induction by ischemia/reperfuion.

Regulation of Heat Shock Gene Transcription

The heat shock/stress response is mainly mediated at the transcriptional level by the activation of a pre-existing transcription activator, the heat shock factor (Hsf). The Hsf binds to the heat shock element (Hse), a cis-acting promoter sequence located upstream of all heat shock genes. The Hse is composed of at least three pentanucleotide modules (nGAAn; n indicates any nucleotide) arranged as contiguous inverted repeats.[4,9]

Heat Shock Proteins in Myocardial Protection, edited by Rakesh C. Kukreja and Michael L. Hess.

Family of Heat Shock Factors

In vertebrate cells, a family of Hsf's has been identified and distinct Hsf family members may differentially regulate the transcription of heat shock genes.[10-14] The Hsf family includes Hsf1, Hsf2, Hsf3, and Hsf4. Hsf1 acquires DNA-binding activity in response to conditions such as elevated temperatures, ischemia/reperfusion, oxidative stress, and exposure to heavy metals and amino acid analogues.[15-17] Thus, Hsf1 seems to be the general stress-response factor.[4] Hsf2 appears to be a developmental Hsf, is activated during erythroid differentiation of human K562 erythroleukemia cells with hemin treatment[18] and is constitutively activated in mouse embryonic stem cells as well as in spermatogenic cells of mouse testes.[19,20] Hsf3 has been cloned in chicken cells only.[13] Although Hsf1 and Hsf3 are activated by various stresses such as heat shock and sodium arsenite, the kinetics and thresholds of Hsf1 and Hsf3 activation are different.[21,22] Hsf1 responds to stress rapidly, whereas Hsf3 responds slowly. In addition, Hsf3 was reported to be activated by heat shock at higher temperatures or with higher concentrations of sodium arsenite than Hsf1. Hsf3 was demonstrated to be involved in persistent and burst activations of stress genes during severe stress. Recently, human Hsf4 was cloned and characterized.[14] Hsf4 lacks the carboxyl-terminal hydrophobic repeat which is present among all vertebrate Hsf's and is preferentially expressed in the heart, brain, skeletal muscles, and pancreas.

Regulation of DNA-Binding Activity of Hsf1

The increase of denatured, unfolded or malfolded proteins triggers heat shock responses.[23,24] Experimental evidence suggests that intracellular levels of free Hsp70 contribute to the feedback regulation of Hsp70 expression.[25,26] Thus, in eukaryotic cells, a model for regulation of DNA-binding activity of Hsf1 has been proposed (Fig. 11.1).[4,27-30] In the model, Hsp's themselves negatively regulate heat shock gene expression via an autoregulating loop. Under unstressed conditions, Hsf1 is present in both the nucleus and the cytoplasm as a monomer that has no DNA-binding activity through transient interactions with Hsp70 or other Hsp's. Under stressed conditions, such as hyperthermia or physiological stresses, an increase in denatured, misfolded or aggregated proteins creates a large pool of new protein substrates that compete with Hsf1 for association with Hsp70. Thus, such stresses initiate the removal of the negative regulatory influence on the DNA-binding activity of Hsf1. Hsf1 assembles into a trimer, translocates into the nucleus, binds to Hse, and acquires transcriptional activity. This activation of Hsf1 DNA-binding activity results in increased transcription and synthesis of Hsp's including Hsp70, which then interact with Hsf1 and interfere with the DNA-binding activity of Hsf1.

Damage by Ischemia/Reperfusion Injury

Ischemia

During ischemia, cells are deprived of not only oxygen for mitochondrial respiration, but also other substrates, such as glucose, that are essentially supplied by blood flow. In addition, physiologically toxic metabolites that are washed out with normal circulation accumulate in the tissue (Table 11.1).[2,31]

Oxidative metabolism, electron transport, and adenosine triphosphate (ATP) production by oxidative phosphorylation in the mitochondria rapidly decline as a result of oxygen deprivation. At early stages, some ATP is still produced with a compensatory increase in anaerobic glycolysis. Intracellular acidosis develops due to the accumulation of lactate and hydrogen ions, and anaerobic glycolysis is suppressed. These alterations contribute to damage to the cell

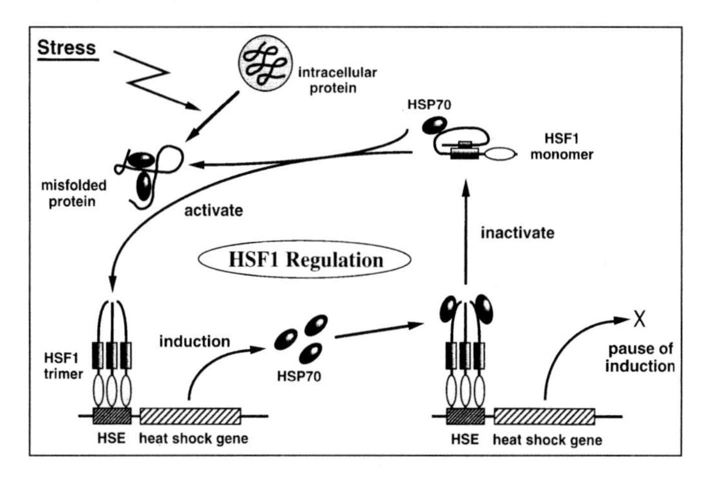

Fig. 11.1. A model for regulation of DNA-binding activity of Hsf1. Under unstressed conditions, Hsf1 is maintained as a monomer that has no DNA-binding activity through transient interactions with Hsp70 or other Hsps. Under stressed conditions, an increase in misfolded proteins creates a large pool of new protein substrates that compete with Hsf1 for association with Hsp70 and initiates the removal of the negative regulatory influence on the DNA-binding activity of Hsf1. Hsf1 assembles into a trimer, translocates into the nucleus, binds to Hse in heat shock gene promoters, and acquires transcriptional activity. This activation of Hsf1 DNA-binding activity results in increased transcription and synthesis of Hsps including Hsp70, which then interact with Hsf1 and convert Hsf1 to non-DNA-binding monomers.

Table 11.1 Changes associated with ischemia/reperfusion

Accumulation of various lipid species
Acidosis
Altered osmotic control
Arachidonic acid and its metabolites
ATP loss
Calcium overload
Cell swelling
Intracellular ionic derangement
Loss of membrane integrity
Reactive oxygen species
Structural disorganization

membrane and induce cell swelling, intracellular accumulation of calcium, loss of intracellular potassium, and other disturbances of membrane ion transport.

Cellular injury as a result of advanced ischemia is mediated by progressive membrane damage involving several contributory factors.[31] Accumulation of calcium on other metabolic alterations induces phospholipase activation, phospholipid degradation, and release of lysophospholipids and free fatty acids. Reduced mitochondrial fatty acid metabolism induces the accumulation of various lipid species, such as acyl CoA and acyl carnitine which can be incorporated into membranes and impair the function. Reactive oxygen species, such as free radicals and toxic oxygen species, are produced in ischemic cells and activated leukocytes. The activation of protease probably induces damage of cytoskeletal filaments resulting in the loss of their stabilizing effect on the sarcolemma. These changes result in a progressive increase in nonspecific membrane permeability, further breakdown in the intracellular ionic environment, and ATP depletion. Cellular metabolism and ATP generation nearly cease, and glycogen stores are depleted. As glycolysis and mitochondrial function are totally lost, autolysis of cells begins, and the leakage of cellular contents increases extensively.

Reperfusion

Although the reperfusion procedure is an effective means of myocardial salvage, evidence obtained under clinical situations as well as under various experimental laboratory conditions has revealed a potential detrimental influence of reperfusion of the myocardium. Additional injury or further damage as a result of reperfusion after ischemia, is referred to as "reperfusion injury" and involves transient contractile dysfunction, called "myocardial stunning", increased deleterious arrhythmia, and cell death.

The effects of reperfusion are complex, and the pathogenesis and mechanism of reperfusion injury are still uncertain.[1-3] Reperfusion is associated with a variety of events including generation of oxygen free radicals, activation of neutrophils and platelets, increased synthesis of arachidonic acid and its metabolites, activation of the Na^+/H^+ exchanger, and abrupt intracellular calcium overload. Considering the variety of underlying mechanisms and manifestations, a single all-embracing theory may not account for reperfusion injury.

Induction of Hsp's by Ischemia/Reperfusion in the Heart

A number of investigators have demonstrated increased expression of Hsp70 mRNA and protein in the heart using different experimental systems in response to global or partial ischemia.[32-37] Dillmann et al first demonstrated the induction of Hsp of ischemic hearts.[32] In the open chest dog model, ischemia of the heart caused by occluding the left anterior descending coronary artery induced high level expression of Hsp70 mRNA and protein using 2-dimensional gel electrophoresis. In the open chest rabbit heart, 5-minute coronary artery occlusion was reported to induce a 2-fold accumulation of Hsp70 mRNA in the ischemic area after 2-hour reperfusion as measured using Northern blot analysis, whereas four repeated cycles of 5-minute ischemia and 5-minute reperfusion resulted in a 3-fold increase in Hsp70 mRNA.[35] Moreover, after repeated 5-minute global ischemia and 10-minute reperfusion, the induction of Hsp 27 and Hsp90 mRNA as well as Hsp70 mRNA was demonstrated in isolated and perfused rat hearts with the Langendorff method.[36] We examined the time course of the accumulation of mRNAs for Hsp70 and Hsp90 during ischemia, postischemic reperfusion, or heat shock.[38] The levels of mRNAs were very low during global ischemia and clearly induced during heat shock or postischemic reperfusion. Although the expression of Hsp70 mRNA during heat shock was greater than the expression during ischemia/reperfusion, Hsp90 mRNA was significantly more strongly induced in ischemia/reperfusion than in heat shock indicating the presence of regulatory mechanisms other than Hsf. On the other hand, Hsp70 mRNA was shown to be localized around the border of the necrotic region after ischemia/reperfusion using in situ hybridization analysis of isolated rat hearts.[39]

Hsf Activation by Ischemia/Reperfusion

Benjamin et al first demonstrated the induction of binding activity of Hsf by hypoxia in cultured mouse myogenic cells with the gel mobility shift assay using a double-stranded Hse oligonucleotide.[40] Mestril et al also reported the Hse-binding activity of Hsf due to hypoxia and found that Hsf1 binds to Hse during hypoxia as well as during heat shock with supershift assays using specific antisera against Hsf1 and Hsf2 in a cell line derived from embryonic rat hearts, H9c2.[41] The Hse-binding activity due to ischemia was demonstrated in the liver, kidney and brain of rats.[42-44]

In the heart, we systematically investigated the induction of Hse-binding activity of Hsf by ischemia/reperfusion as well as by heat shock.[38] Using the Langendorff method, isolated and perfused rat hearts were subjected to global ischemia by clamping the aortic cannula followed by reperfusion or no reperfusion, and the Hse-binding activities of whole cell extracts were analyzed with a gel mobility shift assay (Fig 11.2). The activation of Hsf during global ischemia was detected 3 minutes after clamping, reached a peak after 6 minutes and then attenuated. After 20 or 40 minutes of ischemia, reperfusion induced a burst of activity which continued for more than 60 minutes. Thus, although the activation of Hsf during global ischemia was weak and rapidly attenuated, postischemic reperfusion induced significant activation of Hsf. At any time point, the Hse-binding activity was significantly weaker in comparison with that in heat-shocked hearts that were perfused with 42°C buffer. Recently, we demonstrated the Hse-binding activities of Hsf in hearts repeatedly submitted to 10-minute global ischemia and 10-minute reperfusion.[45] The Hse-binding activity during repetitive ischemia/reperfusion increased steadily, and after the third ischemic event it reached a level equal to or higher than that in heat-shocked hearts. With supershift assays using specific antisera against Hsf1 and Hsf2, the primary component of Hsf activated by hypoxia or ischemia/reperfusion was demonstrated to be Hsf1 in various cells[41,46,47] and in the brain.[42] In the heart, we demonstrated that Hsf1 is the primary component activated by ischemia or reperfusion as well as by heat shock[38] (Fig 11.3). The levels of mRNA for Hsp70 and Hsp90 were examined by Northern blot analysis to determine whether or not Hsf activation resulted in the subsequent transcription of Hsp's.[38] Although the induction of Hsp70 mRNA during heat shock was greater than that during ischemia/reperfusion, Hsp90 mRNA was significantly more strongly induced in ischemia/reperfusion than in heat shock. Individual Hsp's may also be regulated by additional mechanisms other than Hsf.

Myocardial Protection Against Ischemia/Reperfusion by Hsp's

A large number of studies demonstrated a phenomenon of ischemic tolerance as well as thermotolerance in various experimental systems after mild heat shock or mild ischemia.[48-50] The association between heat shock response and enhanced postischemic ventricular recovery was first reported by Currie et al.[51] Rats were exposed to 15 min of 42°C hyperthermia and 24 hours later the hearts were isolated, perfused and submitted to global ischemia. In heat-shocked hearts, recovery of contractile force, rate of contraction and rate of relaxation significantly improved, creatine kinase release associated with reperfusion injury decreased, and Hsp70 increased. They also showed a strong relationship between the accumulation of Hsp70 and the postischemic ventricular recovery 0, 24, 48, 96, and 192 hours after hyperthermia.[52] In focal ischemic rat hearts by occlusion and reperfusion of the left coronary artery, Donnelly et al demonstrated the reduction of the infarct size due to prior whole-body hyperthermia.[53] Similar protective effects of pretreatment with hyperthermia or mild ischemia on the functional recovery or the reduction of infarct size after heart ischemia have been reported in various experimental systems or conditions.[54-58] Recently, it was clearly demonstrated that postischemic myocardial recoveries, including the size of infarction, contractile function and release of creatine kinase, significantly improved in transgenic mice that overexpressed inducible human or rat Hsp70.[5-8] Moreover, the protective roles against ischemic insult of Hsp's other than Hsp70 have been demonstrated. In both rat neonatal cardiomyocytes and the myogenic H9c2 cell line, cells infected with an adenoviral construct overexpressing both Hsp60 and Hsp10, which are known to form chaperonin complex in the mitochondria, were found to be protective against simu-

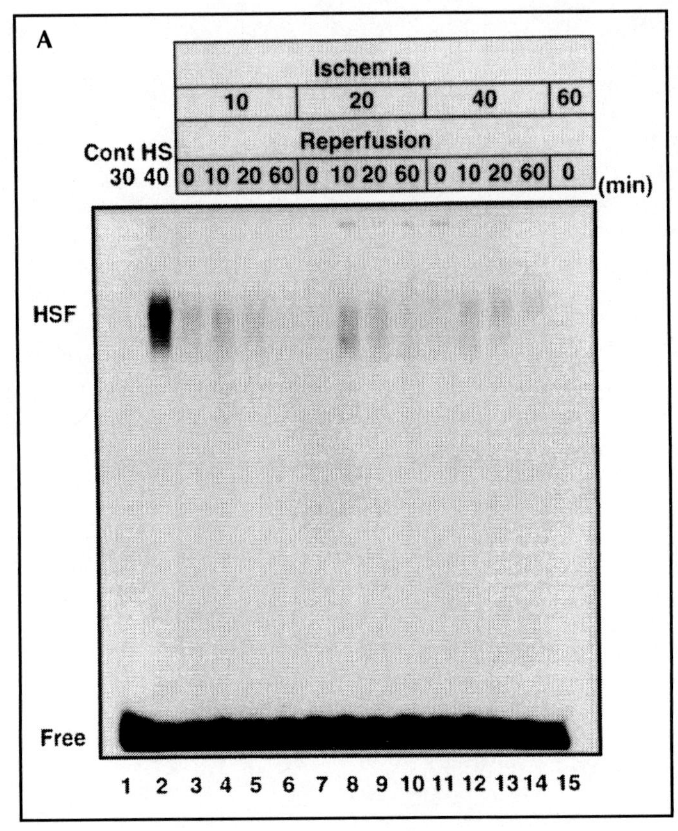
A
Ischemia
10
20
40
60
Reperfusion
Cont HS
30 40
0 10 20 60 0 10 20 60 0 10 20 60 0
(min)
HSF
Free
1 2 3 4 5 6 7 8 9 10 11 12 13 14 15

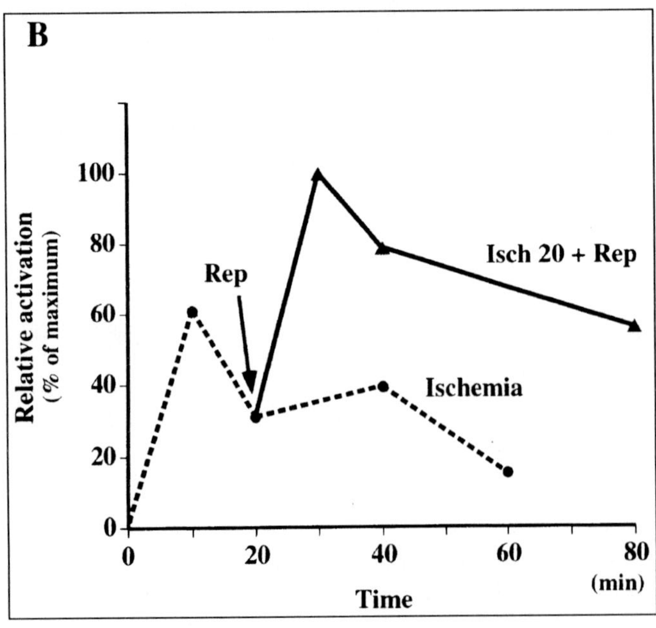
B
Relative activation
(% of maximum)
100
80
60
40
20
0
Rep
Isch 20 + Rep
Ischemia
0
20
40
60
80
(min)
Time

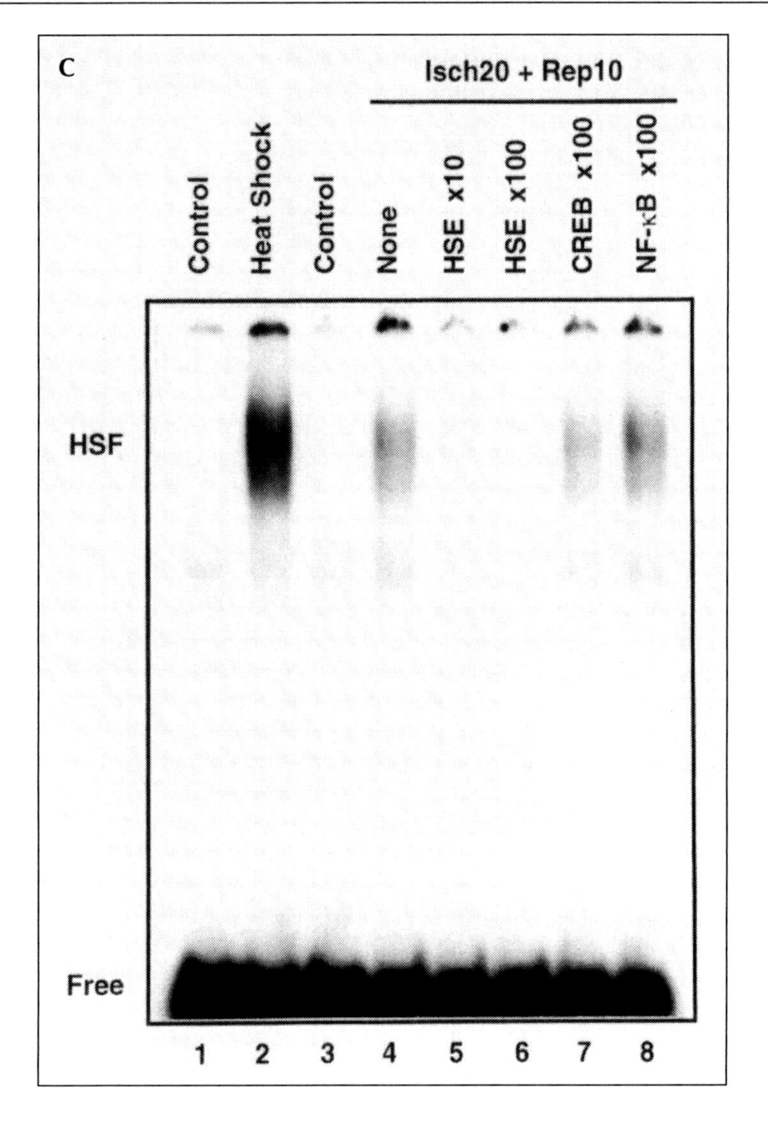

Fig. 11.2. Hse-binding activity of Hsf during ischemia/reperfusion in isolated and perfused rat heart. A gel mobility shift assay was performed with whole cell extracts prepared from control or ischemia-reperfused hearts. Reperfusion was carried out by perfusing with 37°C buffer for the time indicated after global ischemia. (A) Time course of Hse-binding activity during reperfusion after 10 (lanes 4 to 6), 20 (lanes 8 to 10), and 40 minutes (lanes 12 to 14) of global ischemia. Results for control (Cont) or heat-shocked (HS) hearts are also shown. (B) Relative Hse-binding activity during ischemia or reperfusion after 20-minute ischemia (Isch 20 + Rep) is shown. The levels of activated Hsf in (A) were estimated using a bio-image analyzer and normalized to the level at 10-minute reperfusion after 20-minute ischemia. The arrow indicates the onset of reperfusion (Rep). (C) Specificity of the Hse-binding activity during postischemic reperfusion. Competition assays were performed with binding reaction mixtures containing no competitor (lane 4), 10- or 100-fold excesses of unlabeled Hse (lanes 5 and 6), 100-fold excess of unlabeled CREB (lane 7), and 100-fold excess of unlabeled NF-κB oligonucleotides (lane 8). Samples were obtained from hearts reperfused 10 minutes after 20-minute ischemia (Isch20 + Rep10).

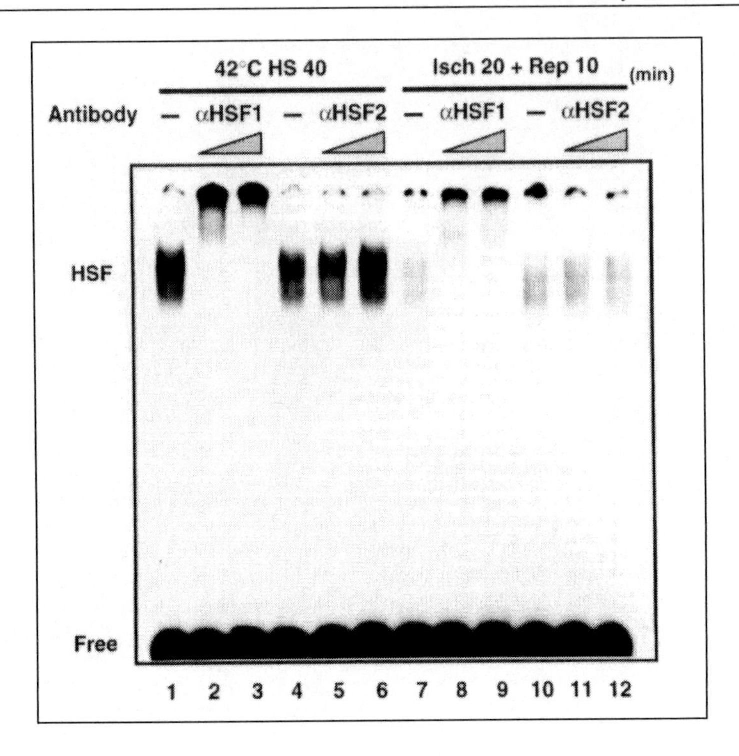

Fig. 11.3. Specific activation of Hsf1 in heat-shocked or ischemia-reperfused heart. Whole cell extracts were prepared from heat-shocked (HS40, 42°C for 40 minutes) or ischemia-reperfused (20-minute ischemia followed by 10-minute reperfusion, Isch20 + Rep10) hearts. Cell extracts were incubated with anti-Hsf1 (lanes 2, 3, 8 and 9) or anti-Hsf2 (lanes 5, 6, 11 and 12) antiserum before the DNA-binding reaction, and gel mobility shift assay was performed. Cell extracts without antiserum (lanes 1, 4, 7 and 10) were similarly analyzed. In both extracts, supershifts or decreases in mobility of the complex were observed when antiserum against Hsf1 was used (lanes 2, 3, 8, and 9), although anti-Hsf2 antiserum had no effect (lanes 5, 6, 11, and 12). The volume of antiserum (diluted 1:10 with PBS) added was 0.5 μl (lanes 2, 5, 8 and 11) or 1.0 μl (lanes 3, 6, 9 and 12).

lated ischemia.[59] More recently, the overexpression of small heat shock proteins Hsp27 and αβ-crystallin was also demonstrated to protect against ischemic change in cardiomyocytes.[60]

Signals for Heat Shock Response During Ischemia/Reperfusion

Multiple and complex pathological changes occur during ischemia/reperfusion as mentioned above (Table 11.1). Although the detailed mechanisms remain to be determined, reactive oxygen species, arachidonic acid, and ATP depletion appear to be the major causes of Hsf1 activation by hypoxia or ischemia/reperfusion. These changes likely disturb protein metabolism and then produce substrates for the molecular chaperones, resulting in activation of Hsf1.

ATP Depletion

Benjamin et al investigated the intracellular signals generated in hypoxic or ischemic cells and indicated that the effects of ATP depletion alone are sufficient to induce DNA-binding of Hsf when oxidative metabolism is impaired in cultured C2 myogenic cells.[61] When the intracellular pH was reduced to 6.7 with normal ATP levels, Hse-binding activity of Hsf was not induced. In contrast, severe depletion of ATP induced the activation of Hsf even at normal pH levels. Van Why et al examined the activation of Hsf and cellular ATP levels in the renal cortex of rats in vivo during graded ischemia and indicated that the intensity of the activity was related to the degree of ischemia indicated by cellular ATP levels.[44]

On the other hand, Iwaki et al examined the induction of Hsp70 mRNA and the amount of intracellular ATP during hypoxia/reoxygenation and metabolic stress using cultured neonatal cardiomyocytes.[62] The appearance of Hsp70 mRNA preceded the intracellular ATP depletion caused by hypoxia. Moreover, in our study using isolated rat hearts, although Hsf activation was very weak during global heart ischemia, during which ATP was reported to rapidly deplete,[63] prompt and significant activation was induced by postischemic reperfusion, during which the ATP level gradually increased.[38] Thus, ATP depletion is likely not the main stimulus for heat shock response during ischemia/reperfusion.

Reactive Oxygen Species

As mentioned above, we demonstrated that the induction of Hse-binding activity of Hsf during ischemia was weak, the activity soon attenuated and that postischemic reperfusion significantly induced the binding activity of Hsf in isolated and perfused rat hearts.[38] Moreover, postischemic reperfusion was reported to enhance the Hsf activity induced by ischemia in livers and kidneys of rats, suggesting that the primary signal that activated Hsf during ischemia/reperfusion was produced mainly during postischemic reperfusion.[43,44] On the other hand, it has been established that a burst of production of reactive oxygen species including hydrogen peroxide (H_2O_2), superoxide radical (O_2-), and hydroxyl radical (OH) occurs during the early moments of reperfusion of ischemic tissues.[64,65] (For a review see refs. 1, 3) These reactive oxygen species are derived from a variety of sources, such as the xanthine oxidase system, activated neutrophils, the electron transport chain of mitochondria, and the arachidonic acid pathway.

Kukreja et al examined the accumulation of Hsp70 mRNA during exposure to exogenous reactive oxygen species and during postischemic reperfusion in isolated rat hearts, and concluded that one of the potential mechanisms of Hsp70 expression elicited by ischemia/reperfusion may involve oxygen radicals.[66] In addition, induction of Hsp70 mRNA by ischemia/reperfusion was reported to be inhibited by intravenous infusion of recombinant human superoxide dismutase in pig livers.[67]

Recently, we concluded that reactive oxygen species played an important role in the induction of the binding activity of Hsf as well as the accumulation of mRNA for Hsp70 and Hsp90 in ischemia-reperfused hearts, based on several observations in isolated and perfused rat hearts.[45] Firstly, we demonstrated a burst activation of Hsf1 in hearts submitted to repetitive ischemia/reperfusion, which was reported to cause recurrent bursts of free radical generation.[68] Secondly, this burst activation of Hsf1 in repetitive ischemia-reperfused hearts was significantly reduced by treatment with either allopurinol, an inhibitor of xanthine oxidase, or catalase, a scavenger of H_2O_2. Thirdly, significant binding activity of Hsf1 was observed upon perfusion with buffers containing H_2O_2 or xanthine plus xanthine oxidase.

Despite the large number of studies, controversy continues regarding the effects of oxidative stresses on the heat shock response. Several studies have shown the induction of Hsp's by various oxidative stresses or reactive oxygen species.[69-71] However, Bruce et al reported that although H_2O_2 or menadione induced Hse-binding activity of Hsf, Hsp's were not synthesized in NIH-3T3 cells.[72] On the other hand, it was reported that phorbol esters did not cause Hsf activation but induced Hsp synthesis in human monocytes, and that increased mRNA stabilization was responsible for this induction of Hsp.[73] Recently, the involvement of the redox mechanism in the heat shock signal transduction pathway has been suggested.[74,75]

Jacquier-Sarlin et al reported that H_2O_2 exerted a dual effect in human premonocytic cells: it reversibly inhibited DNA-binding activity of Hsf as well as induced the binding activity.[75] In addition, they proposed that the time required for thioredoxin induction explained the lack of Hsp synthesis upon exposure to reactive oxygen species, despite the activation of Hsf. Thus, complex, multi-step regulation of the stress response to oxidative stress is suggested, and differences among the studies may be due to the cell specificity, the type of oxidative stress and the subcellular location of the reactive oxygen species generation. Despite the different results, reactive oxygen species likely play an important role in the induction of heat shock response during ischemia/reperfusion.

Arachidonic Acid and Its Metabolites

Arachidonic acid and its metabolites, such as prostaglandins and thromboxane, accumulate during ischemia and are enhanced by reperfusion.[2,3] A relationship between heat shock gene expression and the metabolic pathway of arachidonic acid was suggested by a study that demonstrated treatment of human cells with prostaglandins A1, A2, and J2 induced heat shock protein synthesis.[76,77] Moreover, arachidonate or antiproliferative prostaglandins were shown to induce the Hse-binding activity of Hsf in human cells.[78,79] It has also been observed that treatment with anti-inflammatory drugs, such as sodium salicylate[80] and indomethacin,[81] which inhibit arachidonate metabolism, leads to the activation of Hsf1 DNA-binding activity. Furthermore, pretreatment with arachidonate[79] or indomethacin[81] lowers the temperature threshold for the induction of Hsf1 activation. Although the detailed mechanisms remain unclear, arachidonic acid metabolism likely contributes to the heat shock response induced by hypoxia or ischemia/reperfusion.

Decreased Intracellular pH

The reduction of intracellular pH does not seem to be the main stimulus for Hsf activation during ischemia/reperfusion. Decreased pH to nonphysiologic levels (<6.4) was reported to induce DNA-binding activity of Hsf in HeLa cells.[82] However, severe acidosis (pH 6.7) in the physiological range did not induce the binding activity in cultured myogenic cells.[61]

Clinical Application and Future Perspective

The myocardial protective effect of Hsp's from ischemia/reperfusion injury has been demonstrated as mentioned above. Moreover, recent studies indicate that gene transfection with Hsp's or pharmacological therapies that induce Hsp's may result in new effective treatments although further investigation will be required to establish the general usefulness of these approaches.[83-86] Suzuki et al showed that in vivo gene transfection by intracoronary infusion of the hemagglutinating virus of Japan (HVJ)-liposome caused overexpression of Hsp70 in rat hearts, resulting in enhancement of myocardial tolerance to ischemia/reperfusion injury.[85] In addition, a hydroxylamine derivative, Bimoclomol, demonstrated cytoprotective effects together with a lack of toxicity and side effects under several experimental conditions, including ischemia, by increasing the synthesis of Hsp's.[86]

Further research regarding the underlying mechanisms of Hsp induction, less noxious means to induce these proteins effectively, and improved biotechnology for gene regulation or gene delivery are necessary. We believe that further study will result in valuable clinical applications relevant to high-risk cardiovascular surgery, transplantation, or treatments for ischemic heart diseases.

Reference

1. McCord JM. Oxygen-derived free radicals in postischemic tissue injury. N Engl J Med 1985; 312(3):159-63.
2. Karmazyn M. Ischemic and reperfusion injury in the heart. Cellular mechanisms and pharmacological interventions. Can J Physiol Pharmacol 1991; 69(6):719-30.
3. Maxwell SR, Lip GY. Reperfusion injury: A review of the pathophysiology, clinical manifestations and therapeutic options. Int J Cardiol 1997; 58(2):95-117.
4. Morimoto RI, Tissières A, Georgopoulus C, eds. The Biology of Heat Shock Proteins and Molecular Chaperones. New York: Cold Spring Harbor Press, 1994.
5. Marber MS, Mestril R, Chi SH et al. Overexpression of the rat inducible 70-kD heat stress protein in a transgenic mouse increases the resistance of the heart to ischemic injury. J Clin Invest 1995; 95(4):1446-56.
6. Plumier JC, Ross BM, Currie RW et al. Transgenic mice expressing the human heat shock protein-70 have improved post-ischemic myocardial recovery. J Clin Invest 1995;95(4):1854-60.
7. Hutter JJ, Mestril R, Tam EK et al. Overexpression of heat shock protein 72 in transgenic mice decreases infarct size in vivo. Circulation 1996; 94(6):1408-11.
8. Radford NB, Fina M, Benjamin IJ et al. Cardioprotective effects of 70-kDa heat shock protein in transgenic mice. Proc Natl Acad Sci U S A 1996; 93(6):2339-42.
9. Perisic O, Xiao H, Lis JT. Stable binding of *Drosophila* heat shock factor to head-to-head and tail-to-tail repeats of a conserved 5 bp recognition unit. Cell 1989; 59(5):797-806.
10. Rabindran SK, Giorgi G, Clos J et al. Molecular cloning and expression of a human heat shock factor, Hsf1. Proc Natl Acad Sci U S A 1991; 88(16):6906-10.
11. Sarge KD, Zimarino V, Holm K et al. Cloning and characterization of two mouse heat shock factors with distinct inducible and constitutive DNA-binding ability. Genes Dev 1991; 5(10):1902-11.
12. Schuetz TJ, Gallo GJ, Sheldon L et al. Isolation of a cDNA for Hsf2: Evidence for two heat shock factor genes in humans. Proc Natl Acad Sci U S A 1991; 88(16):6911-5.
13. Nakai A, Morimoto RI. Characterization of a novel chicken heat shock transcription factor, heat shock factor-3, suggests a new regulatory pathway. Mol Cell Biol 1993; 13(4):1983-97.
14. Nakai A, Tanabe M, Kawazoe Y et al. Hsf4, a new member of the human heat shock factor family which lacks properties of a transcriptional activator. Mol Cell Biol 1997; 17(1):469-81.
15. Baler R, Dahl G, Voellmy R. Activation of human heat shock genes is accompanied by oligomerization, modification, and rapid translocation of heat shock transcription factor Hsf1. Mol Cell Biol 1993; 13(4):2486-96.
16. Sarge KD, Murphy SP, Morimoto RI. Activation of heat shock gene transcription by heat shock factor-1 involves oligomerization, acquisition of DNA-binding activity, and nuclear localization and can occur in the absence of stress. Mol Cell Biol 1993; 13(3):1392-407.
17. Fawcett TW, Sylvester SL, Sarge KD et al. Effects of neurohormonal stress and aging on the activation of mammalian heat shock factor-1. J Biol Chem 1994; 269(51):32272-8.
18. Sistonen L, Sarge KD, Phillips B et al. Activation of heat shock factor-2 during hemin-induced differentiation of human erythroleukemia cells. Mol Cell Biol 1992; 12(9):4104-11.
19. Sarge KD, Park-Sarge OK, Kirby JD et al. Expression of heat shock factor-2 in mouse testis: Potential role as a regulator of heat-shock protein gene expression during spermatogenesis. Biol Reprod 1994; 50(6):1334-43.
20. Murphy SP, Gorzowski JJ, Sarge KD et al. Characterization of constitutive Hsf2 DNA-binding activity in mouse embryonal carcinoma cells. Mol Cell Biol 1994; 14(8):5309-17.
21. Nakai A, Kawazoe Y, Tanabe M et al. The DNA-binding properties of two heat shock factors, Hsf1 and Hsf3, are induced in the avian erythroblast cell line HD6. Mol Cell Biol 1995; 15(10):5168-78.
22. Tanabe M, Nakai A, Kawazoe Y et al. Different thresholds in the responses of two heat shock transcription factors, Hsf1 and Hsf3. J Biol Chem 1997; 272(24):15389-95.
23. Goff SA, Goldberg AL. Production of abnormal proteins in *E. coli* stimulates transcription of lon and other heat shock genes. Cell 1985; 41(2):587-95.

24. Ananthan J, Goldberg AL, Voellmy R. Abnormal proteins serve as eukaryotic stress signals and trigger the activation of heat shock genes. Science 1986; 232(4749):522-4.
25. DiDomenico BJ, Bugaisky GE, Lindquist S. The heat shock response is self-regulated at both the transcriptional and posttranscriptional levels. Cell 1982; 31(3 Pt 2):593-603.
26. Craig EA, Gross CA. Is Hsp70 the cellular thermometer? Trends Biochem Sci 1991; 16(4):135-40.
27. Abravaya K, Myers MP, Murphy SP et al. The human heat shock protein Hsp70 interacts with Hsf, the transcription factor that regulates heat shock gene expression. Genes Dev 1992; 6(7):1153-64.
28. Beckmann RP, Lovett M, Welch WJ. Examining the function and regulation of Hsp 70 in cells subjected to metabolic stress. J Cell Biol 1992; 117(6):1137-50.
29. Morimoto RI. Cells in stress: Transcriptional activation of heat shock genes. Science 1993; 259:1409-1410.
30. Mosser DD, Duchaine J, Massie B. The DNA-binding activity of the human heat shock transcription factor is regulated in vivo by Hsp70. Mol Cell Biol 1993; 13(9):5427-38.
31. Reimer KA, Ideker RE. Myocardial ischemia and infarction: anatomic and biochemical substrates for ischemic cell death and ventricular arrhythmias. Hum Pathol 1987; 18(5):462-75.
32. Dillmann WH, Mehta HB, Barrieux A et al. Ischemia of the dog heart induces the appearance of a cardiac mRNA coding for a protein with migration characteristics similar to heat-shock/stress protein-71. Circ Res 1986; 59(1):110-4.
33. Currie RW. Effects of ischemia and perfusion temperature on the synthesis of stress- induced (heat shock) proteins in isolated and perfused rat hearts. J Mol Cell Cardiol 1987; 19(8):795-808.
34. Mehta HB, Popovich BK, Dillmann WH. Ischemia induces changes in the level of mRNAs coding for stress protein-71 and creatine kinase M. Circ Res 1988; 63(3):512-7.
35. Knowlton AA, Brecher P, Apstein CS. Rapid expression of heat shock protein in the rabbit after brief cardiac ischemia. J Clin Invest 1991; 87(1):139-47.
36. Das DK, Engelman RM, Kimura Y. Molecular adaptation of cellular defences following preconditioning of the heart by repeated ischemia. Cardiovasc Res 1993; 27(4):578-84.
37. Myrmel T, McCully JD, Malikin L et al. Heat-shock protein 70 mRNA is induced by anaerobic metabolism in rat hearts. Circulation 1994; 90(5 Pt 2):II299-305.
38. Nishizawa J, Nakai A, Higashi T et al. Reperfusion causes significant activation of heat shock transcription factor-1 in ischemic rat heart. Circulation 1996; 94(9):2185-92.
39. Plumier JC, Robertson HA, Currie RW. Differential accumulation of mRNA for immediate early genes and heat shock genes in heart after ischaemic injury. J Mol Cell Cardiol 1996; 28(6):1251-60.
40. Benjamin IJ, Kroger B, Williams RS. Activation of the heat shock transcription factor by hypoxia in mammalian cells. Proc Natl Acad Sci U S A 1990; 87(16):6263-7.
41. Mestril R, Chi SH, Sayen MR, Dillmann WH. Isolation of a novel inducible rat heat-shock protein (Hsp70) gene and its expression during ischaemia/hypoxia and heat shock. Biochem J 1994; 298(3):561-9.
42. Higashi T, Nakai A, Uemura Y et al. Activation of heat shock factor-1 in rat brain during cerebral ischemia or after heat shock. Mol Brain Res 1995; 34:262-70.
43. Tacchini L, Schiaffonati L, Pappalardo C et al. Expression of Hsp70, immediate-early response and heme oxygenase genes in ischemic-reperfused rat liver. Lab Invest 1993; 68(4):465-71.
44. Van Why SK, Mann AS, Thulin G et al. Activation of heat-shock transcription factor by graded reductions in renal ATP, in vivo, in the rat. J Clin Invest 1994; 94(4):1518-23.
45. Nishizawa J, Nakai A, Matsuda K et al. Reactive oxygen species play an important role in the activation of heat shock factor-1 in ischemia-reperfused heart. Circulation 1999; 99(7):934-41.
46. Mivechi NF, Koong AC, Giaccia AJ et al. Analysis of Hsf-1 phosphorylation in A549 cells treated with a variety of stresses. Int J Hyperthermia 1994; 10(3):371-9.
47. Bergeron M, Mivechi NF, Giaccia AJ et al. Mechanism of heat shock protein-72 induction in primary cultured astrocytes after oxygen-glucose deprivation. Neurol Res 1996; 18(1):64-72.
48. Yellon DM, Latchman DS. Stress proteins and myocardial protection. J Mol Cell Cardiol 1992; 24(2):113-24.
49. Plumier JC, Currie RW. Heat shock-induced myocardial protection against ischemic injury: A role for Hsp70? Cell Stress Chaperones 1996; 1(1):13-7.

50. Williams RS. Heat shock proteins and ischemic injury to the myocardium. Circulation 1997; 96(12):4138-40.
51. Currie RW, Karmazyn M, Kloc M et al. Heat-shock response is associated with enhanced postischemic ventricular recovery. Circ Res 1988; 63(3):543-9.
52. Karmazyn M, Mailer K, Currie RW. Acquisition and decay of heat-shock-enhanced postischemic ventricular recovery. Am J Physiol 1990; 259(2 Pt 2):H424-31.
53. Donnelly TJ, Sievers RE, Vissern FL et al. Heat shock protein induction in rat hearts. A role for improved myocardial salvage after ischemia and reperfusion? Circulation 1992; 85(2):769-78.
54. Liu X, Engelman RM, Moraru II et al. Heat shock. A new approach for myocardial preservation in cardiac surgery. Circulation 1992; 86(5 Suppl):II358-63.
55. Currie RW, Tanguay RM, Kingma J, Jr. Heat-shock response and limitation of tissue necrosis during occlusion/reperfusion in rabbit hearts. Circulation 1993; 87(3):963-71.
56. Marber MS, Latchman DS, Walker JM et al. Cardiac stress protein elevation 24 hours after brief ischemia or heat stress is associated with resistance to myocardial infarction. Circulation 1993; 88(3):1264-72.
57. Hutter MM, Sievers RE, Barbosa V et al. Heat-shock protein induction in rat hearts. A direct correlation between the amount of heat-shock protein induced and the degree of myocardial protection. Circulation 1994; 89(1):355-60.
58. Marber MS, Walker JM, Latchman DS et al. Myocardial protection after whole body heat stress in the rabbit is dependent on metabolic substrate and is related to the amount of the inducible 70-kD heat stress protein. J Clin Invest 1994; 93(3):1087-94.
59. Lau S, Patnaik N, Sayen MR, Mestril R. Simultaneous overexpression of two stress proteins in rat cardiomyocytes and myogenic cells confers protection against ischemia- induced injury. Circulation 1997; 96(7):2287-94.
60. Martin JL, Mestril R, Hilal-Dandan R et al. Small heat shock proteins and protection against ischemic injury in cardiac myocytes. Circulation 1997; 96(12):4343-8.
61. Benjamin IJ, Horie S, Greenberg ML et al. Induction of stress proteins in cultured myogenic cells. Molecular signals for the activation of heat shock transcription factor during ischemia. J Clin Invest 1992; 89(5):1685-9.
62. Iwaki K, Chi SH, Dillmann WH et al. Induction of Hsp70 in cultured rat neonatal cardiomyocytes by hypoxia and metabolic stress. Circulation 1993; 87(6):2023-32.
63. Steenbergen C, Murphy E, Watts JA et al. Correlation between cytosolic free calcium, contracture, ATP, and irreversible ischemic injury in perfused rat heart. Circ Res 1990; 66(1):135-46.
64. Kloner RA, Przyklenk K, Whittaker P. Deleterious effects of oxygen radicals in ischemia/reperfusion. Resolved and unresolved issues. Circulation 1989; 80(5):1115-27.
65. Kukreja RC, Hess ML. The oxygen free radical system: from equations through membrane-protein interactions to cardiovascular injury and protection. Cardiovasc Res 1992; 26(7):641-55.
66. Kukreja RC, Kontos MC, Loesser KE et al. Oxidant stress increases heat shock protein-70 mRNA in isolated perfused rat heart. Am J Physiol 1994; 267(6 Pt 2):H2213-9.
67. Schoeniger LO, Andreoni KA, Ott GR et al. Induction of heat-shock gene expression in postischemic pig liver depends on superoxide generation. Gastroenterology 1994; 106(1):177-84.
68. Bolli R, Zughaib M, Li XY et al. Recurrent ischemia in the canine heart causes recurrent bursts of free radical production that have a cumulative effect on contractile function. A pathophysiological basis for chronic myocardial "stunning". J Clin Invest 1995; 96(2):1066-84.
69. Polla BS, Healy AM, Wojno WC et al. Hormone 1 alpha,25-dihydroxyvitamin D3 modulates heat shock response in monocytes. Am J Physiol 1987; 252(6 Pt 1):C640-9.
70. Jornot L, Mirault ME, Junod AF. Differential expression of Hsp70 stress proteins in human endothelial cells exposed to heat shock and hydrogen peroxide. Am J Respir Cell Mol Biol 1991; 5(3):265-75.
71. Lu D, Maulik N, Moraru II et al. Molecular adaptation of vascular endothelial cells to oxidative stress. Am J Physiol 1993; 264(3 Pt 1):C715-22.
72. Bruce JL, Price BD, Coleman CN et al. Oxidative injury rapidly activates the heat shock transcription factor but fails to increase levels of heat shock proteins. Cancer Res 1993; 53(1):12-5.
73. Jacquier-Sarlin MR, Jornot L, Polla BS. Differential expression and regulation of Hsp70 and Hsp90 by phorbol esters and heat shock. J Biol Chem 1995; 270(23):14094-9.

74. Huang LE, Zhang H, Bae SW et al. Thiol reducing reagents inhibit the heat shock response. Involvement of a redox mechanism in the heat shock signal transduction pathway. J Biol Chem 1994; 269(48):30718-25.
75. Jacquier-Sarlin MR, Polla BS. Dual regulation of heat-shock transcription factor (Hsf) activation and DNA-binding activity by H_2O_2: Role of thioredoxin. Biochem J 1996; 318(Pt 1):187-93.
76. Ohno S. Codon preference is but an illusion created by the construction principle of coding sequences. Proc Natl Acad Sci U S A 1988; 85(12):4378-82.
77. Santoro MG, Garaci E, Amici C. Prostaglandins with antiproliferative activity induce the synthesis of a heat shock protein in human cells. Proc Natl Acad Sci USA 1989; 86(21):8407-11.
78. Amici C, Sistonen L, Santoro MG et al. Antiproliferative prostaglandins activate heat shock transcription factor. Proc Natl Acad Sci USA 1992; 89(14):6227-31.
79. Jurivich DA, Sistonen L, Sarge KD et al. Arachidonate is a potent modulator of human heat shock gene transcription. Proc Natl Acad Sci USA 1994; 91(6):2280-4.
80. Jurivich DA, Sistonen L, Kroes RA et al. Effect of sodium salicylate on the human heat shock response. Science 1992; 255(5049):1243-5.
81. Lee BS, Chen J, Angelidis C et al. Pharmacological modulation of heat shock factor-1 by anti-inflammatory drugs results in protection against stress-induced cellular damage. Proc Natl Acad Sci USA 1995; 92(16):7207-11.
82. Mosser DD, Kotzbauer PT, Sarge KD et al. In vitro activation of heat shock transcription factor DNA-binding by calcium and biochemical conditions that affect protein conformation. Proc Natl Acad Sci USA 1990; 87(10):3748-52.
83. Maulik N, Wei Z, Liu X et al. Improved postischemic ventricular functional recovery by amphetamine is linked with its ability to induce heat shock. Mol Cell Biochem 1994; 137(1):17-24.
84. Morris SD, Cumming DV, Latchman DS et al. Specific induction of the 70-kD heat stress proteins by the tyrosine kinase inhibitor herbimycin-A protects rat neonatal cardiomyocytes. A new pharmacological route to stress protein expression? J Clin Invest 1996; 97(3):706-12.
85. Suzuki K, Sawa Y, Kaneda Y et al. In vivo gene transfection with heat shock protein-70 enhances myocardial tolerance to ischemia-reperfusion injury in rat. J Clin Invest 1997; 99(7):1645-50.
86. Vigh L, Literati PN, Horvath I et al. Bimoclomol: A nontoxic, hydroxylamine derivative with stress protein-inducing activity and cytoprotective effects. Nat Med 1997; 3(10):1150-4.

Index